cook zucchini or can tomatoes. Yes, abundance is one thing we enjoyed last season and are continuing to enjoy year round both from our pantries and from our winter gardens, which last year survived temps of 17 degrees below zero and went on to give us an abundant harvest of garlic, kale, onions and other super hardy vegetables and flowers early last spring,

Gardening is such a great activity for kids. Our daughters love being in the soil, and the soil seems to love being on them as well... Sasha, 7, loves helping with planting, harvesting and saving seeds from any stray pod, and especially enjoys planting fall bulbs. Our daughter Malia, 1, mostly enjoys the harvesting and eating process, with edible flowers being a favorite of both our little plantivores.

We continue to be amazed at the interest in the National Heirloom Exposition in Santa Rosa, California, as well as our festivals in both Missouri and Connecticut. These are all indications of the growth of the heirloom movement as people look to grow their own food and move back toward a simpler way of life.

We always love hearing from our customers and friends. Many of you send us comments and suggestions throughout the year, and we consider every one of them in an effort to continuously improve our customer service. We have also implemented a new order picking and shipping system that greatly improves the turn-around time of filling your seed orders.

Visitors are always welcome here at our farm, restaurant and pioneer village. Please take the time to stop by and say hello when you're in the area. We always have something interesting growing in our gardens from early spring through late fall. Bring your camera and feel free to snap some pictures.

We hope you have a blessed growing season and that your gardens will be abundant. We look forward to hearing about your harvest!

God Bless!

Jere, Emilee, Sasha & Malia Gettle

Ps, please "Like" us on facebook for all the latest varieties, recipes and cool photos!

BAKER CREEK HEIRLOOM SEEDS, LLC
2278 Baker Creek Rd. Mansfield, MO 65704
Published by RareSeeds Publishing, LLC

Seed Index

D0884866

Story Index

Check our website for more rare seeds!

About Our Seed Company

JERE GETTLE always had a passion for growing things, and at age 3 he planted his first garden. Ever since, he wanted to be involved in the seed industry. So in 1998, at the age of 17, he printed the first Baker Creek Heirloom Seed catalog. The company has grown to offer 1,750 varieties of vegetables, flowers and herbs—the largest selection of heirloom varieties in the USA.

Baker Creek carries one of the largest selections of seeds from the 19th century, including many Asian and European varieties. The company has become a tool to promote and preserve our agricultural and culinary heritage. Our company and seeds have been featured in The New York Times, The Associated Press, Oprah Magazine, Martha Stewart, The Wall Street Journal, and many others. Gardeners can request a free 212-page color catalog. Our catalogs now distribute to 400,000 gardeners nationally.

Baker Creek started hosting festivals in 2000 as an idea to bring gardeners, homesteaders and natural food enthusiasts together to exchange thoughts and seeds, listen to speakers and enjoy vendors, old-time music and much more. These festivals gave birth to the idea for our pioneer village, Bakersville. Other projects include our trial gardens that grow each year, seed collecting expeditions, our popular online forums at idigmygarden.com and educational produce exhibits.

Over the last several years, Jere Gettle and his wife Emilee have branched out into other related projects as well, including the nationally distributed Heirloom Gardener magazine, which is now in its tenth year of

Jere with the 1982 harvest

publication. They have also expanded into a location in Sonoma County, CA, in the beautiful town of Petaluma. Their most recent project is the restoration and preservation of the Wethersfield, CT, landmark, Comstock, Ferre & Company, the oldest continuously operating seed company in New England.

The Gettles have published two books with Hyperion. These books feature heirloom vegetables and their work with seeds and food. After publishing The Heirloom Life Gardener in 2011, they released The Baker Creek Vegan Cookbook in 2012.

Jere and Emilee also work extensively to supply free seeds to many of the world's poorest countries, as well as here at home in school gardens and other educational projects. It is their goal to educate everyone about a better, safer food supply and fight gene-altered Frankenfood and the companies that support it.

BAKER CREEK HEIRLOOM SEED CO.
2278 Baker Creek Rd.
Mansfield, MO 65704
Phone: 417-924-8917
www.rareseeds.com

IN OUR 18TH ANNUAL CATALOG WE OFFER:

Over 1750 varieties from 70 countries

300 new varieties

LISA	RICHARD	TIM	LISA
Customer Care Head	Seed Expert	Warehouse	Customer Care

Join us on Facebook

We now have over 300,000 "Likes" on facebook!
Like us for recipes, special offers, and cool photos!

LOVE SEEDS?
Join our Team!
Send your resume
to hr@rareseeds.com

Also Follow Us On Instragram and Twitter!

Printed on recycled paper: please recycle and pass this book on to friends!

Emilee Gettle's 1st Place Bouquet at the Missouri State Fair.

We love flowers, and so do the bees!

This season we are super excited to be introducing a large amount of new flower varieties, from Amaranth to Zinnias, we have you covered! We are working on trialing over 1000 flower varieties each year, so expect more of the same!

JOHN Head Master   **QUINTIN** Chef   **QUINT** Media Man

Visit Our Stores

MANSFIELD, MISSOURI HEADQUARTERS

Come enjoy the beautiful Ozark hills and our farm and pioneer village; shop seeds, see gardens, animals and village. Eat at our restaurant that is open for lunch. (lunch on limited days, during winter) Learn first hand about what we do.

Directions: We are located 45 miles east of Springfield, Missouri. Take Hwy 60 to Mansfield, and at the 2nd exit, turn north on Hwy 5. Go 1½ miles to London Road. Turn left on London Road, then follow signs. Hours: Sunday-Friday, 8 am - 4 pm. Closed Saturdays & major holidays. Come enjoy all the Ozarks region has to offer! Phone: 417-924-8917

PETALUMA, CALIFORNIA STORE

Stroll the streets in the quaint Victorian city of Petaluma. Shop at our unique seed and garden store, that has found its home in a grand, old, former bank building. We also offer hundreds of locally made items! Then enjoy the best food in California at many delicious local eateries all up and down the street!

Directions: Come to Petaluma (30 minutes north of San Francisco) and take any exit west into town. We are on the corner of Petaluma and Washington (199 Petaluma Blvd. N.). Open: Sunday-Friday. Closed Saturdays & major holidays. Phone: 707-773-1336

WETHERSFIELD, CONNECTICUT STORE AND GARDENS

The historic, Comstock Seed Company is located in the heart of old Wethersfield, the "most ancient" town in Connecticut. It is being restored by the Gettle family and staff. Come see this amazing seed company with 11 historic buildings and the founder's 1767 house! We carry all the seeds in this catalog, plus some additional New England favorites. Directions: Come to Wethersfield, CT. (just 5 minutes south of downtown Hartford) We are on Main Street in Old Wethersfield (263 Main St.). Open: Sunday-Friday. Closed Saturdays & major holidays. Phone: 860-571-6590 - www.ComstockFerre.com

DAVY
Packer

MARTIN
Warehouse

DEB
Warehouse

Why Grow Heirlooms?

QUALITY: Decades of modern breeding in vegetable crops has yielded some useful varieties, but at a price: quality has been sacrificed to the producers' convenience in harvesting and shipping. Too often, crops have been bred for uniformity, or to ripen all at once (to facilitate mechanical harvesting), or tough skins (to allow the produce to withstand rough handling and shipping, sometimes thousands of miles!).

Quality, taste, and even nutritional value have been the casualties of this trend. Increasingly, studies are showing that the nutritional values in factory-farmed produce are actually lower. Protein content in corn is one example. Old-style, open-pollinated field corn, the type grown for feed or for milling into flour, often contains almost twice as much protein as the new hybrids. Studies have also shown higher levels of copper, iron and manganese in at least some open-pollinated varieties.

PERFORMANCE: Heirloom varieties are often the product of many generations of careful selection by farmers and gardeners who knew what they wanted from their plants. If a variety has been carefully nurtured and its seed kept by generations of a family or in a small geographic area, it stands to reason that it must perform well in the conditions under which it has been preserved. By taking some care to choose varieties from your own area, or those that come from similar conditions, it is quite possible to select varieties that will be very vigorous and productive in your own garden.

SAVING SEED: A great advantage of heirlooms is the fact that, provided precautions are observed when growing a crop, seed may be saved for use in future years, and it will be true to type, year after year! You can't do this with hybrids; if you save seed grown from hybrid parents, the offspring will show a lot of variation and, in all likelihood, be markedly inferior to the parents. In fact, careful selection in your own garden can actually produce a unique strain of the crop grown, resulting in even better performance under your own unique conditions!

TRADITION & CONTINUITY: Heirloom vegetables represent a priceless legacy, the product of centuries of work by countless generations of farmers around the globe. When we grow heirlooms, we are the living link in a chain stretching back sometimes many hundreds of years. We are taking our turn in a succession of growers, each generation of which cherished their favorite crops and varieties and lovingly preserved fresh seed for coming seasons. As the current custodians, we are endowed with the opportunity to make our mark, as well, because like previous generations, we maintain the varieties that we love the most. Heirloom seeds are our living legacy, bequeathed to us from the past, and passed on, in turn, to the future.

BY RANDEL A. AGRELLA

An heirloom seed saver since 1982, Randel offers heirloom plants in season on his website, www.abundantacres.net. He also manages our seed growing program.

"...the Indiana Jones of Seeds."

-The New York Times Magazine

MARY Shipping

AMY Shipping & Cook

KATHY Cook

JOHN Grounds Curator

Join us at our garden festivals

MISSOURI

Spring Planting Festival
May 3 & 4, 2015
Mansfield, MO

← Join 10,000 gardeners as we celebrate the planting season with thousands of varieties of heirloom plants, seeds, crafts, music and nationally known speakers!

rareseeds.com

CONNECTICUT

Heirloom Festival
May 24, 2015
Wethersfield, CT

← Come to America's historic seed farm of Comstock, Ferre & Co. Join top speakers, vendors and historic craftsmen as we travel back in gardening time.

rareseeds.com

Jere printed his first catalog in 1998, in his bedroom. It included about 70 varieties and was sent to 550 gardeners. The business was started with $100.

In 1999 and 2000 the catalog sales expanded with catalogs shipping to nearly 20,000 gardeners and we even added color in 2000.

the 2000 seed book

By the year 2005 our seed catalog was going to 60,000 homes and we were shipping hundreds of thousands of seed packets annually.

JASON	JACK	JANDI	ROB	RAMONA
Robotics Expert	Gardener	Fulfillment	Customer Care	Gardener

and the Heirloom Expo

CALIFORNIA

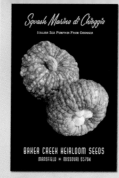

National Heirloom Expo
Sept 8-10, 2015, Santa Rosa, CA

← "The World's Pure Food Fair" Join us at this show-stopping exhibit of over 3000 varieties of heirloom produce. Plus, historic livestock & poultry, display gardens, food exhibits, & over 100 speakers, 350 vendors, historic music, & much more. In Beautiful Sonoma County!

theheirloomexpo.com

In 2006, Jere and Emilee were married, and in 2007 they started to expand the seed gardens and village. We also shipped out 80,000 seed cata-

From 2008 - 2010 the business had steady growth with catalogs shipping to over 250,000 homes and customers from over 70 countries. We also started stores in Calif. and Conn.

In 2014 we shipped 400,000 seed catalogs and continue to expand our seed offerings.

We feel so blessed to be able to pursue our hobby and our passion: growing seeds!

"...the Indiana Jones of Seeds."
-The New York Times Magazine

KATHY	DANIELLE	SHANNON
Media Lady	**Manager**	**Garden Expert**

LETTERS

Here at Such and Such Farm we love heirloom seeds because it tastes like history in every bite. There's never any need to mask the flavors of the vegetables or add much extra to the dish, they always stand on their own. Our chefs love to take these red shishito peppers and make pepper jelly with them. Just the perfect combination of heat and flavor!

-Autumn Blum, Such and Such Farm in DeSoto, MO

My 6 year old, with a harvest from his organic / heirloom 4H garden.
-Sarah Epting

It's the first year I've planted flowers as well as food, and we were dazzled with the results. I planted CA Mission Bell poppies, Bon Bon zinnias, Dwarf Rainbow Asters, and Dwarf Jewel Nasturtium and all were stunning and prolific. We had flowers on our table all season, and I could share with my elderly neighbors.
   Thank you! Our lives are enriched by planting your seeds.

-Linda Robinson

I thought this photo of my son would be a great addition to the catalog! He's holding half of an Orangeglo Watermelon grown from seeds I purchased from Baker Creek.

It was delicious!!!!!"
-Ashley Himes

MIKE	MARY	BILLY	CARL
Manager	Accounting	Packer	Packer

How GMO's Have Invaded Our Lives

Advocates of Genetically Modified crops are quick to dismiss concerns over the harmful economic impact of GMO's. They say, as they indicated in the OSAGATA et al. versus Monsanto suit (in which our company was a plaintiff) that much of the economic damage is only hypothetical, not actual.

In reality nothing could be further from the truth! Our company used to carry up to two dozen varieties of heirloom corn, until we began testing for GMO contamination in 2006. Now, we are barely able to offer half that number, since the remainder have tested positive. That's half of these fine old historic varieties—gone, until or unless we can find clean seed for them! This translates into hundreds of thousands of dollars in lost revenue for our company and the numerous small farmers that supply the seed we ship to our customers. That's revenue we and they will never recover. And everyone is still scrambling to find and increase GMO-free stock seed from the remaining uncontaminated supply.

And despite claims to the contrary, there have been lawsuits initiated over alleged patent violations, including accidental crossing of GMO strains onto organic or other non-GMO varieties. This leaves farmers in fear that they too might be sued over accidental crossing in their fields, by GMO strains being grown by their neighbors.

Add in the cost of testing each seed lot, including cost of testing lots that turn out to show contamination, which then cannot be sold. Multiply the impact by dozens of smaller, independent companies like ours, and the circle of contract growers that supply them, and the actual impact is huge. It might not mean much to a giant like Monsanto, but it's a lot of pain for the little guy to swallow. In fact, it's simply unacceptable!

Days to Maturity? Climate Zones?

Customers often want to know days to maturity on a crop, or what climate zone it's best suited for. We supply DTM information where it's available, but we don't place much stock in it. The reason is simply that there are too many variables for it to be reliable. A day's growth can be very different from one climate to another, and even from one season to another within a single garden. And the methods for calculating them are far from uniform. USDA climate Zones are no better: they only tell the average minimum winter temps. That's great for perennial plants, but most veggies are summer annuals!

A better method is to try varieties that come from a climate whose summer weather is similar to your own. Folks in the northern states should first try varieties that come from there, or from say northern Europe or Russia. Folks in the Southeast should pay special attention to Southern varieties or those from the tropics. And so on. This might seem to be a bother, but, carefully done, this method will give better results than the standard ones, which in our opinion, give a false sense of security. And besides, becoming a bit of an armchair traveler is just more fun!

As a general rule nearly any seed in this catalog will grow in over 95% of the USA, if cultivated properly.

DAVID Tech Dev   **AYANA & LOTUS** Web Dev   **IRINA** Comstock Dev   **ROBERT** Groundskeeper

New Picking System

The new order picking system has greatly improved the order fulfillment process at Baker Creek. In the past, employees would walk from bin to bin picking each individual order that had been printed. The automated process that we use now is much more streamlined and efficient. One employee works with 10 orders at one time, picking the individual seed packets and placing them on the conveyor belt. The conveyor belt sends the packets to a scanner which sorts them by order number and places them in the appropriate package. Then shipping labels are printed automatically for an employee to put on the packages, basically eliminating the task of shipping clerks typing in the information. This process has greatly reduced the number of order errors and has sped up the picking process. Two to three more times the number of orders can be picked through the automated system as when using the individual. We now have more time in the gardens and are able to accomplish our other tasks better and provide you better service is our goal.

DAVE	SHANNON	LAURA	BRIAN
Actor	Groundsman	Photographer	Photographer

Our Gardens

Visitors expect to find gardens containing a wide variety of plants at the Baker Creek farm, and they are not disappointed. Our gardens continue to expand at a rapid rate. The main display garden that is front and center of the pioneer village contains more than 80 individual plant beds separated by slate tile walkways, a hand constructed water fountain that flows into an adjoining koi fish pond, and more than a hundred varieties of flowers and vegetables.

Baker Creek staff plants and maintains a garden at the Laura Ingalls Wilder Home and Museum in nearby Mansfield. Located on the property where Laura wrote her famous Little House books, the garden is reminiscent of the types of things that Laura would have grown in her own garden there.

In addition to our main garden expansion, our Comstock Ferre & Company store in Wethersfield, CT, also has increased gardens for both display and plant-trialing many of our seed varieties.

BOB
I.T. Cowboy

LOUIS
Shipping

WILMA
Head Gardener

JASON
Photographer

The Petaluma Seed Bank

Visit our Petaluma, California Store! We invite our friends and visitors to the West Coast to visit the Petaluma Seed Bank. Occupying the beautiful and ornate Sonoma County National Bank Building that was constructed in the 1920's, the Seed Bank attracts gardeners, foodies, shoppers, and tourists alike. Visitors to the store are awed by its high hammered-metal ceilings, ornate lights, and enormous windows. The building certainly reminds one of a time when foods were more healthful and were not genetically modified.

At the Seed Bank, we offer over 1,500 varieties of heirloom seeds, garlic, tools, books, and hundreds of local hand-made gifts and food items. Remember—everything we offer is pure, natural and non-GMO. We have recently restored and remodeled the lower level of the Seed Bank to enlarge and enhance our retail operation. You will now find a greater selection of garden tools and supplies, kitchen goods, plants and bulbs, as well as locally made foods.

Located just 30 miles north of San Francisco in historic downtown Petaluma, we are part of Petaluma's well preserved historic city center, which includes many buildings that survived the 1906 San Francisco earthquake. We are part of an extensive residential and commercial heritage handed down to us by the early citizens of the prosperous 1880's, 1890's, and 1900's, when Petaluma was the center of commerce for the North Bay counties.

The location has proved to be a good choice as this area of the country has an increasing interest in home gardening, sustainable agriculture, organics, self-reliance and heirloom seed saving. It also serves as an excellent location for our staff to prepare for hosting the annual National Heirloom Exposition in nearby Santa Rosa.

After your visit to the Seed Bank, be sure to stroll the nearby streets to enjoy the best food in California at many delicious local eateries, to view the fine architecture of historic homes, as well as to browse the many antique stores, gift shops, clothing boutiques, art galleries and a wide variety of retail stores, many of which are housed in historic buildings.

Sign up for our online newsletter and visit us on Facebook to keep up with the latest happenings. We schedule regular talks, workshops, and presentations that draw a good crowd. Also, make plans to attend The National Heirloom Expo in nearby Santa Rosa, September 8, 9, 10, 2015. Find it online at www.theheirloomexpo.com. Summer (PDT) Hours: we are open 9:30 am to 5:30 pm, Pacific Daylight Time, Monday through Friday. We are also open Sundays 9:30 am to 5:30 pm. We are closed Saturdays and major holidays.

Winter (PST) Hours: We are open 9:00 am to 4:00 pm, Pacific Standard Time, Monday through Friday. We are also open Sundays 9:30 am to 4:00 pm. We are closed Saturdays and major holidays.

MARTIN
Seedsman

LEAH
Customer Care

DANA
Head Typist

PAUL WALLACE
Seed Bank Manager

ART
Horticulturist

JEANETTE
Store Clerk

SHANNON
Packer

L E T T E R S

Mexican Sour Gherkin Pickles

These adorable cucumbers look like tiny watermelons and have a crispy lemony taste. In our Oakland, CA garden they produced vigorously all summer long. The pickles make a delightful garnish and are a huge hit with kids.

^{1}/4 lb Mexican Sour Gherkins

2 Garlic Cloves

2 tsp Salt

^{1}/2 tsp Ajwain Seeds (or substitute celery seeds)

^{1}/2 tsp Coriander Seeds

Several Strips Fresh Lemon Peel

Put all ingredients in a pint jar and fill with water to cover. You can add a grape leave too, for crispness. Put lid on jar and leave out, away from direct sunlight. "Burp" the jar daily – just open lid and let it off-gas, or, use an airlock lid if you've got one. Taste test for doneness, and refrigerate when fermented to your liking. They usually take 5-7 days to pickle.

From Alisa Kameshvari Thorp

Hello - We are big fans of Baker Creek Heirloom Seeds! Our favorite place in the garden is the pumpkin patch. We love growing many different kinds of heirloom squash and pumpkins. The kids love counting all the pumpkins and squealing with delight to see how much they grow each week. Each year we take a picture of our harvest and use that picture for our annual Thanksgiving card we mail out. Some of our favorite varieties are Long Island Cheese, Galeux D'Esines, Marina Di Chioggia, Cushaw Striped, and Rouge Vif D'Etampes.

Thank you for great seeds!
God Bless, The Lindens, Milaca, MN

These are all Baker Creek pepper seeds I grew out. I started the seeds in little pots under a grow light, set them out in April, watched them grow, and have been enjoying the harvest. I saved seeds from them for next year. I've also had fun arranging my daily harvest, and this is from the day before yesterday.

Middle: Arroz con Polo surrounded by Lemon Drops. Large circle: 3 Spanish Mammoth, 3 Emerald Giant and lots of Yellow Monsters. Outside of the circle surrounded by Lemon Drops are two bowls of pepper seeds.

Yellow monster is now my all time favorite pepper. I have 3 plants and have harvested loads of these. I will have 8 or more growing on a stem. They were also the first of all my 7 varieties of peppers to make. We have eaten them, cooked with them, frozen lots of them, and given them away. Mine seem to be orange and not really yellow, but they are a tasty, prolific pepper. I would highly recommend them.

We also sell your seeds at our health food store: Family Nutrition Center, in Cleburne, TX, and they have been well received and doing great

Thanks so much,
Beverly Adams

The blue breadseed poppies were the easiest poppy I have ever tried to start from seeds, I planted them directly in late winter-early spring with other varieties such as Laurel Grape and Purple Peony and they performed best. The pods fill up with grey blue seeds, yielding enough to share with other visiting gardeners intrigued by the unusual shade of the petals. I plan on using this variety as a staple in our garden for years to come, I will probably grow zinnias near by to cover the leaves when the flowers have given way to pods.

Thanks, Juliette Lanvers

Article and photo by Linda Ly
Founder of gardenbetty.com

It's a common problem among gardeners: we sometimes compost more than we eat. And it's not because we're especially wasteful; we just don't realize that most of the plants we grow, from top to tail, are actually edible. We don't often see them in the supermarket, we almost never come across them in recipes, and through false assumptions passed down over time, we've written them off as bitter, tough, or toxic. But these five delicious vegetables deserve a place in your kitchen beyond the soup stock pot or the compost bin.

1. Leek tops

It doesn't help that every recipe you find tells you to discard the dark green end and use only the "white and light green" parts of leeks. But the dark green end (or top, depending on how you look at it) is just as flavorful as the white end. With homegrown leeks that are freshly harvested, leek tops are far from the tough and woody leaves most people associate with store-bought leeks. Cook them as you would an onion: tossed in oil over a medium flame until they're tender and fragrant.

2. Carrot tops

Oft discarded for having a disagreeable texture, carrot tops are best used as an accent. They have a strong, earthy flavor and can sometimes be used in place of parsley. Strip the tender leaves off the tougher stems and finely chop them into soups and salads, or scatter them over pasta and rice. They're especially good in minestrone or any rustic vegetable soup.

3. Broccoli leaves

When we see broccoli in the store, we usually see a head wrapped in a few wilted leaves, which we immediately remove before cooking. But true broccoli leaves—the billowy rosette of greens that surrounds the bud as it's growing—are a vegetable in their own right. Cook them as you would a sturdy green like kale or collards. The leaves that grow on other cole crops,

such as cabbage, cauliflower, and Brussels sprouts, are also edible and considered a bonus harvest while you wait for the heads and sprouts to mature.

4. Sweet potato leaves

Not to be confused with potato leaves (the two plants are not related), sweet potato leaves are mild in flavor and abundant in summer. They can be harvested all season long while you wait for the tubers to mature; the tender stems and leaves are both edible. Heat brings out their sweetness, so toss them into a soup, sauté, or stir-fry, by themselves or with other vegetables.

5. Squash shoots

The vines of all summer squash and winter squash (such as zucchini, pattypans, butternuts, and pumpkins) have an earthy sweet flavor akin to the fruit they bear. Treat them as you would a leafy green, and try them in recipes where you'd normally use chard. To harvest, snip off the last few inches of the squash vine where you see new growth. This cluster of stems and leaves is called a squash shoot, and it's the most tender part of the vine. Remove the tendrils (which tend to be tough and stringy) and cook the rest.

Linda Ly gardens in southern California and grow a variety of interesting plants, as well as raising chickens in town. She grows many varieties from our seed company, and offers growing tips, fun cooking stories and more on her website. *(Photo by Will Taylor)*

Feeling inspired? Look for my forthcoming book, The CSA Cookbook, due out March 1, 2015 (Voyageur Press). The CSA Cookbook aims to help you cook your way through a CSA box (or farmers' market or backyard bounty) with 105 seasonal recipes that utilize every edible part of the plant, from leaves and flowers to stems and seeds. Think of it as a nose-to-tail approach—for vegetables! Check thecsacookbook.com for more information and upcoming events.

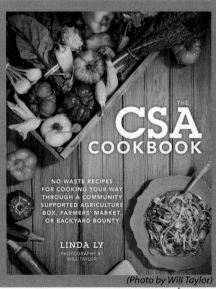

(Photo by Will Taylor)

Tropical Bush Fruits – Eggplant Cousins

We tend to think of eggplant as a vegetable, probably because we usually use it as one in our kitchens. However, botanically, it is a fruit. Here are several close relatives of the eggplant, which are emphatically sweet and juicy, and which are regarded and used as fruits in their native lands.

Pepino: sweet, melon-like fruit.

Pepino *(Solanum muricatum)* Often called a "melon", this tropical fruit often resembles its eggplant relatives: about the size of a fist, round to slightly pointed, and the skin is purple with varying degrees of cream-colored striping. The fruits are usually juicy and mildly sweet, and lend themselves equally well to both sweet or savory preparation in the kitchen.

Pepino seeds are started just like those of eggplant, but pepino does take a little longer to mature. In most of North America, seeds should be started indoors three months prior to the last frost date of spring. Setting out sizable, vigorous transplants is the best way to make sure a crop ripens before fall frosts arrive. Pepino can also be grown in containers, and whisked out of the reach of fall frosts. This may be the best method of all, provided a brightly lit, frost-free, indoor growing area is available. Under proper conditions, pepino is perennial and individual plants will survive for years when grown or moved into frost-free locations.

Here in our zone 6 gardens we have found pepinos are quite easy to grow and are producing fruit for us from August through October. They have amazing potential to be a major crop in the future, with their combination of excellent flavor and beauty. This has become one of our favorite fruits and is sure to be a hit with chefs and gardeners alike!

Tamarillo or Tree Tomato *(Cyphomandra betaceae)* Native throughout most of northern South America, tamarillo is cultivated there in orchard-style plantings. The two- to four-inch fruits are elliptical, pointed at the blossom end, and come in red to nearly purple, or yellow to orange; they are often striped. Their flavor is somewhat similar to that of tomatoes, with the yellow-orange fruits being markedly sweeter. The flesh is scooped out and lightly sweetened, and eaten as-is for a breakfast dish, or spread on toast. The fruit can also be processed into juice (its sweetness being comparable to mango or kiwi fruit). In Nepal it is often used in chutneys, and in South America it is sometimes blended with chiles arboles and used as a condiment.

Tamarillos can be grown as a novelty in a single season by starting seeds indoors in winter and carrying them along as houseplants, setting out sizable transplants after the last frost of spring. Even so, they might require some frost protection the following autumn. Tamarillos are really best suited to the subtropical portions of the country, or farther north in the greenhouse. The plants typically take several months before yielding a single fruit, but in favored climates may reach 15 feet in height and bear for a decade or longer.

Naranjilla *(Solanum quitoense)* The common name means "little orange" and the ripe fruits do taste a lot like oranges! (Some folks compare the flavor to a combination of lime and rhubarb, only much sweeter.) The fruits are spherical and yellow to orange, and the pulp is often orange with a ring of green within the flesh. Uses include juicing, eating out of hand, and desserts, often in sherbets, jellies and marmalades.

Plants may be spiny or spineless, and new growth is covered in felt-like hairs, often in purple; this makes them very eye-catching! At full maturity the plants may reach 8 feet in height, but they bear on two-foot plants starting at about 8-9 months old. This makes them workable as an annual crop in temperate zone gardens; they are easy from seed, started indoors a couple of months prior to last spring frost and grown and handled like eggplants. Naturally they are amenable to greenhouse culture in temperate-zone climates,

State of the GMO Right to Know Movement in the USA

By Ronnie Cummins, Organic Consumers Association

Since genetically engineered (GMO) crops and foods entered the U.S. food supply in the early 1990s, without adequate pre-market safety testing and without labels, U.S. consumers have mobilized to require mandatory labeling of these "Frankenfoods." Most polls indicate that 90% of Americans want to know whether their food has been genetically engineered or not. In Europe where GMO labeling is mandatory, GMO foods and crops have been basically driven from the marketplace.

Consumer demand for mandatory labeling of GMOs has spawned an unprecedented national grassroots Movement that has persevered despite hundreds of millions of dollars spent by the GMO and junk food industries to lobby federal and state lawmakers and regulatory agencies, and to wage vicious anti-labeling campaigns against grassroots powered ballot initiatives in California (2012), Washington State (2013), Oregon (2014), and Colorado (2014). Despite massive lobbying and a lawsuit filed against the state by Big Food and GMO companies, Vermont passed the nation's first mandatory GMO food labeling law in 2014. Vermont's law also prohibits labeling GMO-tainted foods as "natural."

Despite the fact that the Vermont law (which goes into effect in 2016) is only legally enforceable inside the state's borders, it will have a national impact, given the fact that large food and beverage and supermarket brands (Coca-Cola, Pepsi, Kraft, Nestle, General Mills, Kellogg's, Conagra) whose products contain GMO ingredients will not be able, in terms of public relations, to just label their products as containing GMOs in Vermont; while denying consumers in the other 49 states this information. If forced to label (or to reformulate their products to get rid of GMOs, as they've done in Europe) in Vermont, Big Food will have to do the same in all 50 states, and Canada as well. This is why the Grocery Manufacturers Association has sued Vermont in federal court to try to get the labeling law reversed. Unfortunately for Monsanto and big food interests, most legal analysts predict that Vermont's carefully written law will stand up in court.

Of perhaps equal importance to Vermont's law, consumer pressure has prompted the nation's largest retailer of organic and natural foods, Whole Foods Market, to announce that all 40,000 or so food items in the stores will have to be labeled by 2018 if they contain GMOs, including meat, eggs, dairy, and deli or take-out items. Again, although this policy will only affect the 40,000 or so food products sold in WFM stores, brands selling to Whole Foods will suffer a public relations disaster if they label their items in WFM as GMO or non-GMO, but refuse to do so in other stores.

On top of these decisive victories for consumers, one or more additional states, including Oregon, Colorado, and Maine are likely to pass ballot initiatives or state legislation over the next six months. Once this occurs, the federal government will be forced with a dilemma: do they allow these state laws to stand, thereby drastically reducing the presence of GMO foods in the marketplace, or will they attempt to thwart the people's will and stomp on state's rights by trying to pass a federal GMO labeling bill that is industry-friendly, voluntary, or full of loopholes. My prediction is that the we will win this battle, setting the stage for future right to know campaigns (for example labels on meat and animal products coming from factory farms) that will move the country toward a more organic, humane, sustainable, and healthy food and farming system. Please join the Organic Consumers Association and our allies in organizing this world-changing Movement.   OrganicConsumers.org

Join Ronnie at The National Heirloom Exposition, Sept 8 ,9 & 10, Santa Rosa, CA

GMO Industry Produces...

FRANKENFISH Cancer Corn

Human Spliced Rice Round Up Filled Food

BT BEANS Pesticide Proliferation

Patents on Life WORLD CONTROL America's Politicians

Monsanto Lawsuits Contaminated Seeds

Pollinator Poisoning

Super Weeds Allergies Butterfly Death

Leslie Goldman - California's Johnny Appleseed

Leslie Goldman is known as Your Enchanted Gardener and Plant Your Dream Blogger who travels around in a 1968 Volkswagen van spreading the word about value of planting heirloom seeds and ancient grains. He spends his time and money encouraging gardeners along the way to plant heirlooms rather than hybrids.

The inspiration to Grow a Healthier Pizza has become one of Leslie's campaigns in urging others to take control of the food they eat. The campaign began in 2011 when the food industry convinced Congress to define pizza as a vegetable and was further inspired when he received one of the 160,000 packets of San Marzano non-GMO tomato seeds that Baker Creek donated to California's 2012 Proposition 37 initiative that aimed to label genet-

Leslie Goldman and Dave Kaiser

ically engineered foods. Leslie's campaign urges growing ancient wheat and heirloom seeds of many varieties to form the ingredients of a healthier pizza.

Leslie's latest campaign is a grass roots effort to bring more people to the heirloom seed way of thinking. With his knack for using word play, Leslie has created the headline that "Uncle Sam Marries Anti GMO." He hopes this campaign will illustrate that many states have ballot issues involving GMO food labeling and that eventually our government will embrace anti-GMO products. He sees the need to thousands more gardeners and small size farmers producing our food rather than having our food supply centralized in the hands of a few growers.

Leslie is a regular feature at The National Heirloom Expo, and handing out info about it thoughout the year. We thank him for his work.

GMO Labeling Efforts

By Kathy McFarland

Baker Creek has always been a full-fledged supporter of the consumer's right to know what is in our food. The company supplied 160,000 specially labeled packets of San Marzano tomato seeds to raise awareness of California's Proposition 37 when it was on the ballot in 2012. Passage of the initiative would have made California the first state to have mandatory GMO labeling laws. The measure was narrowly defeated in California after opponents from biotech industry and Big Ag companies poured huge amounts of money and misinformation into the campaign. Even though the measure failed in California, it was still a success in that it raised awareness of the need for labeling not only in California, but around the nation.

Vermont became the first state in the nation to pass such a law with no strings attached. Under the law passed in 2014, food offered for retail sale that is entirely or partially produced with genetic engineering must be labeled as such by July, 2016. Maine and Connecticut also passed GMO labeling laws, but those will not go into effect until neighboring states also pass similar laws.

The latest states to join the fight are Oregon with Measure 92 and Colorado with Proposition 15 in 2014. While the outcome of those ballot issues are unknown at the time this catalog goes to press, we at Baker Creek are confident that they have been beneficial to the cause, regardless of whether they were actually enacted into law. We want to encourage our customers to be aware and supportive of any such measures that may come up in your respective states. We all have a right to know what is in our food.

In 2014 we are proud to have supplied free seed packets in support of GMO labelin to Organic Consumers Assoc, GMOInside, Moms Across America and others who fight for pure food.

THE SPRING PLANTING FESTIVAL

Come & Enjoy Our 15th Annual Festival, May 3 & 4, 2015
Sunday and Monday, 10 am to 7 pm both days

Celebrate spring with **150 vendors,** 75 old time musicians, and more than 50 craftsmen. Browse through thousands of varieties of plants and learn how to grow them with our acclaimed guest speakers.

Come and join us and more than **10,000 gardeners** at America's premier event of seeds, plants, music, culture and the celebration of historic foods. Join gardeners from 30-40 states. Bring the kids, who will be admitted free, for a full day of children's fun and educational activities. Area schools are invited to bring their classes.

Enjoy a sense of community with fascinating seed collectors, renowned musicians, international speakers, historic demonstrators, food activists, home schoolers, western re-enactors, organic growers, gourmet chefs, free thinkers, Ozarkian crafters, trendy vendors and herbal hippies!

read more at
www.rareseeds.com

The Spring Planting Festival is held at our village and seed farm, near Mansfield, Missouri. Simply take Highway 5 north from Mansfield for 1.5 miles, and follow signs. We offer free tent and RV camping without hookups; there is no need to register. There are also hotels in the local area. Food is available at the festival. Admission is $5.00 per adult, payable at the event. In keeping with our philosophy of educating about food and gardening, children 16 and under are free. All pets over 20 pounds must be pre-approved. No weapons are allowed. Vendors are welcome! Bring your products to one of the largest heritage garden events. **Vendors and crafters, call for info: 417-924-8917.** (Spaces are limited.) Bring your friends and family to enjoy the festivities.

Meet gardeners, farmers, GMO activists, craftsmen, musicians, herbalists, homesteaders, chefs, nurserymen, re-enactors, seed savers, composters and other seedy souls.

10,000 people joined us last year! Join us this year for the 15th annual celebration of planting, May 3 & 4. Enjoy a close look at Baker Creek's Ozark headquarters.

A Day at the National Heirloom Exposition

The World's Pure Food Fair

By Linda Ly *(Photos this page by Linda Ly)*
Founder of gardenbetty.com

For someone visiting the Heirloom Expo for the first time, stepping foot onto the Sonoma County Fairgrounds is at once exhilarating and overwhelming. Which speaker to sit in on first? Which exhibit to view and which class to take? If you only have ten hours to spend at "The World's Pure Food Fair," as I did (and trust me, that's not nearly enough), here's what I enjoyed most about the expo.

1. A pumpkin wonderland in the exhibit hall.

Hands down, Baker Creek Heirloom Seeds had the best pumpkin patch in all of Sonoma County. Thousands of pumpkins and other winter squash adorned the exhibit hall in all their twisty, warty, bumpy, ribbed, and rainbow splendor. If you thought all pumpkins were orange and squat, the famous Pumpkin Tower in the middle of the hall will have you mesmerized by just how many varieties of heirloom squash exist in this world. And if you thought your pumpkin was a behemoth, the giant pumpkin contest might humble—or motivate!—you.

2. Tomatoes, peppers, watermelons, mushrooms, and garlic galore.

Pumpkins weren't the only stars of the show. Lined up in long rows in the exhibit hall were thousands more fruits, vegetables, and herbs to admire. If you consider yourself a foodie, this is where it all starts—fresh, pure food, straight from the earth.

3. Vendors from every facet of the handmade and homestead movement.

In the next building over, I learned more about gardening, composting, homemaking, and crafting in two hours than I did in two days of random web browsing. Being able to chat face to face with the makers and proprietors behind my favorite (and newly discovered) books, seeds, soil, amendments, plants, and irrigation, as well as fermenting, farming, beekeeping, and chicken-keeping supplies, was an education in itself. But it wasn't all just "work"—the array of handmade jewelry, knits, soaps, baskets, and décor made me wish I had a bigger car to bring it all home in.

4. You won't go hungry.
For billing itself as an old-time fair, the Heirloom Expo outdid itself in terms of food. We're talking more than just hot dogs and lemonade—we're talking grass-fed all-beef dogs topped with freshly fermented sauerkraut, and icy glasses of ginger-mint lemonade. We're talking vegan radish ravioli, Vietnamese bánh mì filled with free-range eggs, beet kvass, artisanal salts, organic jams, and local honey. This is why you need more than ten hours at the expo—you need to sleep off all the food you ate the day before!

5. So many brilliant minds abound at the expo.
Walking into one of the speaker halls at any point in the day had me learning about seed saving, native planting, small-space gardening, the benefits of biodynamic farming, the state of the world's food supply, the progress of GMO labeling initiatives all over the country… and so much more, it boggled my brain. You could easily spend an entire day just listening to speakers and asking questions. The lineup at the expo was back-to-back, highly varied, and incredibly informative, no matter what aspect of gardening, farming, or food activism you're interested in.

6. A mini farm filled with sheep, alpaca, chickens, turkeys, ducks, goats, and rabbits.
I've always had dreams of having my own farm some day, and the livestock area of the Heirloom Expo allowed me to "play farm," so to speak. It was part petting zoo, part agricultural display, and part farm education. I watched a live sheep shearing demonstration (fascinating for a city girl like me) and found new breeds of heirloom hens I'd like to add to my backyard flock one day. The lessons gleaned from the farmers' workshops were invaluable, and made me look at "farm-to-table" and "farm-to-closet" in a whole new way.

National Heirloom Exposition,
Sept 8, 9 & 10, Santa Rosa, CA. theheirloomexpo.com

What began in 2011 as a celebration of pure food and sustainable living has become the world's largest annual heritage food event. Featuring the largest display of heirloom produce, many individual and commercial growers supply an abundance of fruits and vegetables for exhibiting and tasting.

More than 350 related and like-minded vendors include seed companies, tool companies, accessories, food, produce, garden products, and much more.

More than 100 renowned garden and food speakers each year from around the world have included Vandana Shiva, Jeffrey Smith, Carlo Petrini, Ronnie Cummins, Dave Murphy, Percy Schmeiser, Joseph Mercola, and many more top names. Check our website www.theheirloomexpo.com for 2015 scheduled speakers. This event held at the Sonoma County Farigrounds is America's largest educational event for organic farming, gardening & pure food!

Learn from top chefs as they demonstrate different ways to cook with heirlooms, and watch as food artists turn fruits and vegetables into culinary masterpieces. Participate in the many contests such as the giant pumpkin, tomato, and melon contests. Bring your heritage and pure breed animals for entry in to the livestock contests to win prizes.

The Botanical Explorers

Joseph & Patrick Simcox search the globe for edible plants

Last year we introduced the work of Joseph Simcox the Botanical Explorer, this year we are delighted to welcome aboard Joe's dearest colleague, his little brother Patrick. "Patty" as Joe calls him, is one of the most accomplished plant explorers in the world today. His best efforts have been in some of the most remote and dangerous places on the planet. Patty has done the impossible over and over again tracking down plants so obscure and difficult to find that world experts are in awe. By inviting Patty to assist him in his conquests to share the world's food plant resources, Joe acknowledges that it is proof that Patty's work stands alone. "Patty has taken on some daunting expeditions with his fiancé Daniela, and in doing so has earned my deep respect," says Joe. "One of Patty's greatest assets is his personality; he is the type of guy who makes a crowd excited, and as a detective searching out rare plants, the ability to relate to people is incredibly important." Recently Patty told the story of searching for forgotten bean varieties in the highlands of Colombia:

"For weeks we drove around interrogating people. I kept asking for "Don Carlos" in this one mountainous area as this name was my only clue to finding a particularly rare bean; it was only after numerous dead end results that I realized that half the men in the area were "Don" Carlos! after that another tactic was employed and eventually we found our "Don Carlos" bean collector extraordinaire!" 2015 is going to be an incredible year for Baker Creek's Fans... the Botanical Explorers have a veritable treasure chest of some of their favorite food plant discoveries from around the world ready to reveal. Joe's lineup of rarities from 2014 included the one of a kind Kajari melon from India with its sugar sweet green honeydew melon like flesh and brilliant orange red , green and yellow stripes, the magnificent "Royal" corns of Peru; Black Kulli and Giant Incan Yuruckulhua, Chocolate Berries from the Himalayas, Bael Fruit from Afghanistan, rare beans from Peru, giant ancient Cabbage Turnips from Italy, and black and red carrots from India. In 2015 there will be so many amazing surprises spanning the Globe.

The brothers are out on a mission, and that is to show the world how fun good food can be. "Growing your own food or picking your own food is heart warming and brings the human soul closer to all that sustains us: good ol'Mother Earth," says Joe. Planting a garden is also more exciting with so many amazing different varieties and landraces and species of edible plants to choose from. Gardening is like an endless mystery tale awaiting to unfold. Joe remembers as a kid how he was mesmerized by the old Gurneys seed catalogs telling about amazing fruits that astonish your neighbors, " It is funny that those memories have become our reality; we love to astonish people with the treasures of this

Joe and Patrick in Peru

Alicia Simcox with the Marita fruit.

Learn about the explorations and buy seeds at Rareseeds.com

Rare heritage corns in the Urubamba Valley of Peru

Joe in Namibia with the Nara Melon

Browningia candelabra, Chile

Learn about the explorations and buy seeds at Rareseeds.com

earth! Being a plant explorer is hard work, an awful lot of time is spent in the "grey zone," which is what Patty calls the time lapse getting somewhere, the being tired, dirty, worn out and hungry stage. "Eventually our efforts almost always pay off," says Patty " Sometimes it just takes a few years of trying!" He recounts many fruits or vegetables or plants that Joe took years to track down! "A lot of people comment that we have the coolest jobs in the world, and won't discount that for a minute, but at the same time most people see our results and that trophy shot of us having found something amazing. They don't get to see the efforts and perseverance that goes into getting it." What's more, training the eye to notice something special or to find a clue is all important." I often ask myself how much I missed in the past just because was not more astute in looking, " says Joe. "Nature is a giant canvas, and to see its intricacies one has to focus and study." Recently Joe made a trip out to North Eastern Wyoming to find roots of the so called "Prairie Turnip" (Pediomelum esculentum), this plant grows up to almost a foot tall, so for four days Joe drove up and down country roads in the grasslands looking for plants at the end of their blooming period, nothing! Finally, he relocated to near Thunder Basin National Grasslands and there he finally found the diminutive plants already desiccated. He picked one, digging down and found his first Prairie Turnip tuber… his 1600 miles trip would have been worth t for just this one tuber, but after about an hour he had almost 25 of them, making his trip a dream come true! The taste of the raw tubers was impressive: a blend of coconut, green bean and potato! And to all but very few this treasure of peoples past is forgotten. The point of this story is to highlight that we could easily pass an entire lifetime without ever having realized that such a marvel was growing in our midst, so Joe says of his work: "Seek and ye shall find!" Joe's advice to the beginner: "Read a lot and seek books that cover your envisioned region. Learning about the marvels of this world is a work of love and dedication." If you have that curious bone in your body, follow Joe and Patty in 2015. They promise to take us on one of life's most exciting adventures: that of discovering the riches of our plant world and how it feeds us all!

To follow Joe and Patty's work just go to: http://www.rareseeds.com/thebotanical-explorers

Here is a mosaic of unusual fruits and vegetables collected by Joe and Patrick in Panama.

Two beans that are out of this world ! The green fingerprint favas are from the Andes in Peru, and the astonishing yellow and black lima beans from Colombia.

Irina Stoenescu poses with the so called "Desert Rose", Adenium obesum, with its fat swollen trunk for storing water in the desert of Dhofar, Oman

Joe shows off the beautiful "Corazon de Chiriqui" squash from Chiriqui, Panama

Here Patty with his treasure trove of Cionosicyos macranthus fruits in the rainforest of Western Panama

INCAN KULLI CORN

When Joe first found the first cobs of Kulli Corn at a nutraceutical conference, he was blown away. He had seen many "black corns" in the past incuding the Aztec Black Corn but never anything so amazingly dark as Kulli. Recently while on an expedition to Peru with his brother Patty, Joe had the opportunity to see Kulli being used by the descendents of the Incas themselves! Kulli corn has so much anthocyanins in it that some say that it is has more anti-oxidant potential than blueberries! The Peruvians have made a drink called Chicha (which is dark purple like grape Koolaid from the color in the corn!) that is so popular one could call it Peru's "National Drink". Despite the widespread use of Kulli corn, it commands a premium price. Far from being a banal commodity, Kulli to this day, is revered in Peru. Prices average about 30-50 cents an ear even in the biggest markets with thousands of customers, meaning of course, that Kulli is highly appreciated. Kulli Incan Black Corn was introduced here at Baker Creek due to Joe's efforts. With feedback now trickling in, it seems that this high altitude tropical corn actually will grow in the good ole USA. Baker Creek's own seed manager Martin Walsh and family grew mature and gorgeous cobs laden with midnight black kernels right here in Missouri. We are hearing from other growers in longer season areas that their corn produced as well. Part of the thrill of growing something so ancient and admirable as Kulli corn is being able to gradually adapt it to more northern climes. In our prediction it won't be but a few years before even folk in Michigan can ripen a cob. Kulli is one of the great legacies of an ancient people, the Incan People of Peru. It is now a part of the greater legacy of humanity that we preserve these food treasures for future generations. When individuals and families grow these "lost" crops they are helping to re-inforce the importance of preserving biodiversity for all. Who would think some 1000 years ago that their legacy would be a sprouting in a foreign land! **Available online only.**

Chicha morada

Different cultures have different "symbol beverages", which serve not only a nutritional, but a social role. Similar to coffee in Europe, tea in Asia and mate in Argentina, the Peruvian "chicha morada" is a drink widely consumed and present in rituals since pre-Incan times.

"Chicha morada" is a drink prepared with the "kulli corn" (black corn), one of oldest varieties of corn. Its dark color is indicative of its very high content of anthocyanin, making it a superfood, ideal for the preparation of this tasty, health-drink.

The preparation methods vary but the most commonly used ingredients, besides the black corn, are pineapple, lemon and cinnamon. It can be sweetened to taste.

Chicha morada recipe:

- 2 pounds "kulli corn" (the cobs can be used very well)
- 1 pound pineapple
- 1/2 pound lemons
- 1 pound apples
- 1.5 gallons of water
- sugar to taste
- cinnamon to taste

Boil the kulli corn in a large pot, along with the apples, the pineapple, cinnamon and half of the water amount. Make sure water is covering all the other ingredients. Cook, covered, for ¾ hour-1 hour. Allow the liquid to cool and strain it. In other pot, boil the corn cobs a second time for 30 min, strain the liquid and allow to cool. Combine the liquids from the two pots. Add sugar and lemon juice to taste. Serve cold.

Kulli Corn is available at rareseeds.com

Nara Melon

The Nara Melon, (Acanthosicyos horridus), is one of Joe's favorite fruits in the whole world. The Nara melon is unlike any other member of the squash, melon and cucumber family. It is a leafless spiny "vine" that forms colonies in the sandhills of Namibia. The Topnaar people rely on it as a vital food source; in the early part of the year they harvest the fruits for its edible flesh and seeds. The fruit pulp is cooked and the seeds are extracted and dried in the sun. The pureed flesh is then poured onto the sands where it dries to form a fruit leather. The Nara melon is not recorded as being cultivated anywhere; however, it could easily adapt to cultivation if some of its ecological needs are met. Naras grow in sand; they grow in areas with little to no frost and they need access to deep groundwater. For the fortunate few who have a chance to grow a Nara, the possible rewards are worth all the effort! Nara melon fruits look a bit like Crocodile skinned round papayas! They even taste like Papayas! Available at rareseeds.com

Altrei coffee: the natural non-caffeine coffee from the Alps

By Irina Stoenescu

In the idyllic, fairy-tale village of Altrei, nestled in the Italian Alps, locals have long cultivated a very special Lupine: one that can be roasted and prepared into a drink, just like the coffee bean. And it tastes just like coffee, especially when you add a little milk!

This beautiful tradition was almost lost a decade ago. The village of Altrei is a small place with a limited amount of arable land and farmers were abandoning the local tradition in favor of other crops. Fortunately, Marie-Theresa Werth, her brother, Otto Werth and his family were still intrigued by the "café" and continued to grow it, on their small family farm. The dying tradition caught the attention of two German ethnobotanists, who published an article about it. After that, even the Italian government and a lot of foodies became interested. The resultant publicity convinced other locals to resume planting and now a consortium of Altrei growers is producing a limited commercial production of the fabled Altrei Coffee. Seeing it is a tasty coffee, easy to raise, with no caffeine content, it is a nice alternative for those who are avoiding caffeine. It can also be used as a spice for cheeses or added to wine, to give it a unique and refreshing note.

The Italian authorities rallied behind the project and helped the growers obtain all necessary authorizations and the name recognition for this product. With fashionable packaging and witty marketing, Altrei coffee has gained a lot of popularity in Europe.

For the passionate gardener, this is an interesting plant, which does best in cooler regions. It is susceptible to few diseases, but languishes in extremely hot dry weather. **Available online.**

KAJARI MELON

About 10 years ago Joe got wind that a very unusual melon existed in Central India. It was a beautiful melon that was "tri-colored" Copper-Red, Yellow and Green with honeydew green flesh! After extensive research, Joe found a clue that the melon had at least been temporarily offered by a company named Unwins in the United Kingdom in the early 90's. Despite his enthusiasm, all efforts to track down this melon led to a dead end. Joe spent the next 8 years looking for seeds of this beautiful melon. He wrote friends in India and received word back that they had seen this melon but did not have a clue where to get it. Finally in early 2014 Joe made his way to Delhi, India, and while at a local market met a melon man who knew a lot about the melons of Rajasthan. He suggested a place where a seed dealer could have the Kajari variety Joe was looking for. The next morning Joe hired a driver and tracked down the man; sure enough and beyond belief, he had finally after 10 years of searching, tracked down seeds of the Kajari! By summer 2014 a tiny number of Kajari seeds were shipped from India, and the first round of trials started. A number or grow-outs were made around the USA, and the Kajari did amazingly well. The fruits are absolutely gorgeous, about 3 pounds in weight and delicious! They were juicy and similar to honeydews in flavor. We expect this to be as big a melon hit as the Tigger melon was when we introduced it way back in 2004! Enjoy!

TARWI

Deep down in South America and high in the Andes grows a plant that has been cultivated for centuries by the mountain peoples. Depending on the location, it goes by names as diverse as Tarhui, Tarw, Chocho and Altramuz. Tarwi, as I'll call it, is a super plant. It grows at very high elevations often over 13,000 feet, can support drought and produces seeds that contain up to 56% protein! Tarwi was for a long time a poor man's food. It was being abandoned by small land holders even 30 years ago, but now thanks to a resurgence in interests in all things indigenous, it is even being marketed in the big cities by top chefs. Recently while I was in Lima, Peru, I was served Tarwi soup in one of the city's top restaurants. It proved to me that the humble mountain bean had a new following.

For gardeners, there is great potential to further acclimate a crop to temperate growing conditions. Already passionate gardeners like John Glavis in Bolinas, California, and myself are pushing the limits. John lives at sea level on the coast north of San Francisco. For the last couple of years he has had wonderful results and gets my credit for helping adapt this plant to our northern low altitude gardens.

Tarwi is a pulse that is very easy to process; the dry seeds need to be "leached" for about 3-4 days in running water. After that they can be eaten as is or boiled and cooled. Anyone who is going to experiment with Tarwi can find a lot of information online about its preparation.
  As a general guideline, it will do best in cooler long-seasoned areas. To see our Tarwi varieties go to the " Explorer Series" selections online.

LOCHE
A MAGNIFICIENT SQUASH TREASURE OF NORTHERN COASTAL PERU.

To any one who is familiar with the cuisine of the Lambeyecana, the Loche is an enigmatic yet omnipresent vegetable. Archeological evidence of the most beautiful sort, elaborate Moche pottery, attests that this fruit has been known and cultivated for thousands of years in Coastal Peru. The Loche is special, far from being a primitive "old" variety; it demonstrates remarkable domesticated qualities.

Many Loche are completely seedless. To the experienced Loche buyer, any Loche that is tapered at both ends indicates the likelihood of a squash that is all flesh and seedless. Loche are not infertile hybrids; they just seem to "know" that they don't have to produce many seeds. For a very long time Loche squash have been propagated by stem cuttings. Whether or not a plant can figure out if it needs to make seeds or not is a matter of metaphysical discourse; however, the fact is that this squash although apparently very fertile just does not make many seeds. The few squash that do develop seeds have only few in the cavity. When Joe recently cut some seed bearing fruits open in Peru, he found as few as 5 seeds in one squash!

The Loche is unlike any other squash in its fragrance. Belonging to the *Cucurbita moschata* group, it appears more related at first glance to gourds in the *Cucurbita pepo* group. The Loche stands alone for more than its looks; some people in Northern Coastal Peru claim that they can detect a Loche from more than a hundred feet away just by the scent it emits! The perfume of a fruit is difficult to accurately describe: some call it musky; others call it woodsy; some call it woodsy-spicy- pumpkiny only a lot stronger. The Loche is a squash that is rarely eaten as a staple, small intently fragrant slices are added to food to "season" it. In the Lambeyecana Region a dish without Loche is considered incomplete!

At present thanks to the efforts of the Simcox boys, Joseph and Patrick we are hoping that we have the opportunity to offer this exquisite heirloom in the near future. For the time being, the Loche is just another enigmatic rare wonder from the marvelous history of Peru that we can only dream about!

PUSA ASITA
Black Indian Carrot

When Joe saw slices of the Pusa Asita black carrot on display at the Indian National Horticultural Fair, he was star struck. The purple-black slices were the darkest carrot he had ever seen.

Pusa Asita is one of the "creations" of the brilliant plant breeder Dr. Pritam Kalia of New Delhi, India. Pritam is one of the few modern plant breeders who is actually working on creating open pollinated varieties. His motivation is to create varieties that country folk can grow for food and at the same time save their own seeds for the next season. Pritam explained it in this way: " We are trying to create vegetables that are extremely nutritious to feed our people and at the same time give them the opportunity to save their own seeds."

The Pusa Asita Carrot has a very high amount of anthocyanins in it and hence is an extremely nutritious vegetable for people to grow. We thank Dr. Kalia for his wonderful work and are proud to promote it! Available on our website in limited quanities.

www.rareseeds.com

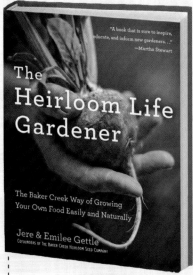

Whole Seed Catalog

This 356 page publication is a new addition that is sure to delight gardeners, foodies and historians everywhere. It is part catalog, plus so much more! We also still have our regular free catalog. Both publications are available on our website. Get a copy for your friends and family!

www.rareseeds.com

check out our COOL HAPPENINGS!

OUR SEED PACKETS

We are excited to introduce even more of our new and improved colored seed packets! So far we have about 1,400 of our varieties in these new packets.

OUR BOOK!

This is a book for a new generation of gardeners, bringing traditional methods and heirloom crops back into practice. This full-color book tells our story, as well as how we garden, save seeds and store the harvest. You'll also learn about our seed saving expeditions and the history of our seed supply in America. A complete guide for the heirloom gardener and a great gift.

OUR MAGAZINE ON NEWSSTANDS

Our full-color, 84 page magazine is on the newsstands in many retailers throughout the US! Each issue is filled with mouth-watering images, educational articles, and delicious recipes. We cover everything from seed starting to vegan cooking! Get your subscription today!

THE NATIONAL HEIRLOOM EXPOSITION

Join us at the 4th annual National Heirloom Exposition in Sonoma County, California on September 8, 9, & 10, 2015! The world's largest event of heirloom gardening, farming & food.

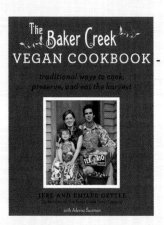

Our Vegan Cookbook!

The Baker Creek Vegan cookbook features over 125 vegan recipes with flavors ranging from Asia to Appalachia. Recipes from our restaurant and a primer on canning and preserving are included!

COMSTOCK, FERRE & CO.

We invite you to celebrate Comstock, Ferre & Co.'s 204th anniversary! Join us in Wethersfield, Connecticut on May 24, 2015 for a celebration of America's agricultural history. The historic buildings and grounds at Comstock are being restored as a living example of our country's agricultural past. We are working to relive history and the seeds that created it. Visit: comstockferre.com

Cool Seed Companies!

Please Support the following companies, they are both friends and exceptional seed farmers! We hope to you check out the many small seedhouses still in America and support them.

It the 1880's America had thousands of small seed opperations, now we just have a few dozen seed catalog companies. Please support your local seed sources and seed libararies and not just our catalog!

Hudson Valley Seed Library is a reliable source for not only heirloom open-pollinated vegetable, herb, and flower seeds but also for beautiful garden-themed contemporary art. Located in Accord, New York, they produce many of their seeds from their own small farm; the rest they source from other local farmers, farmers in other regions, and from trustworthy wholesale seed houses that are not owned by or affiliated with multi-national biotech companies. They also help sponsor the National Heirloom Expo. Hudson Valley Seed Library is both a Certified Organic Farm and a Certified Organic Handler. www.seedlibrary.org

Sand Hill Preservation Center is a family operation located in Calamus, Iowa. They consider themselves to be genetic preservationists interested in genetic diversity of plants and poultry. They produce all of their own eggs for their hatches, tend all of their own flocks, weed and care for the seed crops and produce about 90% of the seed they sell. In addition to the seed they produce on the farm, they also work with several close friends to produce some rare and unusual items to offer a bigger and better variety. Sand Hill provides their customers with an exercise in patience. They do not accept internet or phone orders. They accept no credit card payment. They process orders only through regular mail and with full payment by check or money order included. www.sandhillpreservation.com

Seed Savers Exchange is a non-profit organization dedicated to saving and sharing heirloom seeds in Decorah, Iowa. They have been promoting the preservation and utilization of heirloom varieties since 1975 and helped inspire us to start saving seeds. Working with their members of farmers and gardeners to ensure that these unique varieties are not lost forever, SSE encourages "participatory preservation" through membership in Seed Savers Exchange. Their mission is to conserve and promote America's culturally diverse but endangered garden and food crop heritage for future generations by collecting, growing, and sharing heirloom seeds and plants. Each year thousands of seed varieties are exchanged among backyard preservationists through the Seed Savers Exchange Yearbook for diverse reasons such as connecting to our garden heritage, finding varieties suited to a particular region, enjoying the diversity of heirloom varieties, and sourcing material to use in localized breeding projects.

These preservation methods keep many open-pollinated and heirloom varieties circulating in the hands of gardeners and farmers, making them available to everyone. www.seedsavers.org

Southern Exposure Seed Exchange of Mineral, Virginia, is a worker-run cooperative where every worker has a voice in the decisions of the company and where workers receive equal compensation regardless of the economic value traditionally placed on the jobs done. They offer more than 700 varieties of vegetable, flower, herb, grain and cover crop seeds, emphasizing varieties that perform well in the Mid-Atlantic and Southeast. They offer many unusual Southern heirlooms, including peanuts, southern peas, naturally colored cotton, collards, okra, roselle, turnip greens, corns for roasting and meal, and butterbeans. They do not sell chemically treated seeds. They are leaders in the non-GMO movement. www.southernexposure.com

edible flowers

By Shannon McCabe

Why not bring some of the natural beauty of your garden to your kitchen? Edible flowers are not just for gourmet restaurants; you can plant beautiful flowers to be used in a range of dishes. Educating yourself is the key to success in cooking and baking with edible flowers. After a bit of research to determine if a flower variety is edible, there is no limit to what you can create.

Some flowers lend a strong flavor to a dish and can make a strong impact on flavor. Nasturtium flower petals will add a spicy bite to any dish they are added to. Try tossing in salad or topping a sandwich with the flower petals; blend petals in with butter and lemon for a unique flavored spread. The flowers can also be stuffed with anything from chicken salad to soft cheese. The leaves of nasturtiums can be stuffed like grape leaves or ground into a spicy pesto. One of the most fascinating nasturtium recipes is to pickle the seed-pods to make capers! Rather than buy imported capers from the store, you can make your own! Just don't forget to save a few seeds for next year's growing season!

Cockscomb or Celosia is widely eaten in Nigeria where they eat the leaves and young stems and inflorescence in stew. Celosia is a member of the amaranth family; when eaten young, the leaves taste like spinach. The leaves can be seasoned with lime, hot pepper, garlic and palm oil as a side dish.

Edible flowers look great on cakes and other baked goods. Try topping a cake with your favorite Dahlia variety as a main focal point or create intricate designs with smaller flowers or individual petals. You can also add colorful, chopped flowers to white cake batter and frosting to make a confetti cake. As crazy as it sounds to dig up your dahlias, the bulbs taste like a cross between potato and carrot.

Some flowers are perfect for stuffing; the Tulip is great stuffed savory or sweet. Try a savory stuffing like hummus or cheese, or a sweet stuffing like panna cotta. Daylilies similarly work well stuffed.
The beautiful thing about edible flower recipes is that you can do anything from a complex recipe to something very simple. A great place to start in your edible flower adventure is to freeze them in ice cubes and serve them in light colored tea or lemonade. Whatever you choose to do with your beautiful flowers, just remember to be sure that they were not sprayed with chemicals that can harm you. If you buy flowers in the grocery store that are not specified for eating, you can run into pesticide problems because there are different rules for pesticides used on plants that you eat and plants that are just pretty to look at. That is why growing your own flower is best!

Above: Nasturtium flowers provide a touch of spicy-sweetness to salads.

Try Flowering Herbs! Any edible herb species will have edible flowers if allowed to bloom. Some commonly used ones include basil, borage, hyssop, anise or Korean hyssop, chamomile, lavender and shungiku.

We are excited to have Shannon McCabe recently joined our Baker Creek staff. With a degree in sustainable agriculture, she brings her farming experience from Rhode Island and is a welcome addition to our gardening and writing teams.

Sasha holding a **Mom's Special Dahlia**. Both the large tubers and flower of dahlias can be delicious! See our new bulb section on page 334!

pollinator POWER!

By Shannon McCabe

The plight of our pollinators has been gaining the international recognition that it deserves. The small but industrious workers that keep many of our plants flowering have taken a huge hit in recent history. People have become more aware of how important it is to keep these pollinators from harm's way; and despite the immense forces that have posed a threat to some pollinators, there have been a few significant victories for pollinators recently.

The honeybee has experienced the most dramatic downfall, confounding scientists and stunning the public. The impact of honeybee decline is far-reaching and potentially devastating. Aside from a scarcity of honey, the effect on agriculture would be huge. Honeybees help to pollinate many different agricultural crops from fruits and vegetables, as well as wild growing plants. A class of pesticides known as the neonicotinoids has been one of a few factors implicated in the case of the missing honeybee; they are affected by these pesticides in a few different ways. The neonicotinoids have been shown to cause bees to become more easily infected by the gut parasite nosema. A study in France showed that the neonicotiniods can fog the brain of the honeybee and alter its behavior. A British study also showed that the same class of chemicals can keep bees from supplying hives with enough food for the queen. This year the European Union has decided to eliminate the potential threat that the neonicotiniods pose to honeybees by placing a two-year ban on the neonicotiniods that are attractive to honeybees. This is not an altogether ban on the entire class of pesticides; however it is a step in the right direction and will likely set an example for others. The restriction of GM foods in Europe has likely had an impact on a big victory in the Yucatan in Mexico.

Indigenous groups and beekeepers in the Yucatan state of Mexico have won a court decision against Monsanto's permit for commercial planting of Roundup Ready soybeans in the area. The judge found that the planting of GM soybeans would negatively impact the honey production in the area. The majority of the honey produced in the state is exported to the EU. If the honey is contaminated with GM pollen, the Yucatan honey market will lose its biggest customer. While this ruling favored the beekeepers and indigenous peoples (and ultimately, the bees), it is very likely that Monsanto will try to appeal the decision. The beekeepers' livelihood is not the only factor at stake in the equation; if the GM crops are planted, pollinators would

face a critical loss of habitat. Roundup Ready crops are genetically modified to be resistant to the chemical herbicide Roundup. This would allow the farmer to spray the entire field and kill all plants except the desired crop, which has been genetically modified to resist the chemical. The spraying of Roundup effectively kills a particular weed that is very common on farmlands and also happens to be the sole food source for a very common pollinator: the monarch butterfly.

For many, the Monarch butterfly invokes a sense of nostalgia; most children's first classroom introduction to biology is the hatching of a monarch on a leaf of milkweed. The Monarch is famous for its multi-

generational migration from Mexico to Canada and back. Unfortunately, because of the planting of Roundup ready crops, the Monarch's only food source, milkweed, is quickly being eradicated throughout its migratory path and over wintering habitat. In fact, the population of Monarchs has declined by 90 percent in the past 20 years. In the mid 1990s there were 1 billion Monarchs; this past winter hit an all time low of 35 million monarchs. Concurrently, the Monarch has lost 156 million acres of habitat and 1/3 of ITS summer breeding ground. There are a few factors that have led to the decline of Monarchs, the leading cause being loss of food source and habitat, followed by global climate change, urban sprawl and logging on Mexican wintering grounds. This drastic population decline has prompted the center for Biological Diversity and The Center for Food Safety, along with the Xerces society and well-known Monarch expert, Professor Lincoln Bower, to file a petition to get the Monarch on the endangered species list. This will be a first step in ensuring the once common Monarch does not meet the same fate as that of the passenger pigeon. As an endangered species, it would become illegal for anyone to intentionally kill Monarchs, as well as to modify their habitat without a permit. It will also help to get funding for research on how to help the declining Monarch population. The protection will also help to designate and protect Monarch habitat.

While some of the issues facing pollinators seem insurmountable, the incredible fact is, beekeepers and indigenous peoples in Mexico have exacted huge change to the fate of their pollinators; this is an inspiring win for lovers of wildlife the world over. The home gardener has a unique opportunity to help protect the pollinator populations in peril by planting milkweed and other pollinator-friendly flowers. Milkweed is the sole food source for the Monarch butterfly, and planting a species that is native to your area will help to boost their dwindling food supply. Milkweed has a bright umbrel of flowers that looks beautiful in the garden, especially when adorned with clusters of grateful butterflies! You almost can't go wrong when choosing plants to promote pollinators; however, it is crucial that you do not spray your plants with harmful pesticides. You must also ensure that the plants were not treated with harsh pesticides before you bought them; 51 percent of garden plant samples purchased at top retailers in 18 cities in the U.S and Canada contained neonicotinoid pesticides. These are the very chemicals that we need to avoid in order to keep honeybees and other pollinators safe.

Many hybrid varieties of flowers are bred for desirable traits other than pollen and nectar; breeding for disease resistance and flower size can leave a flower with less nectar and pollen and therefore less desirable for bees. This is why heirloom varieties of flowers are often recommended for attracting butterflies and bees. It is best to choose flowers that bloom throughout the season and to plant different varieties to provide pollen through the whole season to suit each different pollinators' needs. Be sure to plant the varieties of different flowers in clumps to attract more pollinators than one individual flower in a bed would attract; it is best to plant in four foot clumps. Planting flowers of different shapes is also important because there are so many species of bees and other pollinators and they each fit into different shapes and sizes of flowers. It is also important to plant a variety of colors; for example bees are specifically attracted to blue, purple, violet, white and yellow. Whichever colors, shapes and patterns you decide to plant, as long as your plants are pesticide free, you will be making a contribution to the pollinator cause.

The spraying of Roundup effectively kills monarch butterflies food source, Milkweed.

COMSTOCK, FERRE & CO.:
AN AGRICULTURAL JEWEL OF THE COUNTRY
Wethersfield Seed Gardens, Wethersfield, CT

By Irina Stoenescu

Located in Old Wethersfield, Connecticut, Comstock Ferre & Co. is the nation's oldest, continuously operating seed house. Historically very prosperous, Wethersfield was one of the first towns established in the "New World", in the early 1600s. With great entrepreneurial spirit, Wethersfield gained its fame for at least two trades: ship building and agriculture. The Beldens and, later, the Comstocks were an integral part of the town's development and played a major role in the country's agricultural evolution.

By 1811, Comstock Ferre & Co. (then under the name of Wethersfield Seed Gardens) had already printed their first seed catalogue in the Hartford Courant. They had been selling seeds since the late 1700s, but this was the first "documented" list of their offerings. It was only the beginning of a revolution in farming; coinciding with the development of the railroad system, Comstock Ferre became one of the nation's most prominent companies, shipping large quantities of seeds across the country.

Today, almost three hundred years later, Comstock Ferre continues to sell old varieties of seeds, all non-GMO and all responsibly raised. Acquired by the Gettle family in 2009, the company maintained the historic name and is presently offering the "Baker Creek line", as well as the "Comstock line". With its focus on healthy living and pure foods, Comstock remains revolutionary, inspiring people to rethink farming and gardening and raise "pure food".

Although the central piece is the seed collection, over the last year, Comstock has been expanded to include many other divisions. Among those, one of the most popular has been the unique gift section, featuring many local artists and selecting products that fit the Baker Creek philosophy: artisanal, organic, natural materials, with a twist of imagination and a whimsical approach. Comstock is currently building its own imported selection of the world's finest gourmet foods and other enticing goods for the house. Chic and progressive blend harmoniously with the classic aspects of this beautiful store.

The exterior of the property has been upgraded, in keeping with the historical standards and the aesthetic "canons" of a seed company. The front lot has been bricked and five edible gardens are now adorning the property. Botanical Explorer, Joseph Simcox, has selected and planted over 500 varieties of edibles and ornamentals, making the Comstock gardens a model for urban biodiversity and productivity.

In conjunction with the retail aspect, Comstock Ferre has an educational and community building program . Organizing classes and festivals on a regular basis, Comstock seeks to provide, to adults and children alike, information about gardening and stimulate them to indulge in nature's wonders.

Our oldest building. Originally *Silas Dean's* Mercantile in the 18th century

The 11 buildings on the 2 acre property are a fascinating part of local seed history.

Please, join us for our
Annual Heirloom Festival
a celebration of spring and the planting season! **Save the date: May 24th, 2015!** 10:00 a.m. – 6 p.m. – Rain or shine!

Every year, Comstock, Ferre & Co. organizes the Heirloom Festival, featuring charismatic garden, health and sustainability speakers, diverse music, education and entertainment for adults and children. Delicious foods from around the world, as well as popular American main-stays will entice you throughout the day! Many of the area's most talented artists will come to enchant you with their amazing creations. A not-to miss opportunity to acquire your heirloom seeds for spring plantings, heirloom fruit and vegetable plants and gifts chosen for their uniqueness from around the world!

Come celebrate autumn at our
Annual Harvest Festival!
Please come and enjoy the fall's beauty and abundance with us. **Save the date: October 4th, 2015** 10:00 a.m. – 5 p.m. – Rain or shine!

This fall tradition at Comstock, Ferre & Co. brings our visitors the opportunity to spend a relaxed day with the family and indulge with delightful foods, world music and fine arts and crafts. Prominent speakers will offer presentations on gardening, pure foods and healthy living. Children are in for a special treat: every year we have fun and educational programs just for them!

COME SHOP FOR SEEDS, GIFTS, TOOLS, PLANTS & SUNDRIES

Visit Comstock, Ferre & Co., immerse yourself in the nation's history and shop for heirloom seeds and gifts with flare! Our "Library of Seeds" hosts the Baker Creek heirloom seed line, comprised of over 1600 varieties and the Comstock Line, with more than 200 varieties. Diverse and hard to find books, hand-made items of décor and clothing, fine stationery, gourmet foods and sophisticated antiques are all awaiting for you!

Comstock, Ferre and Co.
263 Main Street
Wethersfield, Connecticut 06109
Phone (860) 571-6590
sales@comstockferre.com

Come enjoy our historic seed property and see the amazing city of Wethersfield.

The new brick work and historical gardens on the property

THE VEGGIE PALACE

Everyone has a season of change. Here at Baker Creek, we are always striving for ways to educate and give practical steps to "The Whole Life Approach." The main goal of this concept is to continue our education-based passion for teaching folks how to prepare their harvest. Sometimes the most difficult problem (not really a problem) is what to do with your bounty. Here at our restaurant, we are striving to seek out uncommon foods and prepare them for our visitors. We cultivate creativity. All of our recipes are tested, followed up with a recipe on our website. Our kitchen test garden will be expanding by an acre next year, to account for all the new varieties that we plan to grow.

The next phase of our growth will include an outdoor demo kitchen and video center. We will make culinary videos and invite local chefs to cook and teach at our festivals. We would love to have you send in your favorite Baker Creek harvest recipes.

Our vegan restaurant is filled with local color and flavors from our Ozark gardens. We grow 100% of our produce and pending the seasons, have a large diversity of plants to choose from. Please come by and join us for a "donation only" lunch. Serving from 1130am-1pm. Monday-Friday. Open Seasonally

RECIPE: MESQUITE QUINOA TOWERS WITH BABY TOMATOES & SQUASH BLOSSOMS

INGREDIENTS
2 C Quinoa
1 T of Mesquite Seasoning
4 okra cut small
1 T chopped Garlic
1 C turban squash peeled & diced
1 Lemon cucumber peeled & diced
2 C of green beans
1 T brown sugar
¼ C of fresh mint
2 C Cherry Heirloom Tomatoes
2 T of olive oil
1 Sprig fresh thyme
1 Squash bloom
Sea Salt and Pepper to taste

PREPARATION
1. Cook Quinoa in boiling water for about 10 mins

2. Cool and rinse. Drizzle a little olive oil

3. Small Chop and lightly saute all vegetables starting with squash

4. On a roasting pan drizzle olive oil on your tomatoes and add fresh thyme bake in oven at 275 for 15 min or until wilted. Add half of these to the quinoa mix

OUR CHEF

Quintin Eason is the new chef at the Baker Creek vegan restaurant. After joining the staff of Baker Creek Heirloom Seed Company, he has developed many new recipes and served up exciting and nutritious meals.

Quintin learned to cook from his Italian mother on the old wooden counter tops of his antique home in Memphis, TN. His passion for cooking blossomed when he was in college and began cooking for his fraternity, which led to cooking for other fraternity and sorority events. He then left his undergraduate major of pre-med biology in Mississippi and continued his education at the Scottsdale Culinary Institute in Scottsdale, AZ. He later cooked for culinary greats as Eddie Matney and Chef Michael D. Maria and also cooked for private dinners for Senator John McCain, Tiger Woods, the Arizona Cardinals and the Phoenix Suns.

While running his own garden business, Quintin was introduced to Baker Creek heirloom seeds and using them with his customers. When he saw a Baker Creek post on Facebook calling for potential employees to apply, Quintin sent an email with his resume and was soon a part of the Baker Creek team and was busy finding creative ways to use produce from the Baker Creek restaurant gardens.

He hopes you enjoy his recipes scattered through the catalog this year!

JOIN US FOR LUNCH. Serving Lunch From 11:30-1Pm, (Monday-Friday.)

ABOUT OUR SEED

All of our seed is non-hybrid, non-GMO, non-treated and non-patented.

We do not buy seed from Monsanto-owned Seminis.

We boycott all gene-altering companies. We are not members of the pro-GMO American Seed Trade Organization!

We work with a network of about 150 small farmers, gardeners and seed growers to bring you the best selection of seeds available! Many of our varieties we sell were collected by us on our travels abroad.

We offer over 1,700 varieties of incredible seeds from more than 75 nations.

We take special precautions to ensure that all of the seeds that we sell are pure and viable. We work in our own gardens and with our farmers to try to grow the best seeds possible.

One of our biggest concerns is GMO contamination, particularly of our corn seeds. We routinely test all of our corn varieties and sugar beets listed in the catalog for genetic modification contamination.

Germination: We meet or exceed the federal standards for germination testing on the seeds we sell. Our germination process takes place in our warehouse year round and each seed lot is tested at least every 10 months. Our full-time germination supervisor uses a rotation method of germinating seeds in different planting media, temperatures, and level

of available light. We also grow almost every variety we sell each year! A major feat for us, but this provides us with a real life look at germination and quality.

come visit our farm
near mansfield, mo

SEEDGROWERS

Baker Creek Seeds welcomes applications from potential seed growers. Maintaining a commercial quantity of seeds for 2000+ varieties of plants and vegetables is not easy. We depend upon both professional growers for our seeds, as well as small gardeners and farmers who produce smaller quantities but nonetheless equally important varieties. In 2013 we had approximately 130 individual growers who had received assignments from us. In 2014 the number of private growers had increased to approximately 140. Some of these growers have several acres of ground committed to seed production. However, most are growing seed for us in their own gardens.

Most growers receive a small assignment their first year producing for us. This gives both them and Baker Creek Seeds a chance to make sure that the grower and the company are a good match. Sometimes a grower decides that seed production is not something they want to participate in. We're ok with that....every farmer's goals and situations are unique.

Growing for Baker Creek Seeds is not without risk, just like any other farming practice. There still exists the chance for crop failure . There are also stipulations. Before we can accept seed from a grower, the seed must be tested for percentage of germination. The seed must test at or above the Federal Minimum Standard for germination rates. Another challenge for some growers is that Baker Creek Seeds does not satisfy the contracts until after January 1 of the year following production. This is mostly due to logistical issues involving the testing, packing, marketing, and selling of the seed.

Another issue to consider in becoming a seed producer is that most vegetable types require specific isolation distances from other varieties of the same type. This could potentially prohibit a grower from producing some varieties that they enjoy every year. Finally, a grower must decide their own risk-reward exposure. Growing, processing and selling a seed crop can take less time than growing produce for fresh market, but it also might not have the returns that selling fresh produce can have.

But no matter what makes one grower's situation different from another grower, one fact remains and that is that Baker Creek Seeds cannot exist without the help of private seed producers. All of our growers, no matter the size, are important to us. Getting the world's rarest reeds distributed to the world's farmers is a team effort--one which relies heavily on the private grower.

If you would like to become a grower for Baker Creek Seeds, please contact our Seed Production Manager, Randel Agrella at seeds@rareseeds.com or Martin Walsh at rareseedswarehouse@gmail.com.

← **David Johansen
Seed Grower, Belize**

We use a network of over 140 small farmers and seed growers to produce the seed in this years catalog.

We also produce a good variety of seeds and do seed trials at our Missouri farm

BAKER CREEK VARIETY TRIALS

Baker Creek has access to about 4,000 varieties, all actively maintained in our seed bank. Many of them are offered in our catalog and/or at our web site: www.rareseeds.com.

Because we need a relatively small supply of seeds for each variety, we have to work with a network of more than 140 grow-out locations, usually small growers or even expert home gardeners, plus a small assortment of seed professionals from around the globe. This active network of seed growers across the country allows us to benefit from various micro-climates each adapted to a certain species. We first developed this network in our home state of Missouri, but quickly expanded from coast to coast. For crops that cross-pollinate like squash, it also allows us to find better isolations.

This is a very unique business model in the seed industry, where a vast majority of seeds are imported from China and India or are grown domestically in large mechanized fields. It gives us the opportunity to support small part-time growers and to provide a supplemental income to home gardeners. In that way, the manual skills of saving seeds are not lost.

Beyond this huge task of maintaining and growing out seeds, Baker Creek has also a network of variety trials. What are variety trials for? They in fact are critical to maintaining our varieties true to type (we call them "purity trials") and to finding "new" introductions to our commercial offering (we call them "research trials"). The trials also serve other purposes like catalog photos and display for the National Heirloom Expo, regional fairs, and for the seasonal festivals at Baker Creek farm in Missouri.

Our original trial site is at Baker Creek in Mansfield, MO. This is where we trial most of our flowers, herbs, bulbs and vegetables like peppers, eggplant and many others that do well there in a pretty humid environment. Visitors to Bakersville Pioneer Village are welcome to stroll through our trials and provide their input. At our Missouri location we will trial upwards to 2000 varieties, types and lots each season.

Our largest trial site is now in California at Durst Organic Farm in Esparto on the western edge of the Central Valley. Jim Durst is doing a wonderful job at growing our trials of tomatoes, squash, melons, watermelons and gourds. Most of the varieties are displayed at the National Heirloom Expo in Santa Rosa mid September. This summer, we had more than 400 hundred entries in our mile long tomato trial. We also had more than 200 squash varieties, not mentioning melons, watermelons and gourds.

Monitoring such trials requires a lot of meticulous preparation and timely communication with the grower. We are responsible for planting the trial, the grower grows it for us and it is handed over to a team of enthusiasts and brave Missourians to do the evaluation and the harvest under the very hot sun of California. Paul Wallace, our Seed Bank Manager in Petaluma, has been a great facilitator and helper in this project. Special thanks also to Robert Ramming at Pacific Star Gardens who grew all our tomato starters.

We are expanding our trial network to benefit from season extension under different environments. This year we are trialing a lot of our Brassicae (cabbage, broccoli, cauliflower, kale) and rooted (radish, rutabaga, turnips) varieties at the Center for Environmental Farming Systems in Goldboro, North Carolina where Marisa Benzle, the Small Farm Unit Manager does a wonderful job.

Finally, our store in Comstock in Connecticut did a trial and display gardens, thanks to Irina Stoenescu, Joseph Simcox and team.

We are still looking at expanding this network, more specifically into an overwintering location in Southern Florida, Thailand, Mexico, etc. If you are a grower or an organization interested in this type of work, please contact me: richard@rareseeds.com

Our Seed Expert, Richard Bernard

Jere Gettle in our Missouri flower trials

Flower inspector, Malia Gettle

Marisa Benzle with our fall trials in NC

We trial about 2000 varieties a year at our Missouri gardens.

California squash trials

Jim Durst, Esparto, CA

Planting tomato trials at Durst Organic Farm. Thank you all!

By Kathy McFarland

Whether you are driving down US Highway 60 or perusing a Baker Creek Seed Catalog, you surely must have seen a photograph of our own David Leroy Kaiser, more simply known as Dave. While he has been a fixture around Baker Creek since the inception of the company, he has recently achieved "celebrity" status as the star of Baker Creek silent films.

With a new videographer on staff, we are now making and posting films to our website, our You Tube channel, our Facebook page and other venues. Dave was the starring character in a history of bread film called The Life and Death of Wholesome Bread in which we showed how bread making had remained largely unchanged for thousands of years before modern methods brought unsavory ingredients to the average dinner table. In a longer and more involved film starring Dave as the main character along with other Baker Creek faces is a western themed film titled The GMO Round Up.

Dave says that it seems like yesterday when he was growing up barefoot and with a butch haircut on a small farm in Iowa. Cultivating a garden with two-row equipment and hand hoeing, he was raising lots of tomatoes, corn, potatoes, squash "and such." He calls this "good food from yesteryear." Dave sums his thoughts of Baker Creek when he says, "Good seeds leads to good produce which leads to good health. That's what it's all about!"

Dave's history with Jere Gettle began in the early 1990's when Dave Kaiser moved his family from Iowa to rural Mansfield, Missouri, and settled just down the road from where the Gettle family was living. Dave recalls Jere showing off his gardens and saying that someday he was going to sell seeds. Dave thought that was a nice little hobby for a home schooled boy. As time passed and Jere's "little hobby" grew, Dave continued to be involved with the process that was quickly evolving into a business. Dave and Jere would travel from the East Coast to the West Coast of the United States, and to Mexico and Thailand "seeing the world and gathering seeds and learning about life."

Dave Kaiser says that he was long a neighborhood "roamer" when he made his home in an older, used travel trailer that he parked wherever he could find a spot, often on Baker Creek property. Then Jere conceived the idea to build a cabin for Dave to live in. It would be placed in a prominent location on the Baker Creek farm, would architecturally blend in with the other historic-looking buildings, and would provide a living area for Dave to be the "eyes and ears" of Baker Creek during nights and weekends when the business is closed. As a result, visitors to Baker Creek headquarters often see Dave walking his dog, Soldier, playing the fiddle as Rocky the donkey "sings" along, or tasting the garden produce. Being a "people person," Dave loves the Baker Creek festivals when he gets to meet and converse with all the different visitors. Judging from the questions and comments that we get, visitors love Dave, too.

Watch Dave's new food films on our website and on our youtube channel.

The Kaiser's Food Fight.

Baker Creek was active in opposing Amendment 1 on the August ballot in Missouri. Misleadingly called the "Right to Farm" admendment, it was backed by Monsanto and other big ag companies. It will allow for large industrial farms owned by foreign conglomerates to continue to buy up Missouri farm land that is now in the hands of family farmers, and may allow large big chemical company based farms to do as they please without any legal recourse by other farmers in the case of GMO and pesticide contamination, etc. Baker Creek staff wrote letters and editorials, distributed flyers, made TV commercials, and produced a video starring Dave Kaiser, all in an effort keep Amendment 1 from passing. While it did pass by less than ¼ of 1% of the vote, we are pleased with the awareness citizens raised in a short amount of time with a little amount of money when the corporate supporters had a huge head start and much more money to pour into the campaign. We encourage everyone to be vigilant in looking out for these types of laws (Right to Farm) being introduced is several states. As well as laws trying to override any GMO labeling for America. Working together, we can keep family farmers farming and bring goodness back to our food supply. Join Dave and fight for a more local food supply.

THE MAN BEHIND THE CAMCORDER

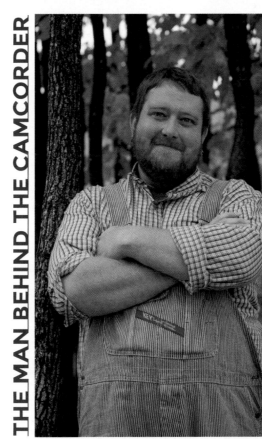

Quint Smith, Baker Creek's new and first full-time videographer, is adding a whole new dimension to sharing our mission and message. Having a degree in photo-journalism from the University of Missouri, Quint experienced Baker Creek when he was working on a filming project for school and came to shoot a video of the Baker Creek operations.

After his college graduation, Quint was working as a free-lance videographer and met up with Jere Gettle again. For some time, we had already been entertaining the idea of adding someone with video skills to the staff. We and Quint worked together on some free-lance projects, and now Quint became a full-time staff member. His main task is to provide video content for food and farm related issues that are important to the company. Video ranging in content from footage of our festivals, to growing tips and tricks, to gardening activities and happenings around the farm, to our politically themed films will be posted on our website, YouTube & our Facebook page.

Seed Starting

By Shoshanna Easling

I grew up in a little Amish community called Cane Creek, full of beautiful rolling hills and spring water. We moved there from Memphis when I was three years old. Although we were not Amish, we learned a lot about sustainable living from them, and soon began to grow and preserve all of our own food. Summer always meant lots of watermelons, tomatoes, and cantaloupe. Perfect for my favorite pastime: seed spitting! The gravel bar always had several watermelon plants springing up from the seeds we left behind. That is when I learned that seeds are not fussy; they WANT to grow. You can eat a watermelon, spit the seeds, and get a plant—in a gravel bar. Our compost pile of discarded veggies always had 25 little tomato plants growing around it. This year I was reminded of it again when I went over to my mom and dad's house and there were a dozen volunteer tomato plants loaded with sweet little red tomatoes. Life is good!

Stage 1: Starting Your Seeds

This method involves sprinkling seeds in shallow containers and then transplanting them into individual cells/pots after seedlings have two true leaves. This is the best way to start most seeds.

1. Put 1–2" of potting soil in tray/container drilled with drainage holes. Sprinkle seeds on top, not too thick. Cover with ¼" of soil for larger seed, less for fine seed.

2. Water gently with liquid fish solution or compost tea (checkout Making Vegetables for more info.) until soil is thoroughly moistened but not waterlogged. Don't forget to label!

3. Cover trays with plastic or put inside a plastic bag to retain moisture. Place seeds in a warm spot that is about 70–80°. DON'T place covered trays in direct sunlight.

4. Check on them at least once a day. If soil gets dry, water again. As soon as you see the first sprouts, remove the plastic & place in direct sunlight with temp. of about 65–70°.

Stage 2: Growing Seedlings

It is important to get your seeds in sunlight as soon as they start poking out through the soil. Keep them in germination temperatures until they are all up. Keep a close eye on them because as soon as they have all emerged they are ready to start building their strength by being exposed to the elements. Cooler weather, (just not below 40°) and some wind will help them grow properly. This will make them strong and healthy.

Seed Starting

Stage 3: Transplanting Seedlings & Growing Plants

Seedlings are ready to transplant as soon as they start to grow their second leaf. Fill containers with potting soil, but do not pack.

1. Pull up a whole clump of seedlings and disturb roots.

2. Pull seedlings apart.

3. Poke hole in the middle of a pot and plant seedling, being careful not to break the stem.

Tip: Water with full-strength fish solution or compost tea until soil is thoroughly moistened.

Growing Happily

Give your new transplants extra care of optimum temperatures and sunlight, and make sure they don't dry out. Be careful not to over-water though. After a week or so, they will be established again and growing happily. Pretty soon you'll be harvesting your very own nutrient rich home-grown veggies!

Thank you Shoshanna for this story.
Visit www.bulkherbstore.com

WILLIAM WOYS WEAVER:

LIMITED EDITION SEEDS FROM THE ROUGHWOOD SEED COLLECTION

William Woys Weaver, PhD

The Roughwood Seed Collection, which now comprises about 4000 varieties of heirloom food plants, was begun informally in 1932 by my grandfather H. Ralph Weaver (1896-1956). During the depths of the Great Depression, when food was scarce for many households, he set out to feed his family from a one-acre plot in West Chester, Pennsylvania that he eventually transformed into a kitchen garden of impressive scale. Since he had been working on the Weaver family genealogy, with direct connections to some of Lancaster County, Pennsylvania's oldest families, my grandfather began collecting seeds from relatives with the same passion that genealogists have for significant dates. His plant passion snowballed thus by the 1940s he managed to build up one the finest kitchen gardens in Southeastern Pennsylvania.

My grandfather was also visionary and ultra bio-diversified long before the concept of biodiversity existed. Sustainability was his unspoken rule of thumb. His rare racing pigeons provided nutrient rich manure for the gardens, his bee hives did the work of pollination for the fruit trees, and because bees and their stings were accepted as cures in folk

remedies at the time, local African-American folk artist Horace Pippin struck up a friendship with my grandfather in order to be stung. Mr. Pippin (as he was known to our family), became a regular at the lunch table of my grandparents, and because he wanted to be stung as a way to mitigate the pain of an old World War I injury, he bribed my grandfather with seeds from the African-American community, seeds which are now considered rare and culturally significant: the Fish Pepper is just one of many that came into the collection through Horace Pippin.

My grandfather's untimely death brought to an end his chapter of the story, but I discovered his seed collection at the bottom of a freezer many years later and decided to take on the responsibility of growing out the rare and unusual plants he had accumulated. Since then, I have added thousands of new plants to the collection (and given it the name Roughwood, after my 1805 house in Devon, Pennsylvania) having acquired, for example, many beans and corns from the Cornplanter Senecas who in the 1960s were displaced by the US government from their guaranteed-by-treaty homeland along Pennsylvania's Allegheny River. As a result of that eviction and its sad consequences, I managed to inherit many beans and corns not known to seed collectors or

to the US Department of Agriculture. As things now stand in 2014, the Roughwood Seed Collection has, among other things, 55 bean varieties of indigenous Pennsylvania origin and many tomatoes that are unknown in any other seed collections. Owen Taylor, well-known in New York City for his creative workshops on urban poultry, has agreed to come on board as the Roughwood Seed Collection Manager. Owen has already built an ingenious machine for processing and cleaning seeds for large-scale distribution.

The original focus of the Roughwood Seed Collection has always been early America, thus many of the accessions reflect the type of culinary materials of interest to historic sites, but beyond that culinary and nutritional value are of utmost importance to the overall collection mandate. In the fall of 2014 Kutztown University offered us 49 acres of prime farm land to grow out rare varieties in the collection. This partnership needs to raise money to make best use of the land and to take it out of GMO corn production, not to mention rejuvenating the soil from the toxins now left in it. In any case the long-term plan is that this will become an "experimental lab" for regional heirlooms and their best use in food tourism.

Our initial catalog offerings with Baker Creek are listed below, but over the next 5

to 10 years Owen and I will be honored to list more of our rarest varieties with Baker Creek Heirloom Seeds because everything we grow will be open-pollinated, organically raised and GMO Free. All of our seed listings will also provide the name of the farm or site where the heirlooms were grown because seed sourcing is important to the authenticity of seed origin not to mention credit due to those who did the hardest work. Thus part of your seed purchases will be given back to those growers who labored to get these rare seeds up to commercial scale for your benefit.
In the very near future look for such Roughwood Seed Collection rarities as the Tom Thumb Celeriac, Caulet de Flandre, Arbogast Sugar Pea, Purple Kinsessing Pole Bean, Neskopeck Wampum Bean, Shalgram Afghan Cress, Makataan South African Preserving Melon, Rice Beans, Royal Minquas Corn, Eight-Leaf Gluten-Free Flour Sorghum from Inner Mongolia, Chile Rama from Nicaragua, and several kinds of Native American maycocks (small squash). Please check the Baker Creek online listings for varieties we plan to add as seed comes available.

William Woys Weaver, Roughwood Seed Collection
Owen Taylor, Roughwood Seed Collection Manager

We are excited to be offering seeds from the collections of our friend and food historian, William Woys Weaver.

Mr. Weaver is a regular speaker at our festivals as well as a contributer to our Heirloom Gardener magazine.

We hope you will enjoy learning about these exciting varieties from the past, and try a few in your garden this season!

Mr. Weavers seeds are only offered on our website, supplies are limited, so hurry and get your now.

Seeds of History

EARLY CHINA BUSH BEAN

(Phaseolus vulgaris) Known among the Pennsylvania Dutch as the Cuckoo Bean and in New England as Early China Red Eye, this hearty heirloom is one of the earliest to set pods. It is valued both as a snap bean and as a baking bean. Documented in Germany in the early 1820s, it was introduced to the US about 1854. In spite of its name, this bean is thought to originate from South America. Allow 60 days. 12-14 inch bushes should be spaced 10 inches apart. Grown for the Roughwood Seed Collection at Field's Edge Farm, Lititz, Pennsylvania. (Availiable online only at www.rareseeds.com)

GOLDEN HEIRLOOM (HERITAGE D'OR) BEAN

(Phaseolus vulgaris) This delicious old Quebec heirloom bush bean with mustard yellow seeds is used as a soup or baking bean in traditional French-Canadian cookery. A good short-season bean originally grown by the Cantin family of Portneuf, Quebec, it is a local selection of Coco jaune de Chine (China Yellow) mentioned by European seedsmen as early as 1821. Allow 60 days. 12-14 inch bushes should be spaced 10 inches apart. Grown for the Roughwood Seed Collection at Field's Edge Farm, Lititz, Pennsylvania. (Availiable online only at www.rareseeds.com)

OLD DUTCH WHITE CUCUMBER

(*Cucumis sativus*) Dating from before 1850 this is the oldest white cucumber grown in the US and one of the most popular heirloom cucumbers grown among the Pennsylvania Dutch. The original seed was saved by the late Ida Risser of Leola, Pennsylvania and in 1985 acquired by the Landis Valley Farm Museum. The short, ivory white, warty fruits are best when harvested 3 ½ to 4 inches long and some even taste slightly sweet at that stage. The 6 to 8 foot vines prefer to ramble over the ground, thus Old Dutch White is ideal for field culture. This is also one of the most productive cucumbers we have ever grown and it will continue to yield fruit long after most other varieties have declined. A real show stopper in mixed pickles and salads.

Grown for the Roughwood Seed Collection in the kitchen garden of the historic Sheradin House at Kutztown University, Kutztown, Pennsylvania. (Availiable online only at www.rareseeds.com)

MAMMI HUBER'S STUFFING PEPPER

(*Capsicum annuum*) This Lancaster County, Pennsylvania heirloom was developed during the 1920s in the garden of Mammi Huber, an Old Order Mennonite who operated a fruit and produce stand near Hinkletown, Pennsylvania. The small, sweet, crunchy peppers measuring 1 ½

to 2 inches in diameter were normally stuffed with shredded cabbage and spices and then pickled. Also great for snack trays. Each 3 foot bush is a prolific producer from mid-summer to frost. Plant 16 inches apart. Grown for the Roughwood Seed Collection in the kitchen garden of the historic Sheradin House at Kutztown University, Kutztown, Pennsylvania. (Availiable online only at www.rareseeds.com)

QUAKER PIE PUMPKIN

(*Cucurbita moschata*) The Quaker Pie Pumpkin was developed among the Quakers of Washington County, New York (hence the name) and then released commercially in 1888 by Philadelphia seedsman W. Atlee Burpee. The original strain featured creamy white skin and weighed as much as 10 to 12

pounds. English Quaker missionaries later took this squash to Africa where it developed into several strains. We acquired the "Mamouza Strain" from Dodoma, Tanzania in 2001 and offer it here for the first time. This sub-variety features off-white somewhat flesh-colored skin and small round fruits weighing no more than 3 to 4 pounds. The flesh is dense, sweet, and has good storage qualities, lasting as long as 6 months. Furthermore the large, oversized male flowers are ideal for stuffing. Allow 120 days.

Grown for the Roughwood Seed Collection at Field's Edge Farm, Lititz, Pennsylvania. (Availiable online only at www.rareseeds.com)

ATLANTIC PRIZE TOMATO

(*Lycopersicon lycopersicon*) Our original seed was acquired in 1993 from a local farmer in Salem County, New Jersey. Considered the quintessential Jersey tomato, Atlantic Prize was developed by a tomato grower in Atlantic County, New Jersey during the early 1880s. It was then introduced commercially by Johnson & Stokes of Philadelphia in 1889. It is still one of the best of the Jersey-grown stewing and canning tomatoes, and remains highly productive from midseason to frost. The 2 ½ to 3 inch oblate fruits normally hang in clusters of 4 to 6. Heavy fruiting requires staking. Grown for the Roughwood Seed Collection in the kitchen garden of the historic Sheradin House at Kutztown University, Kutztown, Pennsylvania. (Availiable online only at www.rareseeds.com)

GOLDEN JUNIATA TOMATO

(*Lycopersicon lycopersicon*) This is probably one of the best of the Victorian-era yellow tomatoes. We acquired our seed in 1984 from the late Betsy Gotshall Kulp, a produce vendor and country store keeper in Harleysville, Pennsylvania. Developed in the 1870s by George M. Keasey of Mt. Wolf, Pennsylvania, this sweet, golden yellow tomato is now considered a Pennsylvania Dutch classic. The 3 inch diameter fruit is used to make yellow tomato-and-peach soup, peach-and-tomato pies, and peach-and-tomato preserves. It is extremely productive as a midseason tomato and has generally exhibited a resistance to early blight. Grown for the Roughwood Seed Collection in the kitchen garden of the historic Sheradin House at Kutztown University, Kutztown, Pennsylvania. (Availiable online only at rareseeds.com)

Atlantic Prize Tomato

LONG GREEN or LONDON LONG CUCUMBER

(Cucumis sativus) This is one of the oldest cucumbers grown in English and early American gardens. Introduced to England in the 1770s as Long Turkey, it underwent breeding improvements in the 1790s after which it became known as London Long. It was again reselected in 1874 and marketed under the name Long Green Improved. The skin is dark green and slightly warty. Best harvest size 5 to 6 inches. A prolific producer especially when the cucumbers are harvested continuously, it can be trellised or grown on fences. Begins to fruit about 45 days from planting. Grown in the kitchen garden at Roughwood, Devon, Pennsylvania. (Availiable online only at www.rareseeds.com)

CYPRIOT DROUGHT-RESISTANT WATERMELON

(Citrullus lanatus) We discovered this classic Cypriot watermelon in 1996 in the picturesque mid-week farmer's market within the walls of Old Nicosia. Grown then by only one villager, it is now gone from the island's markets and is considered one of the most endangered of the Cypriot heirlooms. Dating from at least the 1700s if not before, this melon is known locally as the Pastiha Kypriaki "Anidri," which means that it requires very little irrigation. The traditional practice was to pack mud around the base of the plants in the early morning and let Nature do the rest. The melons feature thin black-green skin with rich, bright red flesh and weigh from 5 to 10 pounds, depending on soil fertility. We have gotten some to weigh as much as 20 pounds. Highly productive, with several fruits on one vine, this watermelon can be grown successfully on trellises or netting. Grown for the Roughwood Seed Collection at Field's Edge Farm, Lititz, Pennsylvania. (Availiable online only at www.rareseeds.com)

COMMUNITY GARDENS IN POLAND:
A GARDENER'S PARADISE

By Richard Bernard

Community gardens first appeared in Poland in the very first year of the 20th century in the same period when community gardens, more accurately called workers' gardens, were spreading in the quickly developing urban areas in Europe as a consequence of the Industrial Revolution toward the end of the 19th century (see the excellent article "Jardins Ouvriers" by Irina Stoenescu in the Fall 2014 Edition of the Heirloom Gardener).

Unfortunately, Poland then went through a very unstable period of its history when parts of the country were integrated into the German Empire. During those troubled times, the community gardens were in reality subsistence gardens which is what their essence still is at least in part: finding a local reliable source of fresh food when the outside world was in trouble.

At the end of World War II and during the time of communism in Poland, the community gardens really expanded. The country was very poor and for an average family, growing a garden was the only way to eat fresh vegetables. The Polish government issued a law in 1946 allowing workers' families to have a place to rest and to grow fresh food. Another dimension was then introduced in the garden: a dimension of pleasure and rest from the stress of working hard in factories, in industrial farms, in mines.

Until the end of the communist period in 1989, the community gardens were the only place where the common people of Poland could spend their week-ends and holidays, as there were not too many other options. Each family received a lot of land of up to a little bit more than 4,000 sq ft in communal areas allocated by the city government.

The gardens then started to play a major role in social life. There are some good stories like the ones about famous musicians giving free concerts for their friends who tended gardens and later on evolving into unofficial concerts more or less tolerated by the government. It is even said that Western modern music was first played live in some of those community gardens.

Today, the situation is a bit different. Community gardens, covering about 100,000 acres, are still a very strong and very alive component of Polish society, however they are facing serious challenges. People have more possibilities to spend time and money elsewhere. Another threat, especially in larger cities, is the real estate pressure from developers. When we were visiting some garden locations in small towns close to Poznan and Wroclaw, we could see that some lots were even becoming more of a leisure place surrounded by a lawn and a few ornamental plants; it was a minority but a new trend.

Community gardens' lots are passed from one generation to another one, but can be lost if the next generation is not interested in tending the allocated garden.

The gardens that we visited with my wonderful and passionate Polish guides, were lush and diverse. Passing through the gate of a community garden, was like entering a world of colors and scents isolated from the nuisances of the surrounding urban life. What a place for a family to gather, do some physical work together, enjoy food and relax! Some of the gardeners that we talked to, were self-taught experts in botany and agronomy and were even able to grow some tropical plants and bamboos; some of them using a tiny greenhouse.

A little bit of everything is grown in those gardens; some of the favorites are beets, heirloom tomatoes, pickling cucumbers, paprikas, potatoes, cabbages and many types of root vegetables (radish, carrots, celeriac, parsnip, turnip, salsify) along with herbs and flowers. Most gardens also have fruit trees: apples, pears, prunes, grapes and even kiwis.

Special thanks to Anna Cwiklinska, Mateusz Janicki and Anna Chlebowska who introduced me to this wonderful world and to Wieslaw Legutko, whose seed company W. Legutko, strongly supports community gardens and supply them with a diversity of seeds.

RARE VARIETIES IN EUROPE

Last July, I flew to Europe on a journey to find some of those Old World heirloom varieties that had not yet made the trip west across the Atlantic Ocean or that had come from our side of the world and had been adopted and locally selected. After a visit to my family in Southern France, a short drive through rolling hills painted bright yellow by sunflower fields took me to the foothills of the Pyrenees Mountains in Ariege where the Association Kokopelli is now located. The organization is dedicated, since 1999, to the protection of food biodiversity, to the organic seed production and to supporting the GMO free movement as well as the free access to seeds within the European Community. You can visit their web site at: www.kokopelli-semencs.fr

Then I headed north west towards the fertile region of Anjou by the Loire River, where a lot of the seeds are being grown. There I visited GSN Semences, a local seed production company that has been tasked by the European Community to maintain an active seed bank of old heirloom varieties from France.

I had to say goodbye to sunny France and head north to cool and misty Holland, but still THE place to go for flowers' fans and seed professionals. The variety of flowers, not just bulbs, that can be found there is amazing and is intrinsically part of the national culture. Nowhere else in the world, such diversity of domesticated flowering and ornamental plants can be found on such a small territory: 16,000 sq miles out of which 20% is water.

Poland: I had heard rumors that Poland was a place where I could find a thriving and very active community of home gardeners, where gardening would still combine ornamental and food production, in brief: where biodiversity in gardening is a reality.

From Warsaw, the train took me to Wroclaw in the South Western part of the country that has been torn through history between the German and the Russian Empires and that is now fully and proudly back to the Polish Nation. There, between the historical and beautifully restored cities of Wroclaw and Poznan, hidden among thick pine forests and fields of rye and sugar beet, small towns and villages display their colorful community gardens and grow an amazing diversity of flower and vegetable seeds.

From this trip to Europe, I brought back many varieties of flowers, herbs and vegetables for Baker Creek. More than two thirds of them come from Poland. For instance, we offer now nine local Polish varieties of radish which is a very popular fast crop from early Spring all the way to late Fall (see our radish section). Because Poland has a short season, a lot of their local vegetables are early and because their community gardens are small and diverse, many plants have been selected to have an upright bush habit.

Take a look at and try in your garden (outside or under cover) these amazing early to very early varieties of papryka (sweet peppers) like Etiuda, a blocky bell pepper, sweet, maturing bright orange and one of the best tasting peppers we have tried. And Oda pepper, a very early and compact plant variety with glowing violet-colored fruit. Plus many others!

Polish Summer Beet Soup

This is a cold and refreshing dish for summer and early fall days when fresh beet roots are available at the market. Choose the deeper red ones for this recipe.

Grate the roots and bring to a boil in a small quantity of water with crushed garlic and a little bit of salt. Reduce the heat and let it gently boil; add one table spoon of lemon juice at the end when the liquid is deep red and homogeneous.

Let it cool at room temperature and then in the fridge; then mix with plain whole milk yogurt and kefir (a fermented milk drink) at the rate of about 30% of the whole mixture. The result should be a fairly thick soup.

Add fresh dill and thinly sliced radish on top before serving.
Optional: traditionally, a boiled egg cut in quarters is served with each portion.

Note: soy products can replace dairy products in this recipe

Favorite Farmers

cool farmers who are challenging the way we look at food, soil and of course seeds!

by kathy mcfarland

Abdellah Boudhira
havests watermelon

Mac Condill— The Great Pumpkin Patch

Illinois, the heart of the Midwest, is home to the most diverse pumpkin patch in the world. The Prairie State stakes claim to being the top pumpkin-producing state in the country. With its hot, dry summers, it's the perfect place to grow pumpkins. Mac Condill grows 400 varieties of pumpkins on the farm that has been in his family for more than 150 years near Arthur, IL. While his family always had pumpkins on the farm, Mac became really interested in them when he was 12 years old. He has channeled that love of pumpkins into a profitable business that includes The Great Pumpkin Patch which hosts more than 50,000 visitors each fall, a popular bakery, and a growing seed business.

Mac admits that he views the world through "cucurbit-colored glasses." His great love is for the botanical family of cucurbitaceae that includes pumpkins, squash, cucumbers, luffas, and melons. Mac is particularly interested in pumpkins, though he branches out to gourds, too. He has traveled the world in search of rare or unusual cucurbit seeds. After searching for varieties on six of the seven continents and in 30 different countries, Mac has been able to introduce a lot of pumpkin varieties to the United States. He celebrates the diversity of pumpkins and has a good collection of seeds of Native American and European varieties, as well as some from Africa, Australia and Asia. Mac points out that it is only in the United States that people think of pumpkins as being only orange. Visitors to the the Great Pumpkin Patch will realize that pumpkins come in many different shades of various colors that include white, green, blue, and striped.

The Great Pumpkin Patch has garnered recognition when featured on the Martha Stewart Show multiple times. Mac traveled to Washington, D.C. In 2010 to erect a huge squash display on the White House lawn. He has also made his fourth appearance at the National Heirloom Exposition in Santa Rosa, California, to construct a magnificent squash tower in the exhibition hall.

The Homestead Seed company launched by Mac Condill offers many varieties of cucurbits. He uniquely packages his seeds (at least 15 each) in small clear or amber colored bottles with cork stoppers. He takes pride in the purity and continuity of the cucurbits offers by The Homestead Seeds. He takes great care and very specific measures to ensure those qualities in the seeds he sells.

Mac Condill building his famous 'Pumpkin Tower' at the National Heirloom Expo, Santa Rosa, CA.

Abdellah Boudhira—Moroccan Farmer

Abdellah Boudhira is an organic farmer in Agadir, Morocco, nestled just 25 kilometers to the east of the Atlantic Ocean, where the mild climate is conducive to growing year round. His grandfather and father were farmers since the early 1950's when Morocco gained independence from France. While growing many different crops, their chief crop was tomato. His grandfather never bought seeds but rather only saved seeds from ripe healthy tomato plants until the late 1980's when Hybrid F1 seeds became available. The hybrids had the advantage of a long shelf life and could be exported internationally. These advantages caused Moroccan farmers to stop saving their heritage seeds and turn to using the hybrid seeds.

Abdellah's grandfather passed away in 1998, the farm was split among the descendents, and much of it was sold off. Abdellah's father kept his share of the small farm and continued to work the land, growing tomatoes, green beans, squash, potatoes, lettuce, cauliflower, and edible gourds. They marketed their produce in a way that included intermediaries, which meant that farmers received low prices for their produce but consumers paid high prices for the same produce. Abdellah chose to change the way he marketed his produce by selling directly to consumers in the city. Realizing that food sold in the wholesale market came from conventional farms that were sprayed with chemicals, he would have an advantage if he could produce healthy food. He knew that in order to grow healthy food, he would first have to select healthy seeds. Unfortunately, the only seeds available in his area were the hybrid seeds. However, because Abdellah was competent using the English language, he created a Facebook account and quickly gained friends in the United States. Those friends told him about the availability of heirloom seeds from Baker Creek. Those same friends purchased seeds from Baker Creek and mailed them to him. However, Moroccan authorities blocked the seeds coming into the country and returned the seeds to the American senders. He then asked his American friends to put the seeds in the bottom of boxes of chocolates and send them as birthday gifts. He has been using Baker Creek seeds since 2011 and has saved seeds from some of them for replanting. Abdellah now farms the way his grandparents did generations ago when they never used any chemicals or hybrid seeds, and when GMO seeds had not yet made their way to Morocco.

Abdellah graduated from high school in 2001 and began farming full time with his father, who had continued farming the land with conventional methods. Abdellah set out to switch to organic farming and worked hard to defy all the challenges to build up the soil fertility with compost and manure and to bring organic heirloom seeds to the farm. Other challenges facing Moroccan organic farms include the depletion of the underground water table, climate change and and some serious insect problems, particularly with the Tuta Absoluta and white fly TMV. These insects cause serious damage to tomatoes, as well as zucchini, peppers, cauliflower, cabbage, and others. Many farmers turned to growing vegetables in isolated greenhouse to keep up with these pests. His Facebook farm page has gained favor and become dear to people around the world.

Anna Peach— Squash and Awe Farm

Anna Peach, squash grower extraordinaire, may run the geographically smallest commercial farm in the state of Hawaii, but the farm is large in other ways. Known as the Guerilla Farmer, Anna is the only farmer to grow edibles year round in a state that imports 92% to 93% of its food. Most farmers gave up due to poor soil, insect pests, and an extended drought.

When Anna first arrived in Hawaii with the intention of farming there, her first challenge was the poor soil. She rented some farmland with soil that just blew away in the wind and would not support growing plants. Fortunately, Anna had spent considerable time volunteering at Brooklyn Grange farm, a one-acre farm on top of a six-story warehouse in Queens, New York. There she learned how to build up the soil from nothing. With that knowledge, she knew that she could build up soil anywhere and set out to organically create farmland that would produce a crop.

Focusing on squash as her super crop, Anna trial-planted many varieties and discovered that her favorites were Thai Kang Kob and Thai Rai Kaw Tok from Baker Creek Heirloom Seeds. She fell in love with those varieties because they naturally repelled the 2 main insect pests of melon fly and pickle worm. Starting from scratch, Anna Peach has built up a successful farm that provides hundreds of pounds of squash to elite chefs, farm stands, and markets on Hawaii Island. *squashandawe.com*

Anna Peach will be a speaker at our Spring Planting Festival, May 3 & 4, Mansfield, MO

Guatemalan seed savers

By Sarah Montgomery

The Garden's Edge teaches gardening and seed saving to widows and families of Guatemala's civil war.

Our journey to find old seed varieties and reintroduce them to Guatemalan villages started thirteen years ago. We started with a few handfuls of seeds collected from Mayan elders who were still hanging on to them, packed away in dusty jars or stored between roof tiles. Each family in our project plants a home garden and leaves a portion of their vegetables to go to seed. After the harvest, each family saves enough seed to re-plant their garden and sells any excess back to the project.

Seeds are not just important for a family's food security; they are often tied to a person's culture or history. Corn, beans, squash and amaranth are a few of the crops that play a significant role in the history of the Mayan people.

The traditional Guatemalan diet consists of corn tortillas at every meal. Corn is a cen-

tral part of the diet and is part of the Mayan creation story. The first Mayan people were molded out of corn masa and sent to live in the four directions. The diversity of native corn in Guatemala is immense. Thousands of varieties exist. They are adapted to different microclimates in a country that is just a little bigger than the state of Tennessee.

Beans are another important part of every meal, and native greens like macuy, chipilin colis and amaranth are combined with eggs or used in soups. Amaranth seeds were once a sacred food. But the Spanish banned them during conquest for their use in ceremonies. The Garden's Edge is working to reintroduce this important grain. The leaves can be eaten like spinach and the seeds toasted and ground into nutritious flour. The flour is boiled to make a traditional cereal drink called atole, and also can be used in bread, pancake, cookie and cracker recipes.

Our project is known as The Garden's Edge, and in Guatemala, the "Qachuu Aloom"

Mother Earth Association. Our board of directors and staff in Guatemala are all local Maya farmers whose dream is to preserve the agricultural traditions of their ancestors.

In September four members of Qachuu Aloom traveled from Guatemala to California to take part in the Heirloom Seed Festival. It was an amazing experience. We shared our exciting and successful work battling the Monsanto Law in Guatemala. Meeting so many other people who care about protecting heirloom seeds was the highlight, as well as seeing the amazing diversity of crops in the exhibition hall. We hope to be back next year to share more of our heirloom seeds. If you missed us at the festival, you can order some of our seed varieties from Baker Creek.

For more information on the Garden's Edge visit: www.gardensedge.org, and look for our booth at the 2015 Heirloom Seed Expo in Santa Rosa, California.

.

Rosalia with a Cassabannana

Guatemalan Seed Bank

Seed Cleaning

GUATEMALA:
CRADDLE OF EDIBLE DOMESTICATED PLANTS

By Richard Bernard

The Mayan people of Guatemala and Southern Mexico will never be credited enough for their major contribution to the diversity of our food. Those skilled agriculturists have domesticated and brought to us a variety of edible plants; among the most famous are tomatoes, chile, amaranth, corn, squash and beans.

While we enjoy growing those crops in our beautiful gardens, there in Guatemala, such a treasure of diversity is now in danger of not only shrinking but disappearing. Tomato is a perfect example of how local heirlooms have been replaced by one single hybrid variety of Roma tomato whose seeds are imported. The process of replacement is simple and took less than five years: local growers started to grow tomatoes under hoophouses to benefit from a longer growing season and therefore created a suitable environment for white flies to multiply, feed heavily on their tomato plants and inoculate a deadly virus to the plants; the growers' only alternative was then to apply pesticides and grow an imported hybrid variety with tolerance to the virus and not save seeds anymore.

Read the story of Qachuu Aloom, a local Mayan seed saving and social organization that demonstrates how people are able, not only to survive but fight and re-build local communitie affected by a terrible civil war and a loss of diversity in their food supply.

I have visited Qachuu Aloom in April 2014 in their region of Baja Verapaz in the central part of the country. It was the end of the dry season when a lot of seed crops are harvested.

Baker Creek and Qachuu Aloom have started to cooperate, and sales of their seeds here in the United States will help support their organization. Some of their best varieties that you can now find in our catalog are:

Three amaranths, green, red and orange, that can bring colors to your garden but also are a prolific grain crop high in proteins and vitamins. They can also be seeded at high density and be harvested as greens to be consumed like spinach. Each one has been named after the ladies who were founders of Qachuu Aloom: Aurelia's Amaranto Verde AM141 (green amaranth), Elena's Amaranto Rojo AM142 (red amaranth), Juana's Amaranto Ananjarado AM143 (orange amaranth).

Colish OG147 is a "criollo" plant from the Brassicae family. "Criollo" means a plant that was brought by the Spanish colonists and has been adopted by the natives and locally selected for adaptation and consumption. Colish is a green that grows in cooler areas; leaves are added to stews or can be fried. The yellow flowers are extremely attractive to bees and are edible.

Another amazing plant brought to us by Qachuu Aloom is the Cassabanana MC101 also called Melocoton in Central America: an amazing tropical cucurbit that can grow in our summers; it also makes a beautiful ornamental vine; fragrant and edible fruits are about 2' long and brown red at maturity; they also store pretty good.

Picture Credit this page: Juan Carlos Lemus Dahinten: jclemus-dahinten@yahoo.com
Juan Carlos Lemus Dahinten is a self-taught photographer from Coban in Alta-Verapaz region of Guatemala. He has focused his work on documenting traditions, rural life and traditional attires of the Mayan people.

Sara Patterson– Red Acre Farm

By Kathy McFarland

Red Acre Farm is a small sustainable family farm near Cedar City in rural southern Utah. The farm began several years ago as an idea with home-schooled eleven-year-old Sara Patterson, who had relocated with her family from southern California. Finding that it was much harder to grow things in the new location, Sara made sure the family garden got planted and grew. By the time she had become a teenager, she was growing more food than her family could use and she started selling baskets of food to family, friends and her mother's co-workers.

A friend of Sara's mother had just started a CSA and became a mentor to Sara. At age 14, Sara started her own CSA with just 5 shareholders. It was one of those early and continuous shareholders who told Sara about "this young guy who home schooled and had an amazing seed catalog." Then a neighbor shared the same information, but it was not until Sara's 16th birthday that she held a Baker Creek Heirloom Seeds catalog in her hands. She says, "I was hooked! I devoured, treasured—okay, maybe even drooled! Every time I taught a class, I suggested having a catalog, if for no other reason than for their coffee table. I have been ordering seeds from Baker Creek ever since!"

Her mother created a website for Sara's new enterprise and hoped that getting the word out would increase CSA shares from 5 to 10. After selling an amazing 20 shares, Sara said, "No more," and announced that her shares were sold out. Still growing more produce than she needed to fill share baskets, Sara started going to the local farmers markets. There she met her next mentor who inspired her to grow year round. While a little scared at first, she sold out of her Fall, Winter and Spring shares each time.

Sara Patterson is still a teenager but now farms full time. Both of her parents, Symbria and Lynn, now work for her at Red Acre Farm. She says she eats and wants everyone else to be able to have access to locally grown food—the purest, cleanest, nutrient-rich dense food possible—year round. In addition to her nearly 100 CSA shares and farmers market sales, she also runs a farm-pick program, a "Volunteer for Veggies" program and has a farm stand called "The Back Porch," where they offer food they raise, gardening supplies, biodynamic compost and Baker Creek seeds. She works with local stores and chefs to sell locally raised food, sells out their Farm to Fork dinners, and hosts numerous events at the farm. Sara says she is coming full circle, going back to what her grandparents did—how they raised food growing up, how they ate and live. She loves the model of a small family farm and how it can fit in today's world. She points out that striving to do it "bigger and more" had and is taking a toll on the earth and its people. She has dedicated herself and others by example how to come full circle.

As part of that teaching, Sara will be a presenter at Baker Creek's annual Spring Planting Festival on May 3 and 4, 2015, near Mansfield, Missouri. The first garden conference of any kind that Sara ever attended was the first National Heirloom Exposition in 2011. She has travelled to Santa Rosa, California, every year since to attend the Expo. She says that what she learned and who she met there changed the way she farms. Sara sums up that the best part of farming is "that it is always changing, and looking for better ways to live and eat healthier on this planet is more in harmony with nature than trying to conquer it." www.redacrefarmcsa.org

Sara Patterson is still a teenager but now farms full time.

Sara is a regular at The National Heirloom Expo and this year will speak at the Spring Planting Festival.

Saving Seeds

By Randel Agrella

Beginning Seed Saving

Part of the attraction to heirloom/open-pollinated seeds is that gardeners can save seeds from their treasured varieties year after year, allowing their plants to complete their life cycles, renewing themselves endlessly as nature intended.

Saving your own seed is easy to do—after all, it's something the plants would do on their own anyway. All you need to do is set them up to do it and then keep out of the way, allowing nature to take its course! Still, a little knowledge and some advance planning can eliminate a lot of trial and error, helping you to achieve successful results from the beginning.

Keep them pure. A basic piece of the puzzle is understanding that, left to themselves, plants within the same species will cross-pollinate. It's natural: Crossing between individuals is what keeps specific traits circulating, and also constantly creates unique combinations of traits, making plants more adaptable to changes in their environment. It also leads to surprises, which suits nature, but doesn't necessarily work in your garden. After all, if you wanted a large red slicing tomato, then a nice yellow cherry type isn't necessarily a wonderful surprise!

Avoid this by keeping your varieties pure by isolating them from other members of the same species. Each crop has its own pollination requirements, and in the garden, the easiest way to eliminate chance crosses is to allow ample distance between varieties within the same species. This can be tricky in small gardens, especially those in town, as some species can be pollinated over great distances by bees or wind. To start, focus your seed-saving efforts on crops that are mainly self-pollinating, or whose pollen seldom travels over long distances. Avoid saving seed of corn, squashes, melons, cucumbers, watermelons and gourds unless you're fairly certain you have good isolation.

Keep them vigorous A concern in seed saving is avoiding inbreeding—you need a sufficient breeding population to ensure sufficient genetic diversity. Inbred plants lack vigor, productivity, and overall good health. It so happens that those crops that need the greatest isolation (those that cross over the greatest distances) also need larger populations to protect against inbreeding. On the other hand, those which pollinate only over very short distances are usually self-pollinating, and are far less bothered by inbreeding caused by saving seed from small populations. Self-pollinating types should have at least 3-5 plants, the others at least 20 plants. More is definitely better in all cases, but large populations of sprawling plants, like the squash family, are difficult to fit into small gardens.

Select the best. When you save seed, you are in the driver's seat in terms of selecting the parents of the next generation. So be aggressive in saving only seed from your best plants. "Best" means whatever you want it to mean! Size, earliness, overall productivity—these are examples of traits that will vary somewhat from one individual plant to another, within each variety. Over generations, your home-selected lines will be better adapted to your unique gardening conditions and style than off-the-shelf versions of the same varieties. Gardeners and farmers have done this for millenia—now it's your turn!

Allow proper maturity to be viable and vigorous, and for good storage life, seeds must be fully mature before harvesting. This is a no-brainer for types where the crop we normally grow is the seed crop (dry beans, grain amaranth) or where mature seeds are already contained in the crop we normally grow (tomatoes, melons). It becomes more problematic with crops that are normally harvested before seed maturity (lettuce, cucumber, eggplant). Most mystifying of all are biennial crops like onions, carrots, beets and chard, and most cabbage relatives. These crops are normally harvested for food the same year as planted, but they won't bloom and set seed until they've experienced a winter's chill, so you must overwinter them somehow to allow them that all-important second season to mature.

Extraction: Each crop type has its own kinks and quirks when it comes time to extract the seeds. Broadly speaking, extraction is either "wet" or"dry," depending upon the nature of the plants themselves. Dry extraction is appropriate for those seeds that are dry right on the plant at maturity (beans, corn, and okra are some examples): You simply break open the pod to release the seeds. Wet extraction is necessary for crops that are still juicy at full maturity, like tomatoes, cukes, squashes and melons. For all these types, pulp is removed from the fruits and subjected to a fermentation process; the seeds are then washed and quickly dried.

Drying: After extraction your seeds must be quickly dried for good storage and viability. A spot out of the rain, having good air circulation, will do. Indoors, a fan playing over the seeds is excellent. Avoid excessive heat, such as direct sun or heaters

Storage: Seeds keep best in cool, dry conditions, and most will keep for several years in ordinary indoor environments. Avoid humidity and excessive heat. For long-term storage, keep fully dried seeds in the freezer, preferably in jars with silica gel dessicant inside. Stored this way, seeds will literally keep for decades!

Get more information: There's lots of great information available online. Or consider purchasing one of these excellent titles: Breed your Own Vegetable Varieties by Carol Depp; Seed to Seed by Suzanne Ashworth; Organic Seed Production and Saving by Bryan Connolly; The Heirloom Life Gardener by Jere and Emilee Gettle

Christopher Carter "Coconut Chris"

Seeing Chris Carter climb a tree isn't much different from seeing a monkey do so. Chris has been given the nickname "Coconut Chris" because of his tree climbing prowess.

Chris is a local celebrity on the Big Island of Hawaii where he maintains a permaculture garden that is truly a wonderland. He has dozens of varieties of rare Hawaiian bananas, some of which he found on hiking expeditions to remote valleys on the island. There are hundreds of fruits and vegetables growing in Chris's gardens, and people come from near and far to see them. Chris has spent years planting fruit trees all over his beloved Waipio Valley. Anywhere that one goes with Chris in the valley, there are delectable fruits to pick that were planted by his hand. Chris also runs a volunteer training/apprentice program to introduce modern folk to the art of serious permaculture gardening in a tropical setting. Each year Chris welcomes gardeners from around the world. They find him on websites and also on the WOOFER platform. His farm is clearly unique, and his own lifestyle gives it a definite personality of it's own. Chris himself is a raw vegan who basically does not eat any processed foods. He drinks only stream water, and takes with him a glass jug of his own "untamed" water when he travels. Visitors to the farm are selected partly for their ability to adapt to Chris's vegan agenda and many temporarily accept his agenda to experience its merits.

If you are interested in a real-life learning work experience led by a master in beautiful Hawaii, you are welcome to contact Chris at: chriscoconut@gmail.com

We loved visiting the legendary fruitarian, Chris Carter on the Big Island of Hawaii. His selection of plants is truly remarkable and his energy and skill for swinging from branch to branch in the tree tops is an amazing feat in itself.

THE GOVERNORS' VISIT

Nixons visit Baker Creek

Baker Creek Heirloom Seed Company was pleased to host a visit from Missouri Governor Jay Nixon and First Lady Georganne Nixon on Memorial Day, 2015. Owner Jere Gettle enjoyed the opportunity to have lunch and give a personal tour of the seed store, various gardens, and business operations. The Nixons appeared to be delighted to be guests at our farm located in the rural Ozarks community of Mansfield, MO.

First Lady Georganne, an avid gardener, enjoys studying seed catalogs and was quite familiar with the Baker Creek seed catalog. She has also read and subscribes to the Baker Creek publications. She enjoyed discussing gardening with Baker Creek owners Jere and Emilee Gettle and the Baker Creek staff. Missouri's First Lady also expressed her concerns about current trends with modern food production. This was the 1st lady Georganne's second visit.

The Governor himself displayed interest in many projects around the Baker Creek farm and asked multiple questions about the operation of the business. He also updated the Gettles about the different related projects with which he is involved, including a new orchard that has been planted at the State House from trees purchased from local nursery, Stark Bros.

Malloy visits Comstock Ferre & Co.

Comstock Ferre & Co. had the honor of receiving Connecticut Governor Dannel Malloy and his delegation this past summer. Comstock manager, Irina Stoenescu, led a tour of the operations that included a presentation about the two lines of seeds, the eclectic gift sections. Botanical explorer Joseph Simcox led a tour of the Comstock Ferre urban gardens designed specifically to demonstrate how diversity can be achieved in very limited spaces, maintaing the aesthetics and mixing ornamental and edible plants.

The Governor enjoyed learning more of the history of our 200 year old Seed Store and is quite interested in the Non-GMO movement. Located in Wethersfield, Connecticut, Comstock Ferre is New England's oldest operating seed house. Currently owned by the Gettles.

A tribute to a great seed man; Blane Bourgeois and the Atchafalaya Swamp Pea

By Joseph Simcox

In late 2013 Jere received a phone call from Karen Bourgeois. She was calling to ask us if we would be willing to take her late brother's seed collection. It was big she said, "There are several dozen ice chests, dozens of five gallon buckets and two freezers filled to the brim." Jere agreed to pick up the collection, so he and I made our way to Salem, Arkansas, to the Bourgeois farm to pick up the seeds. As I helped go through the mountains of seeds, I started to see packets that I had given to Blane or that I had worked with him growing out. In one big ziplock there was a cowpea that Blane had shown me years before, one that he was particularly proud of. I can still remember what he said as he showed it to me: "Here is a really cool cowpea I've selected; I've named it the 'Atchafalaya Swamp Pea' after my Louisiana childhood." It was a very cool cowpea indeed.

Years passed and I lost contact with Blane; in the fall of 2013 I discovered through a third party that Blane died in 2011. Thanks to the incredible gesture of his sister Karen, Blane's love for preserving diversity is now our responsibility. We here at Baker Creek hope that we can do his work justice and share it with all, even the "Atchafalaya Swamp Pea"!

ANNOUNCING THE 2015 SCHEDULE!

ASHEVILLE ★ N.C.	*NEW!* ALBANY ★ ORE.	*NEW!* WEST BEND ★ WIS.	SEVEN SPRINGS ★ PA.	TOPEKA ★ KAN.
APRIL 11-12	JUNE 6-7	AUG. 8-9	SEPT. 18-20	OCT. 24-25

MOTHER EARTH NEWS
FAIR

FUN-FILLED, HANDS-ON SUSTAINABLE LIFESTYLE EVENTS

Livestock demos

Tons of great advice for self-reliant living

Ed Begley Jr.

Joel Salatin & Pat Foreman

Dan Chiras & Bryan Welch

Experience more than 200 practical workshops presented by the nation's leading experts at each unique event!

RENEWABLE ENERGY ★ SMALL-SCALE AGRICULTURE ★ DIY ★ GARDENING ★ GREEN BUILDING
ECO-FRIENDLY MARKETPLACE ★ CHILDREN'S ACTIVITIES ★ 17 & UNDER GET IN FREE!

www.MotherEarthNewsFair.com

Pre-order your tickets now and save!

Sign up for the free MOTHER EARTH NEWS FAIR weekly newsletter

Find discount lodging ★ Get up-to-date program information

Check out our exhibitors ★ Learn about our sponsors ★ Enter to win special FAIR giveaways

SIGN UP TO HELP OUT	APPLY TO EXHIBIT	SPONSORSHIP INQUIRIES
785-274-4307	785-274-4439	828-298-2139
Help@MotherEarthNewsFair.com	Exhibit@MotherEarthNewsFair.com	Sponsor@MotherEarthNewsFair.com

Save our Soil

The Soil Will Save Us   *By John Roulac*

Many of us are now choosing to eat holistically grown food. We're wanting:

- More nutrition from our foods
- To avoid toxic pesticides
- To create safer conditions for farmers

While these reasons are important, one critical issue is missing from today's conversation about food. Before I identify the major problem we're facing, let me say that the solution is literally under our feet.

If you were to take away only one thing from this article, I'd want it to be this quote from the esteemed soil scientist Dr. Rattan Lal: "A mere 2 percent increase in the carbon content of the planet's soils could offset 100 percent of all greenhouse gas emissions going into the atmosphere."

In the past hundred years we've steadily increased our rate of digging up and burning carbon-rich matter. We're destroying the balance in the carbon trilogy by clearing rainforests, degrading farmland, denuding pasturelands, and burning coal and oil. The carbon trilogy? Yes; think of three carbon sinks: the atmosphere, the oceans, and the humus-sphere.

For those who might not have heard the term, when I say "humus-sphere" I'm not talking about the delicious Middle Eastern dip called hummus, but soil humus: the stable, long-lasting remnant of decaying organic material so essential to the Earth's fertility.

John W. Roulac is the founder and CEO of Nutiva. A leader in the organic food movement, John has made it his life mission to revolutionize the way the world eats. Accordingly, Nutiva has brought to the public awareness such organic superfoods as coconut, hemp, chia, and red palm oil.

John has founded five nonprofit ecological groups—including GMOInside.org and the Nutiva Nourish Foundation, which gives 1 percent of Nutiva's annual sales to sustainable agriculture and environmental programs. He has written four books, including Backyard Composting.

Chemical Ag Is Our Number One Problem, and—Yes—We Have an App for That!

Chemical fertilizers and animal confinement operations give off more greenhouse gasses (GHG) than even transportation, and these fall into the sea. Another leading cause of ocean pollution is chemical runoff from GMO industrial agriculture.

A 2014 Rodale Institute report states: "Organically managed soils can convert carbon CO2 from a greenhouse gas into a food-producing asset." To prevent a massive ocean die-off, let's remove carbon from the atmosphere via organic farming, by sequestering carbon into the soil, expanding the soil's water-holding capacity, and growing nutrient-rich foods through building the soil's humus layer.

Monsanto, the oil industry, and the media ignore the fact that our oceans are becoming acidic carbon sinks. Says Terrie Klinger, Professor of Marine Affairs at the University of Washington, "We can attribute the problems in the oyster hatcheries to the increased carbon in the ocean." If not stopped, this carbon will destroy not only oyster and crab populations but also the phytoplankton that provides more than 50 percent of all oxygen on the planet.

It's time for moms and dads, farmers and ranchers, vegans and Paleo eaters, and climate change advocates and deniers to unite in changing the failing industrial-ag system. We can vote three times a day by eating organic foods. Pasture systems sequester carbon into the soil humus-sphere via intensive grazing, without reliance on toxic, high-GHG chemical fertilizers to grow

carbon-intensive GMO corn or soy. Planting rotational cover crops like vetch or alfalfa is essential. Our path forward is to support regenerative organic farming and pasture-raised meat and milk systems while simultaneously reducing animal consumption.

It's time to revive the ancient wisdom of honoring the land, and in the process heal our oceans and ourselves. Regenerative organic farming is the solution we need.

Are you ready to be part of this solution?

We are excited to have John as a speaker at the Spring Planting Festival (May 3 and 4) and the National Heirloom Expo (Sept 8, 9 and 10)

How To Select Heirloom Varieties For Your Climate

by Randel A. Agrella

There are a number of tools available for gardeners to make good selections from the bewildering diversity of heirloom varieties available. Here are some suggestions, based upon years of experience, working with gardeners.

CLIMATE ZONES—Gardeners often ask for climate zone recommendations. The usual reference point is the USDA Climate Zone Map, (more properly known as the USDA Plant Hardiness Zone Map) which breaks the country into some 11 or 12 climate zones.

While it would be convenient to choose varieties by number, we feel it's an over-simplification, leading to a false sense of security, in making selections.

Why do we say this? Simply because the map is based upon average winter minimum low temperatures. It is designed for evaluating winter hardiness of plants that are expected to overwinter. However, most veggie plants and many other garden plants as well, are summer annuals—they aren't expected to live over from year to year. So summer weather conditions are the main concern, and the USDA map doesn't really address this. For example, a quick glance at the map shows large portions of Alaska's Aleutian Islands to be in Zone 6B. That's the same climate zone as our area of southern Missouri. Obviously, summer on a Pacific island near the Arctic Circle is going to be quite different to a summer in the Ozarks!

So we cannot recommend using USDA Zones in selecting most of the types we list. Fortunately, there are better methods available.

DAYS TO MATURITY--Days-to-maturity means different things in different situations, so care must be used when applying DTM information in your own garden.

For crops that are normally direct-seeded right into the garden, DTM means the length of time from sowing or from germination, to the time of the very first harvest. The figure presupposes more-or-less optimal conditions, but in the real world, gardeners, even very experienced ones, may not have optimal condition, and so maturity is apt to be longer than the given DTM. (In very favorable conditions, actual maturity can come quicker than the listed DTM as well!)

With tomatoes, peppers, eggplants, and probably brassicas like cabbage and broccoli, transplants are usually set outdoors after being started indoors. Here, days-to-maturity means average days from setting transplants to first harvest. So now you've got not just weather factors that can affect the actual DTM, but you've also got the question: how big or how old is an "average transplant"? And it is true that, where larger transplants than 'average' are set out, actual days to maturity will run less than the given DTM figures.

The paragraphs above illustrate the following statement: Days to maturity figures are only average and theoretical, and actual results will vary enormously. They are mainly useful to illustrate relative maturity times: a 90 day tomato is pretty reliably going to take longer than a 70 day tomato to mature. But actual performance is going to vary from year to year.

Furthermore, not all days are created equal! A frost-free day in spring or fall isn't going to support the same amount of growth as a midsummer day would—the sun is lower in the sky and the actual period of sunshine per day is going to be less. So it's necessary to add some time, when figuring days to maturity, if some of the days in question are going to be far removed from the optimal conditions for the plant variety under consideration.

To effectively use days-to-maturity as a selection tool, you must have a clear sense of how long a season you have, that would experience normal conditions for the crop in question. Then seek to grow mainly those varieties that fall within the length of that season.

CHOOSING VARIETIES FROM A CLIMATE SIMILAR TO YOUR OWN—By far the best method we know of for making great heirloom selections also happens to be the most involved, even though the idea is simple: you select varieties that come from similar weather conditions to those under which you will be growing them. Let's cite an example to illustrate:

California--Most of California has relatively mild winters and relatively long, dry summers, with most of the precipitation occurring from late fall into spring. Other parts of the world experience a similar climate: the entire Mediterranean basin including North Africa, also the west coast of Chile and much of South Africa. Plant species, or varieties of these, that come from these areas are likely to succeed well in California conditions. (And in fact, plants originating in California tend to do well in these other areas as well. It works both ways!)

Naturally, the most likely best fits are going to be varieties that originated in your own region, and preference should always be accorded to such varieties! Also, it's important to avoid over-generalizing your climate, or the conditions in other places. Obviously, California isn't all a single climate. Some parts of it are going to be Low-desert Southwest, and some parts are going to be Mountain West, etc.

Here are some recomendations for various regions of the country:

Pacific Northwest—Long frost-free season, often cool summer conditions with lots of rain and cloudy weather. Choose varieties originating in England, Japan, Northern Europe, or eastern Europe, including Russia and Poland.

Low-Desert Southwest—Long frost-free season, intense summer heat, low humidity, mild winters that encourage winter gardening. Choose varieties from the Mediterranean region, Middle East, India, Northern Mexico. Be skeptical about varieties that originated in high humidity loctions, or those from cool summer climates (except that short-season, cool-adapted types make great choices for winter gardening in this area).

High-Desert, Mountain West—Summers are often intense but short. Nights are often cool, resulting in relatively cool soils. Try shorter-season (short days-to-maturity) items from England, Japan, Northern Europe, or eastern Europe, including Russia and Poland.

Southeast—Long frost-free season, intense summer heat, often very high humidity, mild winters encourage winter gardening. Summer garden varieties can be drawn from other hot, humid environments, and preference should be given to varieties originating in Thailand, Brazil, Central America, India. But for winter gardening, varieties grown in summer in some of the coolest climates, may thrive in a fall through spring planting regimen.

Midwest, Plains—Hot summers, sometimes dry and sometimes not, intense heat at times, frequently strong winds, unpredicatable early and late season weather conditions—Select varieties from other areas deep in the interior of Eurasia or even Africa, including: Poland, Russia, Ukraine.

Northeast—Comparatively short summers, often fairly cool, with rain and often fairly high humidity. Choose varieties originating in England, Japan, Northern Europe, or eastern Europe, including Russia and Poland.

As you can see, this method requires you to become somewhat of an armchair traveler. But that's not such a bad thing, as it increases your knowledge of the wider world, and also ties in your own region to the big picture. It can really help you develop deep meaning and a sense of place!

Some crops like Amaranth are well adapted to nearly every climate zone.

Planting Your Juicing Garden

resh vegetable juicing has been enjoying a solar flare of attention and praise for its cleansing and healing properties, as well as its ability to melt toxic fats and to prevent and reverse numerous ailments. However, juicing fresh vegetables will not fade into the dark and dusty closet of fad diets. Juicing is a convenient and delicious way to increase your daily vegetable intake, especially for those with an active lifestyle who might not otherwise find the time to work the daily-recommended dose of vegetables into their hectic day. The health benefits of integrating fresh vegetable juices into your diet speak for themselves. Juicing fresh vegetables from your garden is an incredible way to save time and money in the shopping and cooking process. It is the best way to en-sure that you are always using the safest, freshest produce for juicing. With proper planning, you can enjoy fresh juices year round while most others have to resort to less fresh, and potentially nutrient- defi-cient produce from the grocery store. Each vegetable featured in your juicing garden has its own unique and impressive arsenal of nutritional benefits.

Purple Carrots--All carrots deserve praise for having a high source of soluble fiber, which helps to lower bad cholesterol and glucose. Purple carrots contain higher amounts of anthocyanins than orange carrots; anthocyanins are responsible for the intense purple color of the carrot (this purple pigmented photochemical is also found in blueberries, cherries, plums and beets). Anthocyanins are responsible for much more than just adding a vibrant shade to your juice; they also act as anti-oxidant and anti- inflammatory agents. Anthocyanins improve heart health with a positive effect on cholesterol levels and blood sugar metabolism. Anthocyanins also relieve oxidative stress (a contributing factor in heart disease.) It is best to grow carrots in well drained soil in a spot with full to partial sunlight. You can feature purple carrots in your juices pretty much year round due to a long shelf life and the carrot being a fairly cold tolerant crop. Try adding Baker Creek's Cosmic Purple carrot to your juicing garden this season to keep your heart healthy and your tongue purple all year round.

Beets--The juicing movement has breathed life back into the forgotten work-horse that is the beet. Beets add an earthy and sweet quality to juice that is just not found in any other vegetable. Beets are touted as a blood cleanser, and because they contain anthocyanins (just like purple carrots), they protect against heart disease. Beets are also a good source of fo-

By Shannon McCabe

late, which is very important for pregnant women to eat. The entire beet plant can be put right in the juicer; the root, stalk, and leaf are all perfect for juicing. Beat greens are distinctively salty and mouthwatering. Many people find the cylindrical beet to be a perfect juicing beet; just peel the beet and juice, no need to dice. Just like your carrots, beets will keep for a long time if stored properly. They are cold tolerant, making them available year round. The sweetest beets are those picked after the first frost. The Crapaudine Beet is the perfect size and shape to fit in a juicer, and it is revered by chefs who seek out its exceptional flavor.

Kale and other leafy Greens--Kale is an easy crop to grow with a big nutritional payday. The sulfur and fiber in kale is key in digestion health and lowers cholesterol. Kale also has more iron than beef, making it a staple in the vegetarian diet. The nutrients in kale fight bacteria and viruses and strengthen the immune system. It is important to rotate your leafy greens if you juice regularly. Beet greens, Swiss chard, and spinach lend a rich dark green color to your juice, and they are great for you. It is so important to grow your own leafy greens for juicing to ensure that your delicate greens are always fresh and crisp and have never been sprayed with potentially harmful chemicals. The dark leafy greens are a great source of vitamin C and they help to strengthen the immune system. Kale, chard, spinach and beets are all cool weather crops and can be planted early and late in the season.

Fennel--Fennel is a less common juicing ingredient, despite it having a host of nutritional benefits and an unmistakable flavor. Fennel tastes quite a bit like licorice and goes very well with carrots, celery and apples. Fennel is an excellent source of dietary fiber and is a natural diuretic, which helps to cleanse your body of toxins. Fennel also helps to reduce the inflammation that causes rheumatism and swelling. Fennel is the perfect addition to your juice to relieve an upset stomach. Fennel is a perennial that needs good sunlight and well-drained soil. It is important not to plant fennel near coriander (cilantro) or dill because they will cross-pollinate with the fennel and affect the flavor.

Peppers--The broad range of pepper varieties provide you with a multitude of nutritional benefits and its just up to you to choose which one will suit your needs best. Red peppers add a crisp sweetness and a huge amount of vitamin C. Red peppers actually have more vitamin C than oranges. Red peppers are also a good source of lutein which plays a role in eye health, and the high silicon content of red peppers makes them great for the skin and reduces swelling due to arthritis. Hot peppers are a metabolic stimulant and clear out your sinuses; just a small amount of hot pepper will be perfect to add heat to your juice. Peppers are a warm weather crop that should be started indoors. After the seedling have germinated, it's best to harden them off by putting them outside for a few days before planting them in the ground. Plant seedlings when all danger of frost is gone and the evening temperatures are at least 60 degrees Fahrenheit.

Cucumbers--The ultimate way to add a refreshing and hydrating element to your juice is to add a fresh-picked cucumber (they are about 96% water). Drinking a cucumber juice on a hot day will help to normalize body temperature; this can also be effective when you have a fever. It is also a natural diuretic and will aid in waste removal as well as help dissolve kidney stones. Cucumbers are one of the most exciting plants to grow in your garden; they are a warm weather crop that needs staking or trellising. Choose a sunny spot in your garden, perhaps closest to your fence, to allow the vines to grow up or be trained up. Cucumbers are incredibly prolific and are most available right when you need their cooling juice the most: in the heat of summer. A thin skinned variety of cucumber is ideal for juicing; they are best picked and immediately juiced. The Muncher Cucumber is perfectly thin skinned and prolific.

Parsley--The best addition to your morning juice to freshen your breath, Parsley is known to treat halitosis because it cleans out a toxic colon, which is often the underlying cause of bad breath. Parsley also contains folate, which helps to protect blood vessels and reduces the risk of heart attack. The high levels of carotenoids in this herb make it good for your vision. You may find a lot of similarities in nutritional benefits as well as growing traits between parsley and carrots because they are in the same plant family. Both plants like full to partial sunlight and are true biennials (which means it takes two years for the plants' life cycles to complete) however they are both grown as annuals.

One of the most fascinating aspects of juicing is the ability to customize your juice to your desired health benefits and taste preference. Below are some of Baker Creek's favorite juicing recipes.

Purple Juice

- 1 large beet (cylindrical purple is best)
- 2 apples or pears
- 1 fennel Bulb
- 2 large purple carrots

Wash all produce thoroughly; core and peel apples. Dice the fennel bulb to fit in juicer. Cylindrical beets and carrots should be able to be juiced whole. The vibrant purple color of this juice will be a feast for your eyes (especially since fennel and carrots help improve vision health!)

Green Juice

- 2 large handfuls of kale or any leafy green
- 1 medium handful of parsley
- 1 large cucumber
- 1 half a lemon
- 1 pear or apple (Asian pears are great)

When you grow your own cucumbers, there is no need to peel them; just quarter and feed through the juicer. Wash peel and core the apple. Squeeze the lemon into the finished product. This juice is tangy and filling; it's great for breakfast to ensure good breath and a settled stomach. It's also a great drink when you feel a cold coming on.

Red Juice

- 1 large red pepper
- 1 handful of red grapes
- 1 large handful of spinach or other leafy greens
- half of a fresh hot pepper or a pinch of cayenne pepper
- 2 stalks of celery

Remove seeds and stem from pepper. Wash grapes thoroughly and feed through juicer along with all other ingredients. Slowly add the hot pepper to taste to your desired level of heat. Garnish with a nasturtium to add a peppery element. This juice will clear out your sinuses!

modern farmer

Sign up for 1 year (4 issues) of *Modern Farmer* for only $19.95!

Canadian orders add U.S. $20; all other countries add $35 for shipping and handling.

Modern Farmer is filled with deeply-reported stories from around the world as well as illustrated how tos and seasonal recipes, all to give you more information about the plants, animals, issues, people, weather, tools and travel in today's world of agriculture!

Subscribe online at modernfarmer.com

Planting Seeds of Peace

By Kathy McFarland

Jere amd Emilee Gettle and the Baker Creek staff work extensively to supply seeds to some of the world's poorest countries, as well as here at home in community and school gardens and other educational projects. We have an ongoing partnership with Convoy of Hope and donate hundreds of thousands of seed packets to go to Haiti and other disaster-ravaged countries.

Our friend Asma Eschen

Enjoys handing out our seeds to the children of Afghanistan as part her work teaching people to grow their own food. She is the Co-founder of The Bare Roots Tree Project in conjunction with the First Presbyterian Church of San Anselmo, Ca

Wayne Auto Spa's Victory Garden and Learning Center

Here in the States, many community organizations contact us for assistance in providing seeds for their community garden projects. One such project is The Greenhouse Project at Wayne Auto Spa in Wayne, NJ. Bob Burke operates an innovative and environmentally friendly car wash and lube business in which he treats and recycles water, utilizes solar and wind turbine power, uses only biodegradable soaps and replaces unneeded paved areas with organic gardens, chicken and bee hives. He is using his business to also make a difference to the community.

Located on the grounds of the Wayne Auto Spa, Burke has also created an organic Victory Garden and Learning Center that grows organic produce, eggs and honey for free distribution to nonprofits. Using seeds donated by Baker Creek, the garden has been able to donate bushels of fresh produce to Eva's Village, providing fresh produce full of healthy vitamins and naturally good, delicious flavor to homeless mothers and children.

Paradise Ridge Neighborhood Garden

On the West Coast, Eric Gilson of Paradise, California, requests a seed donation for Paradise Ridge Neighborhood Garden, a community garden with a purpose to also educate. The garden is on land donated by the local grange with which Eric is affiliated, and some of the seeds have already been planted. He plans to start a seed library in addition to the community garden. Some of the goals of the PRNG project include providing food for low income and single parents, offering a place to garden for free, including children and teens, offering canning classes, offering classes taught by master gardeners, etc. In addition to the PRNG project, Eric also volunteers at a head start school for 3 year old children that has a small garden that has 24 wine barrel size garden spots and 8 small beds.

Donating seeds to such school and community garden projects is Baker Creek's way of making a difference in the world as children and adults from all walks of life benefit from growing and eating healthy food.

Algonquin/Lake in the Hills Interfaith Food Pantry Victory Garden

Laurie Selpien of Algonquin, Illinois, provides an update of the result of Baker Creek's donation of seeds to the Algonquin/Lake in the Hills Interfaith Food Pantry Victory Garden. The food pantry gardens utilize available space at 2 locations, comprised of four gardens in total. They work with local government officials, churches, and various civic groups united in purpose to grow food on public land that has historically sat idle. These under-utilized spaces now help feed 300+ families through vegetables harvested from these gardens. The gardens are also used as a means to educate as volunteers highlight the histories behind the heirloom varieties they grow, as well as offering a host of display gardens to demonstrate traditional, vertical arrangements, raised beds, containers, straw bales, and even handicap gardening methods to show gardening can be simple and thought of in untraditional ways.

Laurie points out that everything they grow goes directly to the food pantry the same day it is picked. They distribute the vegetables in a comfortable farmers market setting completely free of charge and include tips and recipes. Employees of Algonquin Waste Water Treatment plant volunteer to plant, care for and harvest the vegetable on their own time. They have also teamed up with Jacob's High School's Green Eagles, who raised tomato plants from seed; those tomato plants were then given to over 50 recipients to take home and grow, many of whom are first time vegetable growers.

Chantilly Montessori School Gardens

Norma Spurlock calls herself the Grandmother Gardener who volunteers at Chantilly Montessori School in Charlotte, North Carolina, where her grandsons attend. Each class there has an organic garden tended by students pre-kindergarten through 6th grades. With the help of teachers and volunteers, students plant donated Baker Creek seeds, water, and ultimately harvest the produce. Some of the harvest is prepared, served, and eagerly eaten by students, while some is donated to the local food kitchen. In this small way, Norma says that with Baker Creek's help, the school aids the community while teaching students how to grow healthy, nutritious food "from the ground up." She also thanks Baker Creek for "fixing our economy 'from the ground up, starting with food.'"

Amaranth

100-200 seeds per packet. Warm-season, New World native adds lots of color to the garden. This crop is easy to grow and makes delicious greens and grain. A good ornamental plant for landscaping. Amaranth seed is one of the most complete proteins available from any plant. Direct-sow the tiny seeds when soil is warm, barely covering, and thin to 1-2 feet apart. Can also be started indoors and transplanted.

Dreadlocks

AURELIA'S VERDE #AM141   *New!*
Native amaranth from Guatemala that flowers light green; primarily used for grain which is rich in vitamin B, vitamin A, vitamin E and iron; this variety has been revived in the Mayan communities of Baja Verapaz after almost being lost during the civil war; named after Aurelia, the woman whose family revived and saved seeds of this amaranth. Pkt $2.50

CONGO #AM140
We loved growing and cooking this delicious variety from the Democratic Republic of Congo, brought to us by a friend who is an aid worker at a religious school. In Congo this crop is one of the staples of their diet, being a source of vitamin A, C, as well as calcium, iron, potassium, and zinc. The young leaves are amazing cooked like spinach, and the tall plants produce abundantly and yield green flower heads. Pkt $3.00

DREADLOCKS #AM144   *New!*
A fountain of eye-catching magenta-burgundy blooms! Here's a different amaranth—curious flower-heads in a weeping habit, with "tassels" sometimes reaching down to the ground. Plants seldom exceed 3 feet in height. A form of Love-Lies-Bleeding, so the seeds and young leaves are edible. Combine with Spider Flower or flowering tobacco for some serious drama! Pkt $2.75

ELENA'S ROJO #AM142   *New!*
Native amaranth from Guatemala that flowers deep red; primarily used for grain which is rich in vitamin B, vitamin A, vitamin E and iron; this variety has been revived in the Mayan communities of Baja Verapaz after almost being lost during the civil war; named after Elena, the woman whose family revived and saved seeds of this amaranth. Pkt $2.50

ELEPHANT HEAD #AM116
This heirloom was brought to the USA from Germany in the 1880's and so named because the huge flower heads often take on the appearance of an elephant's trunk. The 3- to 5-foot plants produce flowers that are deep reddish-purple in color. A striking variety that is among the most unique we sell. Pkt $2.50

GOLDEN GIANT #AM117
Attractive golden-colored flower heads produce up to 1 lb of white seed per plant, making this a very heavy producer. Plants grow to about 6' and are easy to grow. Pkt $2.50

GREEN CALALOO #AM126
A popular green vegetable in many countries, including many islands of the Caribbean where this plant is famous for Calaloo Seafood Soup. Light green leaves are great in stews, stir-fries and soups, having a tangy, spinach-like flavor. Easy to grow in warm weather. Pkt $2.00

Congo Amaranth with our manager John Brazaitis

Pygmy Torch

Love-Lies-Bleeding-Red

Green Calaloo

Love-Lies-Bleeding-Green

Tricolor Aurora Yellow

Guatemala Amaranth: Elena's Rojo, Aurelia's Verde, Juana's Orange

GREEN THUMB #AM145 *New!*

Compact size and velvety, apple-green flower heads make "Green Thumb" a great choice for containers or mass plantings. Bushy little plants grow quickly, making a bold statement in a hurry. The 2' tall plants are often planted with "Pygmy Torch". Pkt $2.50

HOPI RED DYE #AM134

Originally grown as a dye plant by the southwestern Hopi Nation, this variety has the reddest seedlings of any amaranth known, making it a natural for micro-green mixes! Plants reach 4-6 feet and cut a most striking figure in the garden! The Hopis use the deep-red flower bract as a natural dye to color their world-renowned piki bread. Pkt $2.50

JUANA'S ORANGE #AM143 *New!*

A lovely orange variety from Guatemala; primarely used for grain which is rich in vitamin B, vitamin A, vitamin E and iron; this variety has been revived in the Mayan communities of Baja Verapaz after almost being lost during the civil war; named after Juana, the woman whose family revived and saved seeds of this delicious variety. Pkt $2.50

LOVE-LIES-BLEEDING GREEN #AM113

A wonderful green version of the lovely "Love-Lies-Bleeding" with long flower-ropes that are lime green; attractive and easy to grow. A must to blend with the red. Pkt $2.00

LOVE-LIES-BLEEDING RED #AM103

60 days. Tall, 3'- 4' plants are covered with very long rope-like flowers that are a deep, brilliant red color. One of the most striking plants for any garden and so easy to grow. Amaranth is one of our favorite crops! A good seed producer, too. This is a very old heirloom, a pre-1700 variety, that was very popular. Leaves are tasty as cooked greens. Pkt $2.50 *or 1 oz $8.50*

MOLTEN FIRE #AM127

Simply stunning, this old favorite produces leaves that are a fire-crimson color, so intense and beautiful! One of the best varieties for edible landscaping as the young leaves are quite tasty and nutritious when cooked. Pkt $2.25

OPOPEO #AM102

60 days. Beautiful, large, red, upright flower spikes and bronze-green foliage make this Mexican heirloom a real knockout in the vegetable garden. Tasty leaves are tender when picked young. Easy to grow from seed. From Opopeo, Mexico. Pkt $2.25

ORANGE GIANT #AM121

Ornamental 6- to 8-foot tall plants produce giant, golden-orange heads, with the stems golden as well. Each plant can produce up to 1 lb of seed; a beautiful variety that is tasty and productive. Pkt $2.50

POINSETTIA MIX #AM132

Incredible range of foliage colors really lights up the garden! This is a formula mix of Amaranthus tricolor colors: green with creamy top leaves, rose-red to chocolate brown, and brilliant red-orange to yellow. Superb in the border, where it reaches about 2 feet in height. Pkt $2.50

Orange Giant

Elephant Head

PYGMY TORCH #AM146 *New!*

Amazing dwarf amaranth variety offers all the style and brilliant color of ornamental amaranth, but at a reasonable size! Cute little plants reach only to about 2 feet in height, making them perfect for smaller gardens or containers. The rich crimson blooms offer an unexpected pop of color. The flowers dry nicely and of course the green-to-burgundy leaves and shiny black seeds are edible and delicious! Pkt $2.50

RED CALALOO #AM135

Similar to our Green Calaloo, being likewise used as greens in the Caribbean and elsewhere. But this one has gorgeous red concentric zoning on the rounded, slightly lobed leaves. A superior amaranth for greens and salads, and sure to become popular at farmers' markets. Pkt $2.25

TRICOLOR AURORA YELLOW #AM138

2-5 feet tall. Stunning contrast between the dark green lower leaves and the flower-like upper leaves—looking for all the world like oversized, yellow poinsettia flowers. Spectacular in a mass planting, especially when sunshine frames the soft yellow flowers against the dark-green foliage. Pkt $2.50

Flowers always make people better, happier, and more helpful; they are sunshine, food and medicine for the soul.

-Luther Burbank

Asparagus

Beloved early-spring crop in Europe since ancient times, asparagus is a perennial plant that starts slow but yields for many years. The best way to grow from seed is to start indoors 2-3 months before last frost. Be sure that the young seedlings receive bright light, to make the strong growth. Set young plants outdoors when weather is warm, growing them in a nursery bed of your finest soil, where they will receive attentive care. In fall, or the following spring, set the plants into their final garden location—spacing them 2 feet or more from their neighbors. Modest yield may be taken the third year, and a full harvest every spring thereafter.

MARY WASHINGTON #AS101

Popular variety, long green spears. Great taste and has been the most popular asparagus in American gardens for the last century. Pkt (100 seeds) $2.50 *or 1 oz $7.00*

PRECOCE D'ARGENTEUIL #AS102

An old traditional heirloom, this gourmet variety is highly esteemed in Europe for its delicious stems with rose-colored buds that can be blanched white. Italian Seed. Pkt (75 seeds) $2.75

POPPED AMARANTH OR QUINOA

Two ancient Andean grains, quinoa and amaranth (known as kiwicha in the Andes) have gained a common acceptance thanks to their great taste and highly nutritious properties. Both grains are a complete source of protein in comparison to grains like wheat and rice. These super grains contain the essential amino acid lysine, as well as iron to give you a power packed treat.

INGREDIENTS

• 1/2 - 1 cup Amaranth or pre-washed quinoa • 1/2 teaspoon salt (optional)
• 1 teaspoon vegetable oil (optional)
• Get creative and add lime powder, coffee and ancho chili powder

PREPARATION

1. Quinoa is often pre-washed before packaging, which should be stated on the box. If not, rinse quinoa thoroughly and let dry).

2. Heat a large skillet over medium-high heat.

3. Add 1/2 teaspoon of the vegetable oil if desired (this will help the salt adhere to the grains later, if you are going to eat them like popcorn, but it's not necessary for popping them). Add about 1/4 cup of grain, just enough to cover the bottom of the pan with a single layer. Stir grains with a wooden spoon as they pop - you will hear a sound and the grains may jump out of the pan. Amaranth grains pop very dramatically and change from dark yellow to white, while quinoa grains have a more subtle pop and turn a toasted brown color.

4. Once the grains have mostly popped, remove them from the heat and transfer to a plate to cool. Watch quinoa especially closely and remove it from the heat when it is golden brown and toasted, before it starts to burn.

Continue to pop the grains in batches. Toss popped grain with salt and serve.

Mary Washington Asparagus

Artichoke
& Cardoon

Green Globe Artichoke

Originated in the Mediterranean region. Long-season plants won't overwinter reliably north of Zone 7. To get a crop of artichokes in one year, start seeds indoors in pots 2-3 months before last frost date in spring. Move the pots outdoors when four leaves have developed, when temperatures are occasionally freezing, protecting them if temps fall below 29 degrees. 2-4 weeks of exposure to cool temps "vernalizes" young seedlings, preparing them to bloom later in the season after plants have grown large. Cardoon may also be started early indoors but vernalizing isn't necessary. Both kinds are then grown in very rich soil, in full sun. They need excellent drainage but ample moisture. They may benefit from some mid-afternoon shade in hot-summer areas.

GOBBO DI NIZZIA #AR103
A rare cardoon from Italy, its broad white stalks are eaten fried, sauteed, pickled and in soups. Italians eat it raw, dipped in olive oil. The root is also edible, tasty, and can be used like parsnips. The plant is similar in culture and appearance to artichokes. Cardoons have been popular in Europe since ancient Rome. Beautiful ornamental plants. Pkt (25 seeds) $2.50

GREEN GLOBE #AR101
Tasty; needs a fairly long, mild growing season, or grow as an annual. A colorful plant that makes a great ornamental. Pkt (75 seeds) $2.50 *or 1 oz $7.50*

VIOLETTA PRECOCE #AR104
Lovely, pointed, purple artichokes. Purple varieties have been popular in Italy for hundreds of years and are more tender than green types. Needs a mild climate. We are glad to introduce this heirloom to the USA. Pkt (25 seeds) $2.50

VIOLET DE PROVENCE #AR107
This French heirloom is noted for its fine flavor and pretty purple buds that are lovely on the big, ornamental plants, especially when the buds open. Rare outside Europe. Pkt (25 seeds) $2.50

PURPLE OF ROMAGNA #AR105
Large, round-headed purple chokes, tender and tasty, perfect for warm season areas, or grow with shelter. So popular with chefs, and is a sure seller at the finer markets. We are proud to introduce this regional Italian favorite. Pkt (25 seeds) $2.50

ROUGE D'ALGER #AR106
This exciting heirloom Cardoon was developed in Algeria, hence the name. It has big, edible and ornamental stalks that are blushed in pale red, which is so striking against the blue-green leaves. The flowers are also beautiful and can be cooked before the buds open, like a small artichoke. One of the prettiest historic varieties you can plant. Pkt (25 seeds) $3.00

Rouge d'Alger Cardoon

Purple of Romagna Artichoke

Asian Beans

A diverse group of many relatives of the common bean. Many grow much better than common beans in warm weather, and most tend to be more disease-resistant.

ASIAN WINGED BEAN #AB112

(Psophocarpus tetragonolobus) This is one of the most unique beans; it produces delicious pods with four winged edges, the leaves are cooked like spinach and the roots have a delicious, nutty flavor. This high-protein bean is an excellent crop and is so useful in the kitchen. The plants are tropical and do best in warm areas. They will not produce well when the days are long, so it may not yield until fall. Soak seeds 24 hours before planting. We have had a hard time keeping any winged beans on the shelf ever since Mother Earth News ran an article on this bean. Limited quantities. Pkt (15 seeds) $3.00

HYACINTH BEAN "MOONSHADOW"

#AB106 (Dolichos lablab) Beautiful purple pods are used in Asia as a curry and stir-fry vegetable. Pick when small and tender, as **old pods and dry beans may be poisonous!** The long, rambling vine is also very ornamental

with lilac-colored blossoms and purple stems. Thomas Jefferson planted this fine bean at Monticello. Pkt (25 seeds) $3.00

HYACINTH BEAN "RED LEAVED"

#AB115   Here is one of the most beautiful and lovely of all legumes. Vines display pretty crimson-red-tinged foliage! A perfect display of brilliant color and these also produce lovely, deep purple flowers and pods. One of the most fascinating plants for ornamental landscaping. These will amaze your friends. If pods are eaten they must be picked when small, as **old pods and seeds can be poisonous**. Pkt (20 seeds) $3.25

JICAMA OR YAM BEAN #AB105

(Pachyrhizus erosus) 120 days. Long vines can grow twenty feet long and produce delicious tubers. These have become very popular in the last few years. Very long season; these must be started very early in all areas except the deep South. Caution: **The seeds and pods are poisonous**, but the small pods are cooked in the Philippines. Pkt (25 seeds) $2.50

"One who plants a garden, plants happiness."

—CHINESE PROVERB

Winged Beans

Hyacinth Bean "Moonshadow"

Beans

(Phaseolus vulgaris) 40-60 seeds per packet. An ancient staple crop grown throughout North and South America.

ARIKARA YELLOW #BN145

Bush, 80-85 days. A tan to creamy yellow dry bean originally from the Arikara nation of the Dakota Territory, introduced by Oscar Will about 1915. Has been identified as the same variety collected by the Lewis and Clark expedition and grown by Thomas Jefferson at Monticello. Drought tolerant and productive; a living piece of the Old West! Pkt $2.75

BEURRE DE ROCQUENCOURT #BN128

Bush. A productive heirloom wax bean named for Rocquencourt, France, a town in France's rich farming country. Wax beans were introduced to France in the 1840's from Algeria, and this variety is surely a descendant of those early beans. The bush plants set good yields early and produce well in most climates. These beans are favored by cooks for their fine-flavored pods that are a bright waxy-yellow in color. This variety was listed in Mother Earth News as a favorite of well-known writer William Woys Weaver. Pkt $2.75

BLAUHILDE #BN165 *New!*

Pole, 64 days. Spectacular climbing type makes enormous purple pods! Pods stay tender and stringless, even at 10 inches long! Plants are gorgeous in the garden as well, with the rose-purple of the blooms contrasting nicely with the rich, deep purple of the developing pods. Vigorous, productive vines reach a moderate 9 feet in height. The richly-flavored pods are best appreciated when used fresh off the vines. This heirloom from Germany is tolerant to mosaic virus, too.. Pkt $2.75

BLUE LAKE BUSH 274 #BN119

60 days. This dark-green bean has been a standard for over 40 years. The bush plants set heavy yields of flavorful pods that are tender and crisp. Developed in 1961 from the Pole Blue Lake. Pkt $2.50 *or 1/2 lb $5.50*

BOLITA #BN133

Half-runner. This bean was one of the original varieties brought by the Spanish as they settled New Mexico. It is still grown by a few Spanish farms to this day, due to its dry bean rich flavor and creamy texture. Better than the Pinto bean, this small, creamy-tan bean cooks fast and is the tastiest part of several centuries of NM history. Vines produce very early. Pkt $2.50

BORLOTTO BUSH OR TONGUES OF FIRE

#BN141   Bush, 65-70 day. Also known as Horto. Reputedly originated in Tierra del Fuego in South America, but extremely popular in Italy, where cooks like the beans' subtle characteristic of picking up other flavors from a dish. Bush-type plants yield pods of white with flame-like red streaks, making great snaps when very young; beans are light pink with darker red mottling, reminiscent of the Cranberry Bean. Makes an outstanding baked bean. Pkt $2.75

CALIMA #BN144

Bush, 50-55 days. French filet type pods of dark

green color, slim straight shape, and superior flavor! Pods are held conveniently at the top of the stocky bushes; pick them when no thicker than a pencil. Fine for fresh use, canning and freezing. Pkt $2.75

CANTARE #BN153 *A favorite!*
Bush, 50-55 days. Superior producer of nice straight dark-green pods for snaps. The slim 4-5-inch pods are stringless and the flavor is every bit as outstanding as the yield! This French variety makes a fine crop for market growers or home gardeners. Excellent tolerance to bean mosaic virus. Pkt $2.50

CONTENDER (BUFF VALENTINE) #BN102
Bush, 50 days. A superb bush bean with huge yields of excellent-quality pods. Earlier than most others & perfect for market. Intro. 1949. Pkt $2.50

DRAGON TONGUE #BN126
Bush. This famous Dutch heirloom bean has an incomparable flavor. The tender and superbly delicious 7" pods are yellow with amazing purple streaks! Also makes a tasty shelled bean. Popular with chefs and gourmets. Compact plants set high yields. Pkt $2.75

GALOPKA #BN161 *New!*
Bush, 60 days. Delicious yellow pods are produced abundantly on compact plants. The pods are richly flavored. A Polish variety that is especially good for freezing. Pkt $2.75

GOLD MARIE VINING #BN142
Pole, 70-75 days. Rampant vining plants produce tons of large golden pods. The gorgeous pods are ideal when harvested at 6-8 inches, but are often tender at much larger dimensions! The massive pods are a bright, clear buttercup yellow, flat and sometimes almost resemble a loose spiral shape, looking voluptuous hanging from the robust vines. This worthy variety was nearly lost commercially and was preserved by backyard seed savers. Pkt $3.00

GOLDEN WAX #BN104
55 days. Delicious golden-yellow pods are stringless and are of good quality with extra-fine rich flavor. This old-time favorite has bush plants. Pkt $2.50 *or 1/2 lb $5.50*

GOOD MOTHER STALLARD #BN148
Pole, 85-90 days. Gorgeous, plump maroon-and-white beans are great in soups, where their creamy texture and hearty, nutty flavor really shine. Generations of gardeners have grown this pole variety that yields 5-6 beans per pod—outstandingly productive! Originally introduced by our friend Glenn Drowns. Superior in baked beans, and also makes a fine shell bean. Pkt $2.75

HARICOT TARBAIS #BN149
(Pole), 90 days. Plump snowy-white variety has been grown for centuries around the village of Tarbais, in southwestern France. Used primarily as a dry bean, including its traditional forte, as a main ingredient of cassoulet. Skins unusually thin and delicate, lower starch content than other types, and of remarkable tenderness! Pkt $2.75

HENDERSON'S BLACK VALENTINE #BN103
Pole, 53 days. Introduced in 1897 by Peter Henderson & Co., this excellent fresh snap bean

Meraviglia di Venezia

Cantare

Gold Marie Vining

Blauhilde

Borlotto Bush or Tongues of Fire

Heirloom Green Beans with Brown Sugar and Mint

Simple but classic dish. This dish does not segregate green bean types. You can mix and match. The sweetness and the punch of the fresh mint with the green beans will be a family favorite. Add some peppery honey almonds for crunch.

INGREDIENTS

2 handfuls of stemmed green beans
1 T of sea salt
1 T of coconut cream or butter
2 Garlic cloves
½ C of chopped mint
2 T of brown sugar
½ C Slivered raw almonds
1 t of honey
Pinch of cayenne powder (Optional)
cracked pepper (Optional)

PREPARATION

1. Finely chop the mint leaves
2. Toss your almonds, honey, salt and cayenne in a bowl
3. Place on a small greased baking pan and in the oven at 325 for 6-8 mins
4. Cool and reserve
5. Add your butter and garlic to the pan. Follow with beans
6. Top with brown sugar, salt and cracked pepper
7. In the final stages of cooking (beans will be bright green) add the mint
8. Plate up and top with your toasted almonds.

Purple Teepee

Purple Podded Pole

has tasty pods. Also makes a fine dry soup bean. Great yields! Any seed that has "Henderson's" name on it just has to be good—that's why we offer so many of his fine varieties throughout our catalog. A perfect all-purpose bean! Pkt $2.00

HIDATSA RED INDIAN #BN146
Half-runner, 85 days. Here's another Dakota variety, so you know it's rugged! This one comes from the Hidatsa people of the upper Missouri River Valley; was introduced in Oscar Will's Pioneer Indian Collection of seeds in 1915. Plump rose-red beans for dry use; plants climb only 3 feet or so. Pkt $2.75

HUTTERITE SOUP #BN121
Bush, 70 days. This variety is revered for making fabulous soups, having a rich creamy texture and fine flavor. The seeds are an ivory color and the bush plants are productive. The variety was grown and preserved by the Hutterite Christians, who follow the teachings of Jakob Hutter, their Austrian leader. They emigrated to North America in the 1870s, and still have colonies in several Canadian provinces and northern US states. Pkt $2.50

JACOB'S CATTLE #BN115
Bush. An old-time bean from the New England states, the white and maroon-mottled beans have long been a staple for baking and soups. This early, bush variety is also good as a snap bean. Pkt $2.50

LANDRETH STRINGLESS #BN151
Bush, 55 days. This meaty variety debuted in 1885. It is a flavorful, stringless bean and boasts heavy yields. The pods are medium green in color and a little over 5" long. The seeds are a rich chocolate or coffee brown. D. Landreth Seed Co., one of the oldest surviving American seed houses, proudly proclaimed it as a favorite; "one of the finest pod varieties for the home garden, market garden and canner. Pkt $2.50

MAYFLOWER #BN111
Bush. This is the bean that is said to have come to America with the Pilgrims in 1620. This old cutshort green bean has great flavor and the red/white beans are quite tasty. A long-time staple in the Carolinas. Pkt $2.50

MERAVIGLIA di VENEZIA #BN166 *New!*
Bush type. The name translates to "Marvel of Venice" and this stringless sort is certainly that! The pods are yellow, wax type but are wide and flat like Romas. The combination opens exciting new opportunities in the kitchen! Highly recommended for bean salads, especially those recipes using Modeno balsamic vinegar. Very elegant and unusual. Pkt $3.00

MCCASLAN 42 POLE #BN108
62 days. This is a selection of the old McCaslan bean that was grown by the McCaslan family of Georgia before 1900. This strain was selected by the Corneli Seed Company of Saint Louis in 1962. The dark-green pods are stringless and full of flavor. The white seeds are also great for a dry bean. Extra productive and hardy. Pkt $2.00

MISSOURI WONDER #BN112
Pole, 70 days. Old-time cornfield type. Vines produce flavorful pods even under stress. The dry beans look like pintos. Introduced around 1931 and grown in corn fields, as corn stalks support them quite well. Pkt $2.50

MOUNTAINEER HALF RUNNER #BN152 *New!*
55 days. Also called Old Dutch Half Runner) Tender snap bean is a longtime Southern favorite! Plants are amazingly productive, although they reach only 24-

Calima

Royalty Purple Pod

Galopka

36 inches, and may be grown without trellising. For snaps the pods should be picked at about 4 inches in length, at which size they usually contain very few strings; excellent for canning and freezing! Flavor is rich and very "beany." Or use the plump, snow-white beans shelled or dried. This variety originated in Germany and was carried into the Dutch Fork region of South Carolina by early settlers. Pkt $2.50

OJO DE CABRA #BN140
Pole. The name means "Eye of the Goat" and the lengthwise brown stripes that some of the seeds exhibit are certainly reminiscent of the vertical pupil of a goat's eye. There are a number of native varieties of this name; ours appears to be the Tarahumara Indians landrace type, since it throws a few dark purple beans. A favorite variety in Baja California and northern Mexico, this unusual bean cooks up firm and sweet and keeps its rich color. Pkt $3.00

OLD HOMESTEAD (KENTUCKY WONDER POLE) #BN105
65 days. This homesteaders' heirloom was first mentioned in *The Country Gentleman* magazine in 1864 under the name of Texas Pole. It was not until 1877 that it was introduced as Kentucky Wonder by James J.H. Gregory & Sons and has been popular ever since. It is a pole bean with 6"- 8" green pods that are very tender when cooked and have a great flavor. In 1896 Peter Henderson & Co. said, "This we regard as far ahead of any other green Pole Bean." They also said it was 10 days earlier. Pkt $2.50 *or 1/2 lb $5.50*

PURPLE PODDED POLE #BN114
This delicious heirloom was discovered in the Ozark mountains by Henry Fields in the 1930's and is still requested by many old-timers of this region. The pods are bright purple, stringless, and tender. Plants grow to 6' and produce heavy yields. Pkt $2.75

PURPLE TEEPEE #BN162 *New!*
Bush, 60 days. Super-productive bush type, yielding straight, purple pods. These are held above the foliage--a great advantage that makes the pods easier to see and harvest, and keeps them from contact with the ground. Pick them young, at 4-5 inches, for flavorful, tender snaps.. Pkt $2.75

RATTLESNAKE POLE #BN109
This pole bean is easy to grow and produces lots of green pods that have purple streaks. Good flavor and very tender; the speckled seeds are popular in soup. This variety is great for hot, humid areas. Pkt $3.00

ROMA II #BN107
Bush, 55 days. This is an improved Romano, bush-type, green bean that produces loads of 6" to 7"-wide pods that are very flavorful. Pkt $2.25 *or 1/2 lb $5.50*

ROYALTY PURPLE POD #BN101
Bush, 56 days. Tender, bright purple pods turn green when cooked. Very ornamental, beautiful and tasty. A good home garden variety. Pkt $2.50 *or 1/2 lb $5.50*

SAXA #BN163 *New!*
Bush, 60 days. Very compact bush type

Dragon's Tongue

bean that has long been a favorite in Germany and the Netherlands. Disease-tolerant plants thrive in cooler conditions than many bean varieties. 4-5 inch, round pods of fine flavor are best when harvested very young. Deserving of more attention among American gardeners but until now not widely available. Pkt $2.75

SNOW CAP #BN147

75 days, Half-runner. This very large, beautiful bean has a distinctive white half or cap, the other half being beige with barn-red and brown markings which it retains when cooked. Mild, earthy flavor complements the silky smooth texture. Pkt $2.75

STATE HALF RUNNER #BN110

60 days. Short, 3' semi-vining plants produce 4" pods that have a very strong, beany taste. Popular in many areas and high yielding; bushy vines do not require staking. Selected by West Virginia University. Pkt $2.00

WHITE RICE #BN116

Bush. An old heirloom that produces slender seeds that are about 1/3 " long. They are great in rice dishes and casseroles, as they cook fast and have a delicious, rich taste. Pkt $2.50

Good Mother Stallard

Heirloom Bean Soup with Chervil

Soup never fails. This one is great for rainy days and keeps well in the cooler. Make sure to soak. You can use any dried bean but I selected one for flavor and texture.

INGREDIENTS
1 C Good Mother Stallard Beans
4 C water
½ C chopped heirloom carrots
2 T of Olive Oil
½ C fresh garlic
½ C chopped celery
1 C chopped onion
½ C fresh Chervil
2 QT vegetable stock
1 t sea salt
Pinch ground black pepper

PREPARATION
Soak the beans in water overnight. This cut the cooking time drastically.

Small chop all produce. I even use the celery leaves.

Heat olive oil in soup pan on med-high heat and sauté the vegetables. Put a little golden color.

Deglaze with your vegetable stock and add beans. This should cover them by couple inches.

Simmer on med heat covered for 45 minutes.

Place in bowls and stir in fresh picked chervil for a bright blast of flavor.

Snow Cap

Hidatsa Red Indian

Extra Precoce a Grano Violetto Fava

Aquadulce Fava Bean

Fava or Broad Beans

(Vicia faba) Mediterranean native that is quite different from ordinary beans. Prefers cool weather.

AQUADULCE #FB103
85 days. This 19th-century Spanish heirloom produces large, white beans, extra early in the season; a great protein source for cool climate areas. Pkt (25 seeds) $2.50

BROAD WINDSOR #FB101
75 days. Yields gourmet high-protein beans on upright non-branching plants. An old English favorite. Pkt (25 seeds) $2.50

EXTRA PRECOCE A GRANO VIOLETTO #FB105
This extra early variety produces long pods that are filled with 6 large beans that are a pretty purple color and are sweet tasting. A unique and colorful variety from Italy. Pkt (25 seeds) $3.00

IANTO'S FAVA #FB104
Originally introduced by Alan Kapuler of Peace Seeds. A large-seeded Guatemalan variety that reaches 6 ft tall! The bright yellow seeds are reputed to contain elevated levels of dopamine, and may have benefits for those at risk for Alzheimer's disease. A fine plant for improving garden soil. Abundant production of delicious fava beans. Pkt (20 seeds) $3.50

Dixie Speckled Butterpea Lima

Lima Beans

(Phaseolus lunatus) Originally grown in South America.

CHRISTMAS- POLE LIMA #LB104
95 days. Very large white beans with beautiful, dark red splashes, rich flavor; heavy yields even in very hot weather; long vines. Heirloom. Pkt (40 seeds) $2.50

DIXIE SPECKLED BUTTERPEA #LB103
76 days. Very productive. Beans are about the size of peas; red-speckled with a deep purple-rust color and grow well in hot weather. A delicious baby lima. Bush plants. Pkt (40 seeds) $2.00

HENDERSON'S BUSH LIMA #LB101
71 days. Introduced in 1888 by Peter Henderson & Co. and one of their most famous varieties; still popular to this day. In 1888 Henderson offered $100 cash for plants bearing the most pods and proclaimed it *"A VEGETABLE WONDER!!!"* *"Can and should be grown in every garden,"* and also said *"of all the Novelties...ever sent out, there is nothing so entirely distinct and valuable as this New Vegetable."* Dwarf bush plants can be grown like regular bush beans. Very tasty, tender beans, and very early too! Pkt (40 seeds) $2.50

JACKSON WONDER BUSH LIMA #LB102
75 days. Introduced in 1888 by David Landreth & Sons. Heavy yields of small-to-medium-sized, tan and purple-brown-speckled beans. Pods can also be cooked when young. Pkt (40 seeds) $2.50

KING OF THE GARDEN LIMA #LB105
90 days. Large 8'-10' vines yield very LARGE white lima beans and give huge yields over a long season. An heirloom from 1883, introduced by Frank S. Platt. An old-fashioned favorite, excellent for home gardeners. Pkt (25 seeds) $2.00

"Allow the president to invade a neighboring nation, whenever he shall deem it necessary to repel an invasion, and you allow him to do so whenever he may choose to say he deems it necessary for such a purpose and you allow him to make war at pleasure."

—ABRAHAM LINCOLN

Jackson Wonder Bush Lima

Runner Beans

(Phaseolus coccineus) Another New World native. Grown like ordinary green beans with one major difference: they prefer cooler temperatures.

BARNSIDE SWEET #RB110 *New!*
80 days Scarlet-flowered runner bean routinely reaches 25 feet in height! Transform unsightly buildings, including barns, into a wall of hummingbird-attracting flowers. Pods can grow to 10-12 inches. Very sweet and tender when eaten at the immature stage, a great variety for freezing for winter use as green beans. For over 30 years Roger L. Smith of Norton Creek Farm, in Northern California has been selecting for height and aphid resistance. Pkt (15 seeds) $3.50

GOLDEN SUNSHINE #RB108
85 days. Here is something really unusual: it's a runner bean, but the scarlet flowers are displayed above brilliant chartreuse foliage! The striking 5-6 foot vines really crank out the 6-8 inch, hefty pods, so good for fresh use or preserving. Like all runner beans, prefers mild weather. Pkt (25 seeds) $3.50

HESTIA #RB111 *New!*
70 days. Unusual bush-type runner bean variety yields full-sized stringless pods. "Hestia" reaches only about 18" tall, spreading nearly as wide, making it ideal for containers or very small gardens. The two-toned pink and white flowers are pretty enough to qualify it for the patio or flower bed! Straight pods are of very good flavor, or harvest the plump, black and purple seeds for use in soups, stews and more. Pkt (15 seeds) $3.50

PAINTED LADY #RB104
Traditional English bi-color grown since 1596! The name had mention to Queen Elizabeth I, *"who was heavily made up with rouge and white chalk."* The gorgeous flowers of red and white are among the most beautiful of flowering beans. The large beans are also good as snaps, freshly shelled or as dry beans, which are chocolate and tan mottled in color. Pkt (25 seeds) $3.50

SCARLET RUNNER #RB101
80 days. Used by native Americans, large, beautiful, vigorous vines grow over 10'. Flowers are very ornamental, in clusters of the brightest scarlet. Good for snap, shell or dry beans. The huge seeds are very colorful, violet-purple mottled in black. These beans like fairly cool weather. Pkt (25 seeds) $3.00

STREAMLINE #RB107
Amazingly prolific, produces clusters of tender, straight pods suitable to be used as snaps. Pods can reach 18 inches in length and are fine for freezing. Seeds can also be used as shell beans or when dried. Brilliant scarlet flowers are an attractive bonus! Very popular European variety. Pkt (25 seeds) $3.25

SUNSET #RB109
65-70 days. Runner beans are all attractive enough for flower gardens or patios, but this one is in a class by itself: Luminous peach to shell-pink blossoms are absolutely unique in our experience. Vines to 6 feet or so are covered in due course with cascades of runner bean pods, equally wonderful whether used as snaps fresh, canned or frozen, or as shell beans. Lovely! Pkt (25 seeds) $3.00

Golden Sunshine Runner Bean

Hestia Runner Bean

Streamline Runner Bean

Soya Beans (Edamame)

(Glycine max) One of the world's oldest crops. Grown in Asia for thousands of years where it is a staple protein source.

AOYU EDAMAME #SY106 *New!*
85-90 days. Heirloom edamame type from Japan. Plump, pale green soybeans are produced on small to medium-sized plants. First collected in Hokkaido, Japan, in 1930.
Pkt. (30 seeds) $4.00

ENVY #SY101
Early 80-day variety is great for the North. Perfect for Edamame, fresh shelling or dried; nice green-colored beans have good flavor; developed by the late Prof. Elwyn Meader, UNH.
Pkt (100 seeds) $3.00

Aoyu Edamame

Envy Soya Bean

Sunset Runner Bean

Soya Bean Succotash

By Chef Quintin

A lively salad with tons of flavor. Succotash (from Narragansett sohquttah-hash, "broken corn kernels") is a food dish consisting primarily of corn and lima beans or other shell beans. I like the addition of the protein powerhouse Edamame beans.

INGREDIENTS
- 1 C Shelled Soya Beans
- 1 C Grilled Shaved white sweet corn
- 1 C Assorted heirloom peppers
- ½ C of yellow onion
- 2 T of olive oil (extra virgin)
- ½ C of chopped garlic
- ½ C of butternut squash
- 1T of fresh oregano
- Splash of tamari

PREPARATION
1. Small chop the peppers, onion and butternut squash
2. Heat up a sauté pan with olive oil. Add your onions and garlic; sweat these for 2 minutes
3. Add your butternut squash, peppers, soya beans and corn
4. Cook until butternut is tender but still firm (al dente) to the tooth
5. Fold in your oregano and deglaze with your liquids
6. Season with salt and pepper
7. Your Succotash is ready

Chinese Red Noodle *Chinese Green Noodle* *Chinese Mosaic*

Long Beans

(Vigna unguiculata) A staple crop of East Asia, where they have been grown for centuries. Delicious green pods are very tender, crisp and nearly never have "strings". Easy to grow in all but the coldest climates. 25-35 seeds per packet.

CHINESE GREEN NOODLE BEAN #LG102
Here is an early variety of long bean imported from China. 20" pods are straight and smooth, bright green, and of excellent quality. This hardy long bean is easy to grow almost anywhere. Very tasty stir-fried. Pkt $2.50

CHINESE MOSAIC LONG BEAN #LG110
Lovely, lavender-pink-shaded pods measure 12"-18" long and are crisp and flavorful. The vigorous vines produce loads of tender Chinese beans. Very popular here at Baker Creek and sure to become a favorite of gourmets everywhere! A real standout that is quick to come into production. Pkt $3.00

CHINESE RED NOODLE BEAN #LG109
80 days. This is the most stunning and unique bean I have grown yet. Fantastic, deep red, 18" pods are so delicious and full of nutrition, and they even keep most of their color when sauteed! Long vines produce all summer and do well under many conditions. This incredible variety will draw lots of attention in your home garden or at market. We are so excited to offer this unique, Chinese ethnic variety that produces fairly early. Small red seeds. Pkt $2.50

RED-SEEDED ASPARAGUS BEAN
#LG101 75 days. Very long pods grow to 24"! Very tender and tasty; no strings, small seeds; huge yields on 10' vines. They grow well under almost any conditions–very resistant to heat, humidity and insects; great for the South. Pick for snap beans when 12"-14" long; delicious

stir-fried! The '*Vigna*' genus does well for us all summer at Baker Creek. Pkt $2.50

TAIWAN BLACK SEEDED LONG BEAN
#LG103 This is the true "Yard Long" bean, with light green pods 38" long, with black beans. The long vines set heavy yields of these delicious pods that will amaze your friends! Long beans should be lightly fried and not boiled. They have superior flavor to common beans. This variety was collected from a Taiwanese immigrant in the 1970s. RARE! Pkt $4.00

THAI #2 RED SEEDED LONG BEAN
#LG113   Pretty lime-green pods are tender and delicious. This variety has brownish-red seeds and is late-maturing, so it is better for the South. Collected in Thailand. Pkt $2.50

THAI #3 EXTRA LONG BEAN #LG116
Very long, green pods can reach 30" or more! A great-tasting variety that is so fun to grow and produces well, too! It has unique red and white-spotted seeds. Pkt $2.50

THAI PURPLE PODDED YARD LONG #LG117
Vigorous, high-yielding Thai variety. The lovely, deep-purple pods have green tips, are crisp and stay tender to amazing lengths, often reaching 20 inches! The productive variety is a local favorite in Thailand where long beans are appreciated as a very important staple crop. Pkt $2.50

THAI SURANAREE BUSH LONG BEAN
#LG114   A great bush variety of long bean from Thailand, it is easier to grow in small gardens than the pole types. This variety produces 12" long green pods that are perfect for stir-frying. Dark reddish-maroon seeds. Pkt $2.50

THAI WHITE SEEDED LONG BEAN
#LG112 Smooth, light-green, 25" long pods from Thailand. These are delicious and crisp, great in curries and stir-fries. They have creamy-white seeds. I am sure you will enjoy this great variety! Pkt $2.50

Chinese Red Noodle Bean Saute

◆ Any amount of Chinese Red Noodle Beans
◆ Any amount of chopped onion
◆ Green pepper
◆ Olive oil
◆ Italian Seasoning
◆ Salt & Pepper to taste
◆ Zucchini or summer squash (optional)
◆ Any shredded cheese (optional)

Rinse and cut beans into 1-2 inch lengths. Chop onion and green pepper. Using a cast iron skillet or other heavy pan, saute onion and pepper in 3-4 tablespoons of olive oil. Once the onions and peppers are beginning to soften, add the beans and continue to saute over medium heat. Sprinkle with Italian Seasoning to taste. A little water may be added as needed. Cover during part of the cooking time to allow the beans to absorb moisture. Cook until beans are tender and most moisture is absorbed. (Around 30 minutes) If using zucchini or other summer squash, add these sliced or chopped after the beans have cooked for 10 minutes or so, as the beans need a longer cooking time than squash. Add salt and pepper to taste. Sprinkle with shredded cheese before serving.

Note: I have even used Chinese Red Noodle Beans which have gotten to be as long as 12-14 inches. As long as they have not started to wither, they tend to cook up tender. If they get too big on the vine, leave them to dry out so you have beans to save for next year's planting.

From our customer, Alice Brassie of Wildwood, MO.

Beetroot

(Beta vulgaris) 250 seeds per packet. An Old World crop known to the Romans, but not cultivated for roots until much later. A delicious and easy-to-grow crop, sown in early spring or late summer in most areas, succession-planted spring through fall in cooler summer climates. Forage types yield amazing quantities of large roots for livestock, but may also be harvested for table use, both for greens and roots, when taken young. The "seeds" are actually capsules containing several seeds, so thin plantings adequately; be sure to use the thinnings as baby greens.

ALBINO #BT108
55 days. A pure white, fairly smooth round heirloom beet from Holland. Its super sweet white flesh is unusual and tasty. The greens are also good. This beet can be used for making sugar. Pkt (100 seeds) $2.75 *or 1 oz $14.00*

BULL'S BLOOD #BT101
50 days. This beautiful beet has deep reddish-purple leaves! Very sweet and delicious, the baby leaves are a rage in salads. The beets are tasty too, and have pretty pink rings inside. Pkt $2.50 *or 1 oz $5.50*

CHIOGGIA (BASSANO) #BT104
60 days. A pre-1840 Italian heirloom beet, this variety arrived in the USA prior to 1865. They have light red skin and beautiful rings inside, like red and white candy stripes. The flesh is very tender, mild, and sweet. Named after a fishing town in Italy; a favorite here.
Pkt $2.50 *or 1 oz $5.50*

CRAPAUDINE #BT114
In 1885, the French book *The Vegetable Garden* stated this is one of the oldest varieties. Today some experts feel this may be the oldest beet still in existence, possibly dating back 1000 years. This unique variety is one of the most flavorful, with carrot-shaped roots that have rough, dark colored skin which looks like tree bark. Inside, the roots are very dark, with almost black flesh that is of superior quality and sought after by chefs who want real flavor. We are proud to offer this rare old selection. Pkt $2.50

CROSBY'S EGYPTIAN #BT105
55 days. Introduced to this country in 1869 and trialed by Peter Henderson, who recommended it in 1871. This improved "Crosby's" strain was first offered by J. H. Gregory. This beet is early, tender, & fine flavored.
Pkt $2.25

CYLINDRA OR FORMANOVA #BT111
55 days. A wonderful heirloom from Denmark, this one is famous for slicing with its long, cylindrical roots. Produces much more uniform slices than round beets. This tender and sweet variety is also known as "Butter Slicer" because of its wonderful texture. Pkt $2.00 *or 1 oz $4.50*

DETROIT DARK RED #BT110
55 days. The most popular, old standard, all-purpose red beet; uniform and smooth, blood red flesh that is sweet and tasty. 14" tops make good greens. Heirloom variety introduced 1892. Pkt $2.50 *or 1 oz $4.50*

EARLY WONDER #BT103
50 days. An old heirloom, pre-1811 variety. Early, smooth, round beet; makes lots of tall tender greens, too! Perfect pickled, fresh, cooked, or in borscht.
Pkt $2.25 *or 1 oz $4.50*

FLAT OF EGYPT #BT113
50 days. In 1885 Vilmorin said, "An exceedingly early variety, and certainly the best of the early kitchen-garden kinds." This is a very quick beet of great quality, producing flattened 3", crimson purple roots and short leafy tops. Pkt $2.25

Detroit Dark Red

Golden Beet

Bull's Blood Beet

Golden Beet Mash with ground Sumac

By Chef Quintin

Beets are a versatile vegetable. When roasted, the beet takes on a whole new character. I like to use golden beets because the tendency to bleed is minimal. Roasting these in the oven at a low temp creates a sugar concentration inside the meat. You will see the sugar bleeding a little through the skin. Great option for a non-potato accompaniment for your dish and will become a beet favorite.

INGREDIENTS
4 med golden beets
1/2 teaspoon sea salt (optional)
2 T of olive oil (extra virgin)
Artisan Pepper Mill
1 t of ground sumac
1 T of white balsamic vinegar

PREPARATION
1. Rinse Beets well. Pull leaves off and save for garnish

2. Rub beets down with olive oil and sea salt. Bake in oven at 325 for 1 hour or until fork tender.

3. While beets are still warm peel skin off with gloved hands. Place in a mixer with a paddle or mash well.

4. Fold in olive oil, pepper, sea salt.
5. Place on the plate and sprinkle with sumac. Toss leaves in a little white balsamic vinegar. Place on top of mashed.

Chioggia

Albino

Crapaudine

McGregor's Favorite

Mammoth Red Mangel

Giant Yellow Eckendorf

Cylindra

FUER KUGEL #BT119

60 days. Smooth-skinned, dark purple roots remain sweet and tender even to a very large size. Occasional concentric white zoning makes this very pretty for the table. Excellent keeper. Originated in Switzerland. Pkt (75 seeds) $3.00

GEANTE BLANCHE #BT115

A "Giant White" fodder beet that is a mainstay in France as a beet for livestock. Long, pointed white roots with a green collar are sweet and keep well for winter use. Pkt $2.00

GIANT YELLOW ECKENDORF #BT116

The 1927 Henry Fields catalog said, *"Giant, smooth, long roots of cylindrical shape, weighing up to 20 pounds each and growing two-thirds above ground. Solid white flesh with high food value."* These big yellow-skinned roots are perfect for growing as animal food, a tradition that is finally being brought back on many small farms. Pkt $2.50

GOLDEN BEET #BT102

55 days. This variety dates back to the 1820s or before. The beets are a rich, golden-yellow and very sweet. A beautiful beet that won't bleed like red beets. The greens are also very tasty. A favorite of many. Pkt $2.50 *or 1 oz $8.00*

LUTZ SALAD LEAF #BT118

70 days. Quite possibly the best storage beet known. Top-shaped red roots with concentric lighter zones. Pink-stemmed leaves are renowned for use like chard, superb in salads. Roots remain tender and sweet even when grown to quite a large size, having reached 3-4 pounds! Also known as "Winter Keeper." Pkt $2.50

MAMMOTH RED MANGEL #BT107

100 days. Huge, up to 20 lbs each; large yields per acre. Highly used for livestock feed in the 1800's. Or picked small for table use. Pkt $2.50 *or 1 oz $4.50*

McGREGOR'S FAVORITE #BT124 *New!*

60 days. Old dual-purpose variety is grown for both its leaves and its roots. The leaves are unique: long and narrow, incredibly dark ruby red, with an unusual, silky sheen. The long, cylindrical roots, which can reach 6 inches long, are unusually colored: red, yes, but with overtones toward purple-blue. The dark color translates to increased phytonutirents-- among the highest of any beet variety! This Scottish heirloom, also called Dracena, was until recently almost extinct. Pkt (100 seeds) $3.00

OKRAGLY CIEMNOCZERWONY (Bordo) #BT123 *New!*

65 days. Smooth, blemish-free round-to-top-shaped beets are very dark red. Very tender and very sweet! A superb keeper, this variety originated in the old Soviet Union, where beets are an important staple crop. Pkt $2.50

SHIRAZ TALL TOP #BT121

60 days. Dual-purpose variety! Very fast-growing tops may be harvested early in the season—red-ribbed green tops grow lush and succulent. The sweet, very smooth and stylish roots follow in due course. Disease resistance of this newer type keeps the uniform roots blemish free! Excels equally for canning, pickling, roasting or boiling! Pkt (75 seeds) $2.50

SUGAR BEET #BT120

95 days. White-fleshed conical roots are larger than our Albino Beet, and have a very high sucrose content. May be grown for sugar production or as a higher-calorie stock fodder. Roots frequently exceed two pounds in weight, and under ideal conditions are as much as 20 percent sucrose! We sell seed only of tested, GMO-free seed lots. Pkt $2.50

YELLOW CYLINDRICAL #BT106

Very large, oblong, golden-yellow mangel beets are sweet and tasty if picked small, or let them mature for high-quality stock feed. A rare European heirloom that can grow huge. It also makes tasty greens. Pkt $2.50 *or 1 oz $4.50*

ZENTAUR FODDER #BT126 *New!*

60 days (90 days to fodder crop) A nice fodder beet from Europe. Roots get to 5 pounds, staying sweet to a surprisingly large size. Flesh is white, very fine-grained and sweet at smaller sizes; fine for the table. Skin turns emerald green where exposed to sunshine. Where summers are too cool to grow corn, beets are a workable traditional fodder crop. Pkt $2.50

"He that tilleth his land shall be satisfied with bread." —

PROVERBS 12:11

Brussels Sprouts

(B. oleracea) Old World cabbage relatives that are grown for succulent flower heads or buds.

CATSKILL #BS103

(B. oleracea) 100 days. Hardy, dwarf plants produce tasty, uniform sprouts. Developed by Arthur White of Arkport, NY, in 1941. Pkt (150 seeds) $2.50

LONG ISLAND IMPROVED #BS101

100 days. The standard open-pollinated variety since the 1890's. Heavy yields of delicious sprouts. Pkt (150 seeds) $2.50 *or 1 oz $4.00*

How to Grow Brussels Sprouts

BY DR JEFF NEKOLA

One of the most essential pieces of information in the optimum production of Brussels Sprouts is knowledge of their unique climate requirements: being initially developed in the Low Countries of Holland and Belgium, they appreciate long, cool growing seasons. Even though these countries are as far north as Hudson's Bay, their winters are much warmer than similar latitudes across much of North America because of proximity to the Atlantic Ocean. These areas also don't get very warm in the summer for the same reason. As a result, the highly frost-tolerant Brussels Sprouts can be grown year-round in their place of origin, where both the summers and winters are neither too hot nor too cold.

If you live in the cool coastal areas of the Pacific Northwest, you are very lucky indeed, as your climate in broad brushstrokes is the same as Brussels Sprouts' home. In this area, all you need to do is plant seeds when you set out the rest of your garden, with year-round cultivation being an option. But, if you live anywhere else, you'll have to do things differently. Because they tolerate cold spells better than heat waves, if you live in a mild-winter area that does not drop much below 20°F, you'll want to plant Brussels Sprouts seeds once the heat of summer is well past, and grow them as a winter crop. If you live in colder areas, you'll want to set out husky transplants into the garden when there is approximately 100 days remaining before the first frost.

If you're direct sowing seeds, plant about ½ inch deep, and thin to about 2 feet spacing when they are a half-foot tall. Don't forget that you can eat the thinned plants like you would kale. If you're setting out transplants, space them 2 feet apart and set in deeply so that the bottom leaves are just above the soil surface; firm the soil and water well. Mulch the growing plants to help retain soil moisture and keep the ground from getting too hot. Hand pull weeds, rather than hoe cultivating, to protect their shallow roots. Fertilize them lightly twice a month. Stake the plants to keep them from being blown over in high winds. As the bottom-most leaves begin to yellow, pinch them off. This encourages the plant to grow tall, giving you more sprouts per stalk.

Harvest after the sprouts are 1-2" in diameter and have been exposed to a few frosts, as this will help make them sweet. You can prolong harvest by pinching off the first ripe sprouts near the plant bottom first, and then keep harvesting them up the stalk. If the sprouts are not maturing quickly enough and hard winter freezes are on their way, you can remove the plant top, which will force sprout development over a few weeks long period. If a plant-killing freeze of less than 20°F. is on its way, you can uproot stalks with developed sprouts, remove the leaves, and hang in a cool, sheltered place like an attached garage, basement, or root cellar.

Photo: David Cavagnaro

Long Island Improved

Calabrese Green Sprouting

Waltham 29

Broccoli

(B. oleracea) 300 seeds per packet. Old World cabbage relatives that are grown for succulent flower heads or buds. Needs rich soil, abundant moisture, and cool weather (but avoid prolonged exposure to temps below 50 degrees). Broccoli is harvested when the tiny buds are full-sized, but before they begin to open.

CALABRESE GREEN SPROUTING #BR101
An Italian heirloom brought to America in the 1880s; 5"-8" heads and many side shoots. Pkt $2.50 *or 1 oz $5.00*

EARLY PURPLE SPROUTING #BR102
An English heirloom variety, bred for overwintering. Produces lots of purple broccoli sprouts in the spring. Grows slowly through the winter; very frost hardy. A great variety that is very hard to find in this country; delicious! Pkt $2.50 *or 1 oz $8.50*

RAPINI #BR103
(B. rapa) An Italian non-heading broccoli grown for flavorful, asparagus-like spring shoots and leaves. Great to cook or in salads. Pkt $2.00

ROMANESCO ITALIA #BR104
The true and popular Italian heirloom with spiraling, apple-green heads that are so superbly flavored. This variety is widely grown in northern Italy. A must with many of the finest chefs. Pkt $2.75 *or 1 oz $7.50*

WALTHAM 29 #BR105
Standard type, produces 4-8" green heads that are nicely flavored. Compact plants also produce some side shoots. Introduced in 1954. A favorite here at the farm. Pkt $2.50

Romanesco Broccoli

Cauliflower

(B. oleracea) Old World cabbage relatives that are grown for succulent flower heads or buds. All need rich soil, abundant moisture, and cool weather (but avoid prolonged exposure to temps below 50 degrees). Cauliflower is harvested when the heads reach full size, but before the tiny buds (called the curd) begin to develop and open. Cauliflower succeeds best where spring or autumn weather is uniformly cool. Some varieties are blanched (the large outer leaves drawn up and tied to shade the developing bud) to produce a milder flavored curd.

ERFURTER #CA106 *New!*
55 days. (Also known as Snowball A) Great yields of snow-white heads that reach 6 inches across. Self-blanching type that is very early and reliable, even in dry conditions. Fine-grained curd is mild-flavored. Pkt (200 seeds) $2.50

GIANT OF NAPLES #CA104
Large, 3-lb white heads; a vigorous grower; very good leaf cover; a delicious Italian heirloom that is hard to find. Pkt (200 seeds) $2.50

GREEN MACERATA #CA105
A delicious Italian variety with 2-lb, bright apple-green heads that are superb cooked or raw in salads. Very attractive, vigorous plants, fairly early. Pkt (200 seeds) $2.50

PURPLE OF SICILY #CA103
Beautiful, brilliant purple heads weigh 2-3 lbs and are of a fine, sweet flavor. The heads cook to bright green. Insect-resistant variety that is easier to grow than many white varieties; rich in minerals. A colorful heirloom. Select Italian seed. Pkt (200 seeds) $2.50

SNOWBALL SELF-BLANCHING #CA101
An old, white type; ivory heads, good size. The standard American favorite for over 100 years. Pkt (200 seeds) $2.50 *or 1 oz $5.50*

VIOLETTA ITALIA #CA102
Large healthy plants produce nice-sized, beautiful purple heads that turn bright green when cooked; very tasty. A fine Italian variety. Pkt (200 seeds) $2.50

Snowball Self-Blanching

Green Macerata

Cabbage

(B. oleracea) 300 seeds per packet. Cabbage does best in a long season of mild weather, but it is also very hardy and may be grown to mature in the cool weather of late autumn. Spring plantings are best started indoors and transplanted out about the time of last frost; summer plantings may be seeded right in the garden. We recommend early varieties for spring planting, longer-season, large-heading varieties for a fall crop.

Glory of Enkhuizen

AUBERVILLIERS #CB117 *New!*

70 days. Gorgeously crinkled, savoy-type leaves are produced within dense heads. These are round to slightly flattened, and often weigh 3 pounds or more. This European heirloom variety is seldom available in the US. Mainly grown for fresh use, and has been since the turn of the 20th century, when it was a favorite at Paris markets. Usually grown for a fall crop, where its earliness, mild flavor and tolerance to cold are especially valued.. Pkt $2.25

BACALAN DE RENNES CABBAGE #CB112

Listed by Vilmorin in 1867, this French heirloom was grown in the Saint-Brienc and Bordeaux localities. The oxheart-shaped heads grew especially well in the mild, seaside climate along the west coast of France. Early, flavorful, green heads are still grown in France today. Pkt $2.00

COUR DI BUE #CB108

Tender, 3 to 4-lb, pointed, oxheart-type heads; very good for home use or specialty markets. We offer quality Italian seed for this old European heirloom. This type of cabbage was very popular 150 years ago. Fairly early and of superb quality. Pkt $2.00

EARLY JERSEY WAKEFIELD #CB103

70 days. Introduced in the 1840's, with tasty, 2-lb, sweet and flavorful, conical heads. This very early variety was sold commercially by Peter Henderson in the late 1860's. Pkt $2.50 *or 1 oz $4.00*

GLORY OF ENKHUIZEN #CB104

90 days. Introduced in 1899 by Sluis & Groot in Enkhuizen, Holland. Has medium-large, hard round heads. An early, excellent-keeping variety that is a good producer and good for kraut. Pkt $2.00

Tete Noir

GREYHOUND or EERSTELING #CB116 *New!*

63 days. (also known as Express) Super-early European cabbage variety boasts compact, pointed heads, similar to Early Jersey Wakefield but comes in a full 10 days earlier. Very suitable for sowing under glass and often succession planted as it is so quick to mature. A deliciously mild, sweet variety!. Pkt $2.50

HENDERSON'S CHARLESTON WAKEFIELD #CB106 Larger than Early Jersey Wakefield (4-6 lbs), and only a little later, this fine variety was developed by Peter Henderson & Co. in 1892. It is a good variety for the South. Pkt $2.00

KALIBOS #CB119 *New!*

85 days. Incredibly graceful appearance would qualify Kalibos for the flower garden! But this European variety is eminently useful as well. The conical, long, heart-shaped, 2-pound heads of deep red are on the small side, ideal for a single dish. The color is so beautiful when the leaves are shredded into slaw. Flavor is mild and very sweet. And they're good keepers as well, allowing you to enjoy your fall harvest well into winter. Pkt $3.00

KODA #CB120 *New!*

90 days. Nice round heads reach 3 pounds. This treasured European variety is seldom seen in this country. Early and densely packed for a red type. Our seed come from Poland, where cabbage is an important staple crop. Pkt $2.25

Aubervilliers

MAMMOTH RED ROCK #CB105

90 days. A large heirloom cabbage from 1889 with deep red heads that have good flavor and are very colorful. Pkt $2.50

NERO DI TOSCANA OR BLACK PALM TREE #CB101 60 days. This loose-leafed cabbage dates back to the early 1800's at least. It has beautiful, deep black-green leaves that can be 24" long. They are heavily savoyed. This Italian heirloom is popular in Tuscany and central Italy for making fabulous soups and stews. One of the most beautiful and flavorful types you can grow.

Red Express

Early Jersey Wakefield

Topas

Kalibos

Perfection Drumhead Savoy

Pkt $2.50 *or 1 oz $6.00*

PERFECTION DRUMHEAD SAVOY #CB110

95 days. This large drumhead-type has finely-crinkled, savoyed leaves that are mild and sweet in flavor; compact short-stemmed plants. This heirloom was introduced before 1888 and is an excellent keeper. Pkt $2.00 *or 1 oz $4.50*

PREMIUM LATE FLAT DUTCH #CB109

100 days. The standard, giant flat cabbage that is good for storage. 10 to 15-lb heads are of high quality; delicious flavor. This heirloom was introduced by European settlers in the 1860's. Pkt $2.00 *or 1 oz $4.50*

RED EXPRESS #CB114

Newly released open-pollinated red cabbage, the first in many years! Specifically bred for Canada and northern tier of USA. Compact plants, extra early production of solid, split-resistant oval heads to only 2-3 pounds. Pkt $2.50

TETE NOIRE #CB113

The traditional French variety is very rare outside of Europe. Solid, deep-red heads are of good quality and are mostly grown as an autumn variety in France. Pkt $2.50

TOPAS RED #CB121 *New!*

80 days. Medium-early for a red type. Nice round heads, densely packed with mild, nutty-tasting cabbage. Makes a festive slaw! Popular variety in eastern Europe, where cabbage is a traditional staple crop. Pkt $2.50

Mammoth Red Rock

Cour di Bue

Celery & Celeriac

(Apium graveloens) Moisture-loving Old World crop grown since antiquity. They are best started indoors 8-12 weeks before the last frost of spring. The tiny seeds must be surface-sown and never allowed to dry out. The young plants are set out at about the time of last frost, preferring a moister soil than most vegetable crops, and very rich in organic matter. Requiring to be kept moist all season long, they are otherwise easy to grow and surprisingly reliable in most climates.

CELERIAC- GIANT PRAGUE #CE103

110 days. Root Celery, this variety is grown for its large, white roots that are superb fried, or in soup. Taste and culture much like regular celery. Introduced in 1871, popular in parts of Europe. Pkt (200 seeds) $2.00

GIANT RED RE-SELECTION #CE109

A recent re-selection from the European red-stalked celeries. Selection goals were better color, earliness and disease resistance. Red celery has a richer flavor than the green types. Until you've sampled the golden-pink hearts, you haven't tasted celery! Pkt (150 seeds) $2.75

TENDERCRISP #CE101

A very large type of celery, excellent flavor. One of our most popular varieties! Pkt (200 seeds) $2.50

UTAH TALL #CE107

110 days. Thick, crisp, medium-dark green stalks reach a foot or more when well grown, high quality. Introduced in 1953. Pkt (200 seeds) $2.50

Carrot

(Daucus carota) 800 seeds per packet. Carrots are originally from central Asia and they come in so many colors besides orange—purple and red types are actually the original ones! The tiny seed must be sown very shallow; to avoid drying out, especially when sown in hot weather, shade the seed bed or row with boards, paper, or something to exclude the hot sun and hold in moisture. Long-rooted types need a deep, mellow soil; in heavier soils, grow half-long or round types.

AMARILLO #CR114
75 days. Lovely, lemon-yellow roots have sweet, bright yellow flesh. Good for a summer to fall crop, large 8" roots and strong tops. Yellow carrots always taste the best to me; they are so crunchy and full of juice. Pkt $3.00 *or 1/4 oz $6.00*

ATOMIC RED #CR109
75 days. Brilliant red carrots are so healthful and unique-looking, sure to add color to your garden. The 8" roots are high in lycopene, which has been shown in studies to help prevent several types of cancer. Crisp roots are at their best when cooked, and this helps to make the lycopene more usable. Very flavorful. Pkt (300 seeds) $3.00 *or 1/4 oz $6.00*

BERLICUM 2 #CR117
Beautiful 8", good-sized roots are extra-smooth, long and blunt-ended. A deep orange color with a fine carrot flavor makes this variety popular in the markets of Europe. Slender roots tend to stay tender and not get woody. A perfect variety for gourmet cooks and upscale markets. Pkt $2.50 *or 1/4 oz $4.00*

CHANTENAY RED CORE #CR111
75 days. One of the sweetest, this variety was introduced in 1929 and is a large stump-rooted carrot with a deep red-orange center, great for juicing or fresh eating. A good market variety that is smooth and refined in shape. Pkt $2.00

COSMIC PURPLE #CR112
This one is causing excitement at farmers' markets. Carrots have bright purple skin and flesh that comes in shades of yellow and orange. Spicy and sweet-tasting roots are great for marketing. Pkt (300 seeds) $3.00 *or 1/4 oz $6.00*

DANVERS 126 HALF LONG #CR102
70 days. The original Danvers Half Long dates back to the 1870s. This strain "126" was improved in the 1940s. The old standard American carrot, adaptable and dependable. Thick 7" roots have good flavor. Productive. Pkt $2.50 *or 1 oz $3.75*

DARA FLOWERING CARROT #FL134 *New!*
Queen Anne's Lace is the familiar wild form of carrot, and the white-flowered version has been appreciated for years as a delicate filler in beds and flower arrangements. But 'Dara' is a spectacular, vividly-colored variety! Flowers open chaste white, change to soft pink and finally deep, rich rose-red; the lacy flower heads reach to 4 ft tall. Large amount of flowers over a long season. Pkt (20 seeds) $3.00

JAUNE OBTUSE DU DOUBS #CR120
A delicious, bright, lemon-yellow carrot that comes from France. Mentioned in 1894, it was originally used as a stock carrot for livestock. This big, thick yellow carrot has been winning over chefs and gardeners, for it has a fine, sweet taste that is hard to duplicate in modern carrots. Pkt $2.50

KORAL #CR125 *New!*
75 days. Cylindrical deep orange roots are 8-9 inches long and very free of splitting, even when grown in heavier soils. A great keeper and also considered superior for juicing. Widely grown in Europe but practically unknown in this country. Pkt $2.50

Pusa Asita, Available online only.

Amarillo

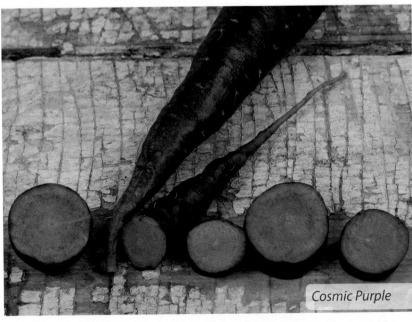

Cosmic Purple

Parisienne

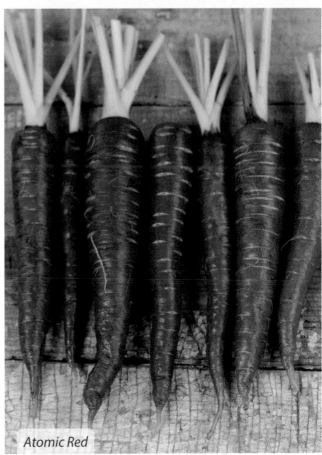

Atomic Red

KURODA LONG 8" #CR107

75 days. Popular variety for Oriental markets; deep orange, stubby roots are mild and sweet. Excellent for juicing. Grows well in many climate conditions; good for home or market. Pkt $2.00 *or 1 oz $5.00*

LITTLE FINGER #CR103

55 days. A superb baby-type carrot with deep orange color; developed in France for canning and pickling. Sweet 3" carrots are great for snacks. Pkt $2.00

LOBBERICHER YELLOW #CR124 *New!*

80 days. Brilliant yellow roots size up plump and large. An old fodder type from Europe, where there are many traditional fodder crops other than corn! Or harvest it small (under 10" in length) for the table; its mild sweet flavor and impressive crunch pleases trendy chefs and discriminating home cooks alike. Makes a fine storage carrot too, and its clear yellow is so cheery on a plate during the depths of winter. Pkt (300 seeds) $3.00

LUNAR WHITE #CR113

75 days. Here is a vigorous producer that has creamy white roots that are very mild, delicious, and have a fine flavor; very small core. White carrots were grown in the Middle Ages, but now they have become very rare. We are glad to offer this productive new variety. Pkt (300 seeds) $3.00

MUSCADE #CR118

A delicious North African carrot that produces blocky, 7" orange roots that have exceptional flavor and a crisp, crunchy texture. They hold up well at market and are late bolting. Rare and almost impossible to find! Pkt $2.50

NANTES SCARLET #CR122

65-74 days. Half-long type reaching 6-7 inches in length, about 1 ½ inches in diameter. Sweet, brilliant orange, blunt, cylindrical roots are very delicate and fine-grained, containing almost no core. High moisture content make this a natural for juicing; fine for bunching or storage. Originally from France but grown in this country for many decades. A good sort to try on heavier soils. Pkt $2.50

OXHEART #CR126 *New!*

90 days. Massive heart-shaped roots to one pound each. Can be a shy seed producer and seed is sometimes scarce, so we are excited to be able to offer this old French variety! Despite their large size, the brilliant orange roots are crisp, sweet and mild. Their blunt shape makes them superior for heavy or shallow soils. Known as "Guerande" in France, it was first introduced in the US in the late 19th century. Excellent storage type. Pkt (300 seeds) $3.00

PARISIENNE #CR115

Small, round carrots that are so popular in France. Tender, orange globes are superb lightly steamed. Easy to grow even in heavy soils. This little carrot is great for home and market gardens, as this variety is fairly uniform. Pkt $2.50

SHIN KURODA 5" #CR106

75 days. The baby Japanese variety having short 3"-5" tender carrots with fine flavor. Perfect for specialty markets. Pkt $2.00 *1 oz $5.00*

SNOW WHITE #CR119

An attractive creamy-white carrot with a delicious, mild-sweet taste and a good crisp crunch. Roots grow 7"-8" long and are great raw or cooked. White carrots are again becoming popular with home gardeners and specialty growers after many years of neglect by the commercial seed trade. White varieties were common in the middle ages through the 19th century but then became scarce. Pkt $2.50 *or 1/4 oz $6.00*

ST. VALERY #CR101

70 days. The Vilmorins of France mentioned this variety in 1885 and said it had been grown a "long time" then. A large handsome variety with bright red-orange roots; smooth, 10"-12" long & 2"-3" in diameter. Sweet & tender. Rare. Our favorite! Pkt $2.25 *or 1 oz $5.00*

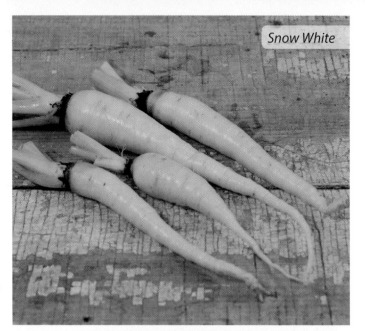

Snow White

Little Fingers

Pusa Rudhira, Available online only

Grilled Heirloom Carrots

By Chef Quintin

Fall planted carrots are so full of sugar. They bode well with the cooler growing season. This simple preparation method is a great addition to your grilled items.

INGREDIENTS

8 heirloom carrots (assorted colors) sliced in half longways
1/2 teaspoon sea salt (optional)
2 T of Olive Oil, Extra Virgin

1 T of Aged Balsamic Vinegar
Pinch of fresh Thyme

PREPARATION

Rinse carrots well. Save tops for soup!

Sliced carrots lengthways and drizzle with olive oil and sea salt; drizzle with balsamic vinegar.

Cook on the grill for 4 mins on each side. Should have a nice carmelized color.

Sprinkle with fresh thyme leaves and serve

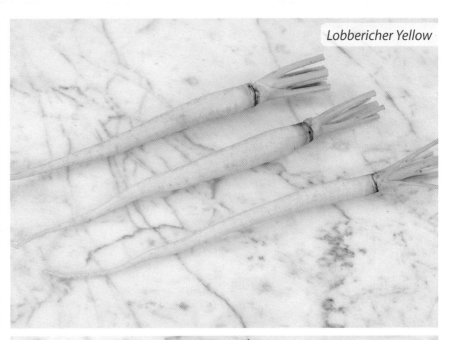

Lobbericher Yellow

Dara Carrot

Kuroda Long

Oaxacan Green

Corn

(Zea mays) The quintessential Native American crop, corn was a staple of indigenous peoples from South America to the Great Lakes. It's believed to have been domesticated in Mexico, and may be of the world's oldest agricultural crops. It's best seeded directly into the garden, in good, rich, well-drained soil, right about the time of the last spring frost. Plant it in blocks rather than long narrow rows, to improve pollination. Corn can be very drought tolerant, but ears fill best when there is good soil moisture when tassels and silk first emerge. Harvest sweet corn when the kernels are full of milky-colored juice; allow other types to remain on the stalks until fully dry. 75-125 seeds per packet.

BEDWELL'S SUPREME WHITE DENT #CN148

Stately plants usually produce 2 ears, 12-14" long. These are white, but the variety has always thrown an occasional rosy-colored ear, and an occasional shoepeg type (random kernels, not in rows). Originally grown in Clarke County, Alabama, where it has been family held in the Bedwell family for at least a century. Fine for roasting ears, cornmeal, and hominy. See Edna Bedwell's recipe, to make incomparable creamed corn. Pkt $4.00

DORINNY SWEET #CN153 *New!*

75 days—Early season sweet corn that yields in cool climates. Dorinny was originally a Canadian cross between Golden Bantam and Pickaninny. Received a Market Gardeners' Award of Merit in 1936. Reliable even where soils are cool. Yellow kernels on 6-7" cobs offer old-fashioned sweet

Edna Bedwell's Southern-style Cream Corn

Harvest 'Bedwell's Supreme' ears when they are at the milk stage. Working with one ear at a time, just nip the tops off the kernels with a corn cutter or very sharp knife. Continue cutting around each ear, shaving more deeply with each pass until all that remains on the ear is the fibrous bases of the kernels, collecting the juice and pulp into a bowl.

When you have two cups of cut corn, pour into a skillet, add a little water, salt to taste, and a stick of margarine. Simmer on very low heat until thickened, about 20-30 minutes. Serve with fried okra, a mess of purple hull peas, and cornbread.

corn flavor. Vigorous plants reach 4-5 feet in height, usually yield two ears per plant. Grown in northern Maine by our friend, activist-farmer Jim Gerritsen. Pkt $3.50

CHEROKEE WHITE EAGLE #CN144

Beautiful white and blue kernels on 8"-10" ears, makes superb corn meal or can be used as roasting ears if picked young. This great Cherokee variety gives good yields on sturdy stalks, some kernels have eagle-like markings on them, hence the name. Very rare and hard to find. Pkt $4.00

CHEROKEE LONG EAR #CN138

100 days. A beautiful blend of brightly colored

long ears (5"-7"), wonderful for fall decorations, and is great for popping. This beautiful corn was selected by Carl Barnes, a world-renowned Cherokee corn collector from Oklahoma. Pkt $3.00

COUNTRY GENTLEMAN #CN105

90 days. Introduced in 1890 by S.D. Woodruff & Sons. Sweet, delicious and milky; tender white kernels on 8" ears. The ears have no rows, as this is a shoepeg type, and kernels are packed in a zigzag pattern. One of the best heirloom sweet corns. Pkt $3.00

DAKOTA BLACK POPCORN #CN136

Dark reddish-black ears are quite attractive for fall decorations, or popping into tasty popcorn! This variety is easy to grow, and does well in almost all growing climates. Fun for children's gardens. Pkt $3.50

GOLDEN BANTAM 12-ROW #CN143

Released in 1922 by the Clark Seed Company of Milford, Connecticut. Although developed from the original Golden Bantam, this is definitely an improved type—larger ears mean higher yields, and the golden yellow corn stays tender longer. Equally suitable for freezing and fresh eating, this variety was for decades the standard for home and market gardeners. Pkt $3.00

OAXACAN GREEN #CN147 *New!*

85-100 days. The stunningly beautiful ears come in a range of greens, from yellow-green through emerald, with every imaginable shade in between. The deeply dented kernels have been used for centuries by the Zapotec people to make a regional favorite, green-flour tamales. Also makes excellent cornbread! The 6- to 10-inch ears are superb in arrangements and for fall decoration. Plants reach 7 feet, are very drought-tolerant, and perform well even at higher latitudes. Amazing and cool! Pkt $3.50

GMO Tested

Genetically Modified Organisms were NOT detected in test samples of any corn varieties listed here.

Each year we have a harder time getting seeds that test GMO-free. It is getting to the point where most heirloom corn varieties test positive for GMO's; even growers in remote areas are having problems with Monsanto's GMO corn.

"Science has tried to assume a monopoly—or, rather, a tyranny—over our understanding of the world around us … We are only now beginning to understand the disastrous results of this outlook." —PRINCE CHARLES

PENCIL COB DENT CORN #CN131
This old classic "shoepeg" type corn has very thin cobs, hence the name. Long white kernels are great for corn meal, or picked young and used as a roasting ear; sturdy 6' stalks produce 2-3 ears. Pkt $2.75

STOWELL'S EVERGREEN #CN130
This is among the oldest sweet corn that is still in production, predating 1949. It is still a favorite of many, producing tasty white kernels. The plants used to be pulled up when completely ripe, and hung upside-down in a cool pantry; the ears would last well into the winter, in a semi-fresh state. In 1873, the seeds sold for 25 cents per pint. Pkt $3.00

STRAWBERRY POPCORN #CN119
The popular, cute, little ears look just like big strawberries, just 2"-3" long. The 4' plants produce 2-4 ears each; great for fall decorations or making delicious popcorn. Pkt $3.00

TENNESSEE RED COB #CN149
White dent-type kernels are produced on deep red cobs! There are a number of red-cob types that hail from The Volunteer State, but this one was preserved and documented by University of Tennessee. Generally yields a single nice ear per plant, and has exceptional drought tolerance. The red cobs open up interesting possibilities for crafters. Superior for grinding into flour, or for roasting ears. Pkt $3.00

THOMPSON PROLIFIC #CN140
Excellent pale yellow dent type, very productive. Sturdy, 8-9 foot stalks frequently make two heavy 8-inch ears. This variety was recommended for Tennessee farmers in the 1936 USDA Yearbook of Agriculture, and was offered in the Richmond, Virginia area in the 1930s. An excellent choice for the middle South. Pkt $3.00

WADE'S GIANT INDIAN #CN141
This is the best Indian flint corn we have found; huge ears are about 12" long, very thick and heavy! This beauty comes in a whole range of lovely hues from yellow, blue, red, orange, white, purple and more. This one is perfect for stunning autumn displays and for selling at market. Also great for producing lots of corn for meal or feed. We were really excited to find this beautiful corn that was carefully selected for giant size and superior quality by Wade Nursery of Macomb, Michigan. Pkt $3.50

Country Gentleman Corn

Strawberry Popcorn

Golden Bantam Corn

Photo: David Cavagnaro

Cowpeas

(Vigna unguiculata) 30-75 seeds per pkt. Very easy to grow, colorful, and tasty. Cowpeas are popular in the Southern US, Africa, and Asia. They originated in Africa, and tolerate heat, drought and humidity much better than common beans do. They are great picked young for use as green snap beans, and stir-fried or boiled. They also make a great cover crop, sown in spring or summer and tilled into the soil when flowers begin to appear. Plant seeds about an inch deep after frosts have ceased and soil is warm. Most types "run," meaning they grow long vines, and so 3-5 feet should be allowed between rows.

Running Conch

BLUE GOOSE #CW103
The 36" vines produce purple-gray peas with up to 20 in a pod! A rare old Southern heirloom (pre-1860). Great for table use. Pkt $2.50

BOHEMIAN #CW139
75 days. This heirloom was brought to America by immigrants from Prague in the early 1800's. Small vining bushes produce small white peas, cream-colored flowers. Pkt $2.50

CALIFORNIA BLACKEYE PEA #CW108
70 days. An old standard variety; vigorous, high-yielding vines. Thomas Jefferson grew Blackeye Peas in the 1770's. Originating in Africa, cowpeas are easy to grow and are very popular in the South. A very ancient crop. Pkt $2.00

CARRAPICHIO #CW130
Good yields of khaki-colored peas and long pods. An attractive pea that is very rare and uniquely colored. Pkt $2.50

CLAY #CW102
This pea was a staple of the Southern armies during the American Civil War. We were excited to be able to find this living treasure of the 1860's. Tasty peas are the earthy color of clay. Rare! Pkt $2.50

Red Ripper

COAT AND JACKET #CW163 *New!*
Seeds are two-toned with with deep brown-red and cream coloring. This variety was introduced to Baker Creek Seeds by a kind couple, visiting our farm from Mississippi. Donor reports that the gentleman had swore he would never like them however, after a friend continued to insist, he not only enjoyed them but would neither grow nor eat any other variety. Pkt $2.50

GRAY-SPECKLED PALAPYE #CW107
Flavorful, gray-speckled peas in large pods; very early and perfect for the North. From a market in Palapye, Botswana. Rare. Pkt (25 seeds) $2.50

GREEN EYED PEA #CW143
Very rare, Missouri heirloom is larger than the standard Blackeye pea. The peas are named for their "green-colored eye" on each seed. We have finally procured some seed for this great variety. Pkt $2.50

HARICOT ROUGE DU BURKINA FASO #CW117
An heirloom from Burkina-Faso, West Africa. Colorful red-purple pods have deep red seeds. This pretty variety produces well even in extreme conditions. Pkt $2.50

HOG BRAINS #CW164 *New!*
These blocky-shaped cowpeas are two-toned with cream and deep brown-red coloring along with some mottling. This variety is not unknown in the south but the origin of its colorful name is somewhat of a mystery. Botanical Explorer Joseph Simcox strongly recommended that Baker Creek Seeds carry this variety after he discovered a quantity of it among the expansive seed collection, being housed at

Stick Up

106

California Blackeye Pea

Cowpea and Potato Curry
By Chef Quintin

INGREDIENTS
1 C of heirloom cowpeas soaked overnight
1 onion chopped
½ C of tomato puree
1 T of curry powder
3 small potatoes medium diced
1 t of cumin
1 T of fresh ginger
1 t of garam masala
1 C of mint and cilantro
1 bay leaf
4 cups of vegetable broth
2 T of olive oil

PREPARATION
1. Heat pan up with olive oil

2. Add your onions, and all spices. (this brings out oil in spices) lightly toast these

3. Then add your potatoes, tomato puree and drained cowpeas

4. Cover with vegetable broth and simmer for 25 min

5. Add your bay leaf and herbs in the final 5 mins of cooking. Cover and let rest on stove top

Hoppin' John

BY DR. JEFF NEKOLA

In the southern USA this dish is traditionally served for good luck on New Year's Day. The standard versions call for some type of smoked meat to be cooked with the dry peas. Here we use a combination of vegetables to make a truly delicious vegan main dish.

- ❑ 1 cup cow/field/black eyed peas
- ❑ 2 tablespoons olive oil
- ❑ 1 diced onion
- ❑ 3 diced stalks celery
- ❑ 1 diced white carrot (optional)
- ❑ 1 tablespoon minced garlic
- ❑ 1 cup uncooked long grain rice (not instant!)
- ❑ 2½ cups vegetable stock or water
- ❑ ½ cup finely chopped green onion
- ❑ 1 teaspoon salt
- ❑ Black pepper (to taste)
- ❑ A few drops liquid smoke (to taste)

Cook the cow peas in boiling water until barely tender. The length of cooking time will vary according to pea size, freshness, and variety as well as elevation. Make sure the liquid does not cook out; add more water as needed. Drain peas. Heat oil in a 10-inch cast iron skillet, sauté onion, celery, and optional white carrot until onion is transparent, then add garlic.

Now add in the raw rice and sauté that until it becomes chalky white. Add stock/water, cooked cow peas, green onion, salt, pepper, and liquid smoke; bring to a boil, reduce heat, cover and simmer for at least 15 minutes, or until the beans are tender. Remove from heat and let sit for 10 minute before removing the lid.

Baker Creek, of the late Mr Blaine Bourgeois, a long time and important seed saver from Arkansas. Pkt $2.50

LADY PEA #CW136
80 days. The tiny and popular, yet hard-to-find, white "lady pea." They are superbly flavored and are very tender. The short plants are great for small gardens, and yields are high. One of our most asked-for varieties. Pkt $2.50

MAYO COLIMA #CW134
80 days. Mixed-color peas, gray, gray-mottled, or orange/tan-mottled. Seed from this variety was collected from the low desert of Los Capomos, Sinaloa, Mexico, from a Mayo village. Pkt $2.50

MITCHELL FAMILY CREAM PEA #CW160
These white peas have been in the Mitchell family for over a century. Originating in Kentucky or Tennessee, the seeds went west when Mitchell ancestors emigrated to Missouri in the mid-nineteenth century. We received our original seed from a Mitchell descendant, whose wish is to preserve this living piece of America's agricultural past. Pkt $2.50

MONKEY TAIL #CW147
Hardy, rambling vines produce extra-long pods with unusual cocoa/tan-colored beans. From the UCD Seed Saving Project, collected in Africa. Pkt $2.50

OLD TIMER or PURPLE HULL SPECKLED #CW138
Short, bush plants produce colorful, purple, 7-inch pods that are filled with medium-sized, tan peas that have dark speckles. A fine variety that is good for small gardens. Pkt $2.50

OZARK RAZORBACK #CW148
90 days. The most beautiful pea we grow; the peas are mottled half white and half red. Very productive bush plants that set on loads of tasty small peas. This fine variety was developed by Horus Botanicals of Salem, Arkansas. Pkt $2.50

PENNY RILE #CW116
Khaki-tan color, medium-sized peas, heavy yields. The peas are great for soup. Grown by a Mr. Martin, whose family grew these vines to feed their livestock and as a food source for the family to help with long winters. Pkt $2.50

PIGOTT FAMILY HEIRLOOM #CW153
A Louisiana variety that has been in the Pigott family, Washington Parish, since the 1850's. Prized by the family as the best-tasting cowpea of them all. Brown seed is speckled and of good size. Pkt. (30 seeds) $2.50

PURPLE HULL PINKEYE #CW109
A preferred variety of many Southerners; delicious flavor. Hulls are purple; an old favorite. Pkt $2.50

RED RIPPER #CW106
90 days. Large running vines yield 12" to 14" pods that are loaded with peas! This heirloom has blood-red seeds and great flavor fresh or dried. Pkt $2.50

RICE #CW112
Tiny white seeds are just larger than rice and cook in 40 minutes. Very tasty. Bush plants yield well. A pre-1860 Southern cowpea. Pkt $2.50

RUNNING CONCH #CW154
Good yields of small, delicious cream-colored peas, one of the parent varieties of "Zipper Cream." An heirloom from the late 1800's, great for growing in the South. Long vining plants. Pkt. (30 seeds) $2.50

SIX-WEEK PURPLE HULL #CW145
An early Pink Eye, Purple Hull type, produces lots of tasty cream-colored seeds that have a "pink eye." Small plants and reddish-purple pods. Sent to us by a customer. Pkt $2.50

SHANTY PEA #CW157
South Carolina heirloom produces peas in varying shades of tan, on vines of medium length. Productive, noted for its ability to yield over a very long season, even up to frost from an early planting. Originally from one A. D. Huckabee. Pkt $2.50

STICK UP #CW129
80 days. Pods tend to "Stick Up" on the vines, hence the name. This heirloom was once popular in French Fork, Louisiana, and it helped the local people of the area get through the Great Depression. Small brown seed. Pkt $2.50

WHITE WHIPPOORWILL #CW155
We at last have the hard-to-find, white-seeded Whippoorwill. Plants produce loads of these creamy-white peas that are great when picked young and stir-fried; or harvested when dry for soup. An old Southern heirloom. Pkt. (30 seeds) $2.50

Cucumber

(Cucumis sativus) 25-35 seeds per packet. Cucumbers originated in India or western Asia, and have been known to gardeners for at least 3,000 years. Their diverse forms and flavors are now appreciated and utilized in local cuisines around the world. Warm growers, they are best sown in place after the last frost of spring. Very rich soil, well-drained yet moist, suits them best. Full sun exposure is usually preferred, except that in hot-summer areas, the plants might benefit from some mid-afternoon shade. The vines run to about 5 feet in length. Or, to save space, grow them on a trellis.

ARMENIAN #CU169

(Cucumis melo) Light-green, mild-tasting, deeply ribbed fruits. The elongated fruits yield uniform, easily digestible, fluted slices. They are apt to twist and coil growing on the ground, but develop nice and straight when hanging from a trellis. Fruits reach 24 inches long, best harvested at about 18 inches. The classic Armenian "Cucumber" which is actually a melon genetically. Pkt $2.50

BEIT ALPHA #CU150

A delicious, very sweet cucumber that is usually picked small and does not need peeling as the skin is very tender. This variety is very popular in the Mediterranean, having been developed in Israel at a kibbutz farm. Now becoming popular with Americans because of the fruits' fine flavor and high yields. They are also burpless and have great shelf life. Pkt $2.50

BOOTHBY'S BLONDE #CU118

60 days. Heirloom variety from Livermore, Maine, where the Boothby family has grown it for several generations. It sets high yields of 6"-8" cream-colored cukes that are mild and sweet, thin skinned. Good producer. Pkt $2.50

BOSTON PICKLING #CU105

An old heirloom dating back to 1880. Vigorous vines give large yields of smooth green fruit. It is excellent for pickles; very crisp and good quality. A very popular variety at the turn of the 20th century. Pkt $2.25

CHICAGO PICKLING #CU181   *New!*

55 days. Originally bred for the markets of the Chicago area. Released in 1888, this has been the go-to pickling cuke for generations of home gardeners and canners, and we are so pleased to be able to offer it! The thin skins take up pickling solutions readily. Black-spined fruits can be allowed to reach 7" without sacrificing quality, but are often harvested much smaller. Amazingly prolific, and disease-resistant, too. Pkt $2.50

CHINESE YELLOW #CU112

Beautiful, yellow-orange cucumber from mainland China, the young fruit is green. 10" fruit are as crisp as an apple. Very mild and delicious, great for slicing or for pickles. This was our largest-yielding variety ever -- just a few plants produced hundreds of cucumbers! Our favorite cucumber for 2003. A very rare Chinese heirloom. Pkt (15 seeds) $2.50

CRYSTAL APPLE #CU149

Small 3" oval fruit are a bright, creamy white, about the size of a small apple; sweet, mild and very tender. This variety has become almost extinct in America after being introduced here from Australia around

Mexican Sour Gherkins

Boston Pickling

Jaune Dickfleischige

Beit Alpha

Miniature White

the year 1930 from Arthur Yates and Co. But this type of cucumber is likely to have originated in China. The small fruit are so tender you can eat them skin and all. Pkt $2.75

DAR #CU182 *New!*

60 days. Here's a gorgeous new all-purpose slicing/pickling type. The plants are of bush habit, usually running no more than 18" or so, making them superior for small gardens, containers, or anywhere space is tight. Fruits hold well on the plants, so avoiding the need for constant picking. Plants are also tolerant to Downy Mildew, which is so often a problem in humid-summer climates. The bumpy, brightly-striped exterior is particularly attractive as well. A superb new Polish variety! Pkt $2.50

DE BOURBONNE #CU144

Tiny pickling cucumbers are ready in about 50 days. This old French heirloom is used to make the 2" long Cornichon pickles that are so tasty. Still popular in France for this purpose. High-yielding vines will be popular with all those who preserve food. Pkt $2.00

DELIKATESSE #CU109

60 days. 10"-long, unique fruits are pale green with small warts. Superb taste, excellent for slicing or pickling; bears abundantly. A rare variety from Germany. Pkt $2.25

DOUBLE YIELD #CU175

55 days—Very productive pickling type. Bright green fruits reach to 8 inches, but may be harvested much smaller. Originally introduced in 1924 by Joseph Harris Seed Company, who wrote: "The remarkable thing about this new cucumber is its wonderful productiveness. For every pickle that is cut off, two or three more are produced." The flavor is also excellent! Pkt $2.75 *1 oz $6.00*

DRAGON'S EGG #CU147

Beautiful cream-colored fruit are about the size and shape of a large egg! Mild, bitter-free and sweet-tasting, this little cucumber set massive yields in our gardens. So fun to grow, and very unique-looking; great for children and all who like delicious cucumbers. We were sent this new favorite by Reinhard Kraft, a German seed collector, but this heirloom originated in Croatia. Pkt (12 seeds) $2.75

EARLY FORTUNE #CU176

55 days. (Also called Special Dark Green) A super dependable garden cucumber, sweet and almost never bitter. Slicing-type fruits grow 7 to 8 inches long, 2 inches in diameter. Originally selected out of Davis Perfect (now believed extinct) by George Starr in Royal Oak Michigan in 1906. Upon its release it was described as "the earliest and best white spine cucumber ever offered." Pkt $2.75

EARLY RUSSIAN #CU130

This early heirloom was introduced in 1854. It produces loads of short, medium-green fruit over a very long season. They are mild and sweet in flavor and uniform in shape. The vines are quite hardy, making it perfect for northern areas with short seasons; a great little cucumber for salads or pickles. We have been selling these at our Comstock, Ferre Store in Connecticut since the 1850s. Pkt $2.75

FIN DE MEAUX #CU145

Slender, little green fruit are picked when 2 inches long and are used to make delicious cornichon pickles. A popular French variety that is hard to find. Very productive plants bear fruit that is darker green than most types. Pkt $2.50

GELE TROS or LARGE DUTCH YELLOW #CU159

This is a large yellow cucumber that was popular in Holland for making yellow, sliced pickles. The Dutch call this cucumber the "ancient race". The ripe fruit are quite colorful in their sunny yellow color. A fine old strain that is very rare now even in Europe.
Pkt (15 seeds) $2.75

HMONG RED #CU152

The fruits are white to pale green, turning golden-orange as they ripen. A very productive and tasty variety that stays mild even when large. This heirloom was collected from a Hmong immigrant. Millions of the Hmong tribe live on the borders of Thailand, China, Burma, Laos and Vietnam, and are a very ancient people.
Pkt (15 seeds) $2.50

JAUNE DICKFLEISCHIGE #CU140

A variety that is described as "ancienne" or old by the French, it also bears a partly German name and is of German origin, making this old heirloom a real piece of European cucumber history. Huge, yellowish-green fruit turn a lovely lemon color at full maturity and can weigh 5 lbs! Beautiful fruit are very crisp and flavorful. Vines produce good yields of this impressive, tasty cucumber. Rare! Pkt $4.00

HOFFMAN'S JOHANNA #CU183 *New!*

57 days. (Also known as Giganta) European go-to variety seldom seen on these shores. Makes a mild, bitter-free slicing type. Fruits are dark green, dense-fleshed and so crisp and juicy. Pkt $2.50

LEMON CUKE #CU103

60 days. The shape, size, and color of a lemon, but the flavor is sweet and mild! This heirloom was introduced in 1894 and is still a favorite today. Pkt $2.50 *or 1 oz $8.00*

LONGFELLOW #CU177 65 days. An unusually long, slender, dark green variety. Not a heavy yielder, but fruits are very large and finely shaped, being 12 to 14 inches in length and very attractive. It has excellent color retention when canned. Also a great cucumber for slicing, it was first offered on the market in 1927 by Jerome B. Rice Seed Company of Cambridge, NY Pkt $2.00 *or 1 oz $6.00*

MARKETMORE 76 #CU101

70 days. Dark green, 8"-9" fruit; great slicer! Good yields! Excellent flavor. A real standard for superb eating cukes. Pkt $2.25 *or 1 oz $6.00*

MEXICAN SOUR GHERKIN #CU125

(*Melothria scabra*) 75 days. Incredible, small cucumber-like fruit are shaped like baby watermelons. They are good added to salads or can be pickled. They have a cucumber-like taste with a touch of lemon. The ornamental vines have tiny leaves and flowers and are perfect for the cottage garden. Very unique and fun for kids. Huge yields. Read about these in "Mother Earth News". Pkt $2.50

MINIATURE WHITE #CU167

50 days. White-skinned, black-spined little pickling cukes. Production is high and begins very early on almost-bush plants that seldom run over three feet making great container plants. Delicious for fresh use as well—this strain has none of the bitterness that has unfortunately come to be associated with the white-fruited types. Pkt $2.25

Telegraph Improved

Hoffman's Johanna

Tendergreen

MONIKA #CU184 *New!*

55 days. From our Polish grower, who recommends 'Monika' for pickles. This one is parthenocarpic, which simply means it doesn't need pollination to set fruit. This is great news to gardeners who find they haven't got sufficient local bee populations to pollinate regular cucumbers. It also means you can grow pickling cukes under glass. Makes a nice slicer as well. Pkt $2.75

MUNCHER #CU174

60 days. Very tender, dual-purpose variety makes great pickles and is excellent for fresh eating right out of the garden! Nearly spineless fruits are 6 to 8 inches long, reaching a plump 3 inches wide. Produces abundantly on strong vigorous vines. Non-bitter, burpless variety, can be eaten at any stage of growth. For pickling, harvest the fruits at 4 to 6 inches long. Pkt $2.50

NATIONAL PICKLING #CU172

52 days. 6-inch, blunt and blocky fruits, dark green with some striping or stippling. Dual-purpose cukes are primarily for pickling; they were bred with a slight taper to fit more readily into a jar! They make great slicers as well, though; with their tender skin, peeling is not really necessary. Medium-sized vines are fine for trellising. Black-spined type produces over a very long season! Pkt $2.50

PARISIAN PICKLING #CU106

60 days. The old French gherkin or cornichon pickler. Listed in America in 1892 by Gregory. Great for making tiny sweet pickles. Rare. Pkt $2.50

RICHMOND GREEN APPLE #CU108

A unique heirloom from Australia and is still popular there. The fruit are the size of a lemon but are of a beautiful light green color. For eating these are excellent, very mild, sweet and juicy. Hard to find and really fun to grow. Pkt (15 seeds) $2.75

RUBY WALLACE'S OLD TIME WHITE #CU153

65 days. Grown for over 50 years by Mrs. Ruby Wallace of Dallas, North Carolina. Ruby first got a start from her mother-in-law Myrtle, who had grown them for many years. The Wallace family uses the fruits for pickles when they are very small. (Be sure to use white vinegar to make white pickles!) Or the family let the fruits get a bit larger for slicers. It's the only one they grow! A real Carolina heirloom. Pkt $2.50

SAGAMI HANJIRO #CU165

Traditional Japanese variety used primarily for slicing. Sagami is an area in Japan; "hanjiro" means two-toned, and this one is dark green and lime green. Like many Japanese varieties, these are fantastic for fresh eating. Few seeds. Pkt (10 seeds) $3.00

SIKKIM CUCUMBER #CU124

The historic cucumber of Sikkim. Fat, large fruit can reach several pounds in size. The ripe fruit is a unique rusty red color and is good eaten cooked or raw. In Asia, cucumbers are often stir-fried and are quite tasty. This variety is grown in the Himalayas of Sikkim and Nepal. Sir Joseph Hooker first discovered it in the eastern Himalayas in 1848. Here is part of what he wrote about it: "So abundant were the fruits, that for days together I saw gnawed fruits lying by the natives' paths by the thousands, and every man, woman and child seemed engaged throughout the day in devouring them." Pkt (10 seeds) $3.50

SOLLY BEILER #CU157

This cucumber makes superior pickles when harvested at about the size of your thumb. Spectacularly productive in our trials, the plants

Crystal Apple

Lemon

Dragon's Egg

yield very uniform fruits, which at full maturity are russeted like a Poona Kheera. Stays crisp and mild even at larger sizes. Developed in the 1930's by Solomon "Solly" Beiler, then a bishop in the Beachy Amish Mennonite Church, in Lancaster County, Pennsylvania. Our original seed was furnished by Martin J. Hughes, a present day member of the same church in Elmira, New York. Pkt (15 seeds) $2.50

STRAIGHT EIGHT #CU168

52 days. All-America winner for 1935! Smooth, straight, deep green 8-inch fruits with rounded blunt ends. Early, vigorous and prolific; tolerates mosaic virus. A superb variety that has stood the test of time. Pkt $2.00

SUYO LONG #CU132

65 days. Long, ribbed, dark green fruit can grow to 18". They are very mild, sweet and burpless. One of my personal favorites for fresh eating. This productive heirloom comes from northern China and is very attractive. Pkt $2.75

TELEGRAPH IMPROVED #CU110

60 days. Smooth, straight, dark-green fruit, 18" long. Flesh is very crisp, tender and mild; superb flavor. Very few seeds, vigorous high-yielding vines, great for greenhouse production; also good cultured outdoors. This is an excellent English heirloom variety, introduced around 1897. Pkt (15 seeds) $3.50

TENDERGREEN BURPLESS #CU173

55 day. Burpless slicing type, free from bitterness, that has been popular for over 80 years! Fruits are medium-dark green, 7-12 inches in length, and quite plump and smooth compared to Japanese long slicing types. Excels as a slicer, because each fruit yields so many slices of uniform diameter, but the tender skin makes great pickles as well. Tolerates cool soil and excessive moisture better than many, as well as downy mildew and mosaic virus. An altogether superior sort! Pkt $2.50

WEST INDIA BURR GHERKINS #CU107

(Cucumis anguria) 65 days. Not a true cucumber, but used much like it. Will not cross with C. sativus. Very beautiful long vines and hundreds of small tasty fruit. Yields better than any cucumber. These are becoming rare. They do great in hot, humid weather. Introduced to the USA in 1793 from Jamaica; it had been pickled and boiled by the Colonists in Jamaica. Pkt $2.50

WHITE EMERALD #CU154

White Emerald cucumber is vigorous and prolific. Fruit is crisp with light green color skin. Thick, cylindrical in shape. A good resistant variety that is well adapted to a wide range of growing conditions, but especially in hot, humid areas. From Thailand. Pkt $2.25

WHITE WONDER #CU104

60 days. A great yielder. Creamy-ivory, 7"-long fruits, delicious and great for pickles or slicing. W. Atlee Burpee introduced this heirloom in 1893 after they received it from a customer in New York. Pkt $2.00 *or 1oz $5.00*

Richmond Green Apple

Suyo Long

Asian Cucumber Salad
By Chef Quintin

INGREDIENTS

- 2 Cucumber
- 1 Red Onion
- 1 Red Bell Pepper
- ½ C of shredded Carrots
- ¼ C of Cilantro
- 2 T Honey
- 3 T Rice wine vinegar
- 1 t of Red Crushed Chiles
- 1/2 teaspoon sea salt (optional)
- 1 T of shredded of ginger
- Pepper to taste

PREPARATION

1.   Slice cucumber in half rounds. Finely julienne onions and peppers

2.   Grab a box grater and shred the carrots into thin long strips. Finely chop cilantro

3.   Whisk honey, vinegar together. Then add the crushed chilies and ginger]

4.   Mix all ingredients together well and season with salt and pepper

Chinese Yellow

Muncher

Sikkim

Antigua

Rosita

Early Black Egg

Eggplant

(Solanum melongena and others) 25-35 seeds per packet. We offer the best selection of quality heirloom eggplants in the USA. This is my favorite crop, as it is easy to grow, and the fruit is nutritious and incredibly delicious. Another of the great staple agricultural crops of India, eggplant varieties have long been appreciated in traditional communities in Africa, Asia, the Middle East and Mediterranean coast, and, more recently, the Americas. With their often large and showy purple or white blooms and velvety leaves, eggplants are ornamental enough to grow in the border or even in the front yard! Heat-loving plants, eggplants are best started indoors about 8 weeks before the last frost date of spring. Be sure to set out transplants only after carefully hardening them to outdoor conditions, and only after warm weather has really arrived.

ANTIGUA #EG189
80 days—Amazingly beautiful lavender-streaked fruits are 6-8 inches long, elongated teardrop shaped. Flesh is tender and mild, snow-white and bitter-free. Pkt $3.00

APPLEGREEN #EG103
70 days. An early, light-green eggplant. Good yield, very tender and delicious. Smooth oval-round fruit growing on small plants. We highly recommend this fine variety! Developed by the late Prof. Elwyn Meader, UNH 1964. Pkt $2.00

ARUMUGAM'S EGGPLANT #EG149
This variety produces an assortment of green, white and lavender fruit, many are striped. It is used in Tamil Nadu State in vegetable stews and curries, as well as stuffed. It was given to a traveler by the Arumugam family of Ambal, India, who have a small rice farm near the island of Karaikal. We are proud to offer this great little Indian eggplant. Pkt $2.00

ASTRAKOM #EG174
Compact plants reached barely two feet in our trials. Each plant yielded several 4-inch, teardrop-shaped fruits, of a rich, glossy purple-black. Grown from seed provided by our Belorussian friend Andrey Baranovsky. Pkt $2.00

ASWAD #EG175
This incredibly delicious Iraqi variety comes from our friend Nael Aziz. Satiny, dark purple-black fruits get very large—to 3 pounds or more. Shaped like a squat teardrop, the flesh is sweet and tender, perfect for grilling or baking. The fruit are abundantly produced. Very heat tolerant and productive in our trials. Pkt (15 seeds) $3.00

AUBERGINE DU BURKINA FASO #EG139
(S. aethiopicum) A unique heirloom from Burkina Faso, West Africa, featuring a tall plant, beautiful enough for the flower garden, which produces many good-sized, red-ribbed fruit. The fruit is wrinkled, flat, and (some think) somewhat bitter and strong flavored. Pkt $3.00

BANGLADESHI LONG #EG146
Cylindrical fruit are very attractive-looking, being purple-gray with dark purple streaks. This variety was collected in Bangladesh. Pkt (15 seeds) $2.25

Turkish Orange

Little Green

Korean Red

BLACK BEAUTY #EG113

90 days. Standard old type, large black fruit of excellent quality. Very tasty but is lower yielding and much later than many types and needs a long season. Pkt $1.75 *or 1/8 oz $3.50*

BLACK STEM #EG168

This ornamental variety is grown for its stunning black stems and red, pumpkin-shaped fruit that are used by florists in Japan in flower arranging. Stunning and elegant in a vase, and a real beauty in any ornamental garden. Perfect for landscaping. Pkt $2.00

CANNIBAL TOMATO #EG153

Beautiful, attractive plants are covered with loads of shiny green and red fruit that are shockingly bitter and about 3" across. They are very cute, as they look like little pumpkins covering the plant. A native to Fiji and Tahiti, this plant has quite a history, as it is said that the fruit was made into a sauce and used on a cannibal's meal! The leaves were also prepared as cooked greens. One of the more interesting and infamous plants we've grown. Hardy and easy to grow. Pkt $2.50

CASPER #EG101

75 days. Medium size, very attractive, smooth ivory-white fruit that have a very mild mushroom-like flavor. Prolific plant. Fruit ripens early. An excellent variety for specialty growers and gardeners. Pkt $2.50

CAMBODIAN GREEN GIANT #EG177

Here is a large, round, flat variety from the kingdom of Cambodia. We collected this variety in 2004, when we were touring this once war-torn southeast Asian country. Attractive fruit are pale green with dark green stripes, and are lightly ribbed. This is a very unique color pattern for a large variety. We are proud to be among the first companies to offer varieties from Cambodia, a country with a delicious cuisine that is in danger of being lost. These are great eating, and have a deep, full bodied eggplant flavor. Pkt $3.00

COOKSTOWN ORANGE #EG173

Tomato-shaped fruits start out green, eventually turning a gorgeous red-orange with intriguing, two-toned green striping. Yellow flesh is non-bitter when harvested young. Very attractive—pretty enough to grow in the border! Pkt $2.50

DIAMOND #EG102

70 days. Mild, dark purple, 6-9" x 2-3" slender fruit; superb flavor and firm flesh. Becoming popular with market growers and home gardeners. This variety from the Ukraine was collected by Seed Savers Exchange in 1993.
Pkt $2.25 *or 1/8 oz $6.00*

EDIRNE PURPLE STRIPED #EG160

Originally collected in Edirne (Adrianople), Turkey, in 1948, and stored by the USDA ever since, until we grew it out in 2008! Gorgeous 6-8 inch fruits are richly striped in purple and off-white. May be even superior to Listada de Gandia in appearance due to its deeper luster, and actually preferred over it in our trials! Vigorous plants, very productive. Pkt $2.50

EARLY BLACK EGG #EG202 *New!*

65 days. Stunning fruits are egg-shaped to teardrop. So purple they really are almost black. Leaves and stems of the three-foot plants are "black" as well. With its purple

flowers, it's really too pretty to hide away—consider growing it in containers, flaunting its beauty for all to see! Originated in Japan. Pkt $2.50

FENGYUAN PURPLE #EG176
Very long, slim, 16" fruit are light lavender-purple in color. One of the best long varieties we have seen: mild, sweet and tender; good yields. Unique Taiwan heirloom. This is one of the main varieties we grow for our restaurant each summer. Pkt $3.00

FINGERS MIX #EG190 *New!*
80 days—A formula mix of various eggplants in a range of colors. The common denominator is, all are smallish, long- and narrow-fruited types. Great fun! Pkt $3.00

FLORIDA MARKET #EG114
85 days. Very large plant; large purple bell-shaped fruit. An old standard market variety and an excellent type for the South. Pkt $2.50

FOO CHOW ROUND #EG195 *New!*
Nearly spherical fruits are large and very lovely—white with lavender markings. Plants are very productive. Good tasting variety that hails from China. Pkt $2.50

GBOGNAME or COLLARD EGGPLANT
#EG154 An ancient vegetable from Togo, West Africa. The young, green leaves are cooked into delicious dishes, like you would cook collard greens. Easy and fun-to-grow plants take heat well and are quite attractive with their green and yellow bitter fruit. A great piece of African culinary history that is rare and hard to find! Pkt $2.75

GOYO KUMBA #EG144
Brilliant, shiny red 3" fruit. This African variety is among the most colorful and ornamental we offer. Tall, spreading 4' plants produce loads of fruit. Perfect for the flower bed as well as the vegetable garden. Pkt $2.25

HOMSI #EG185 *New!*
Pretty fruit grow to about 5 inches in length, are predominantly a lavender to light purple with varying degrees of white striping. Gathered by a local Syrian company directly from farmers, and passed along to us by our friend, Raghad Gorani. Homsi requires a long growing season and is a good to fair producer in dry conditions. Pkt $2.50

JADE SWEET #EG181 77 days. Skin is an attractive soft green. Blocky-shaped fruits keep good eating quality to surprisingly large size. A good producing variety from Australia. Pkt $2.25

JAPANESE PICKLING #EG161
A beautiful, long, slender Japanese variety that produces fruit up to 16" long. Beautiful, glossy purple skin, with pure white flesh that's sweet and mellow tasting. Great for home or market. Pkt $2.50

JAPANESE WHITE EGG #EG110
65 days. Full, rich flavor; lovely 2"-3" white fruit are perfect for stir-frying. The plants give heavy yields all season. Pkt $2.00

KAMO #EG200 *New!*
65 days. This drop-dead gorgeous Japanese sort is delicious, too! Very thin skin is non-glossy dark purple to nearly black. Fruits are round, and frequently exceed a pound in weight. Tolerates cooler conditions than many eggplant varieties. A traditional "kyo yasai" or Kyoto vegetable, originating in the Kamo region. Pkt $3.00

Ronde de Valence

Lao Purple Stripe

Rosa Bianca

Jade Sweet

Casper

Lao Green Stripe

KASHMIRI BRINJAL #EG193 *New!*
80 days. Oval to elongated fruits in clear shades of lavender to pink. Fruits reach 4-6 inches in length. A local type in the uneasy land of Kashmir, north India. Pkt $2.50

KAZAKHSTAN #EG170
Seed collected at a state-run market in Alma Ata, Kazakhstan, by A.T. Whittemore, and donated to the USDA Germplasm Repository in 1991. The plants are rather compact, reaching 24 to 30 inches in our trials. Pale purple flowers give way to dark purple-black, teardrop-shaped fruits to 6 inches or so, produced early and in abundance. To our knowledge this variety has never before been offered for sale in North America. Pkt $2.00

KOREAN RED #EG171
Rounded bush to 3 feet tall, yields tender, sweet green fruits very early for an eggplant. Left to mature, the fruits reach 4-6 ounces, taking on a red-orange color and are quite decorative—perfect for arrangements. Unusual eggplant grown from seed originating in the former USSR. Pkt $2.50

LAO GREEN STRIPE #EG140
Colorful, green-white-purple striped, 2-4" ball-shaped fruit have pleasant eggplant flavor that is perfect for curries, soups and other dishes from Southeast Asia. This productive heirloom comes from the beautiful mountain country of Laos. Pkt $2.50

LAO PURPLE STRIPE #EG143
90 days. A lovely little eggplant that is the size and shape of a ping-pong ball. Fruits are a pale lavender with deep purple stripes. A great little eggplant for using in stir-fries and Asian dishes. This variety was brought to the US by Hmong students from the Southeast Asian country of Laos. Pkt $2.50

LAO WHITE #EG141
White, 2" ball-shaped fruit turn deep yellow as they ripen; a colorful and good-yielding heirloom from Laos. This very rare variety needs to be preserved as it is used in many traditional Laotian recipes. Pkt $2.50

LISTADA DE GANDIA #EG137
90 days. One of the most popular heirloom types; this one has 7"-long fruit that are white with lovely bright purple stripes. They are so beautiful and have fabulous flavor with sweet, tender flesh. This excellent variety hails from Spain, a country that is renowned for fine food. Pkt $2.25 *or 1/8 oz $6.00*

LITTLE FINGERS #EG169
65 days. Small, purple-black fruits are produced in clusters on sturdy, compact plants. The blunt-ended fruits may be harvested when finger-sized, but may also be allowed to grow larger with no sacrifice of their mild, sweet taste and tender texture. Pkt $2.25

LITTLE GREEN #EG172
75 days. Charming, small, single-stemmed plants yield green fruits to 6 inches long, 3 inches in diameter. A new introduction grown from seed sent to us from the former Soviet Union. Try this in cooler-summer climates. A sweet and delcious variety that is one of our favorites. Pkt $3.00

LITTLE SAILOR #EG188 75-80 days.
Rather early type as you might expect from this

Cambodian Green Giant

Bangladeshi Long

variety that we received from the former Soviet Union. The very pretty fruits are oval to nearly round, run to 5 inches across, although most are more like 3 inches. Color is purple with white markings. The flavor is very mild. Productive plants are good-sized, to about three feet, and nearly free of spines. This seed was grown out by our own Sasha Gettle in conjunction with her grandfather! Pkt (10 seeds) $2.50

LOUISIANA LONG GREEN #EG115
100 days. Large, 8"-long, light green banana-shaped fruit that have pale stripes; tender and mild. Excellent quality, prolific yields. A rare heirloom from Louisiana. Pkt $2.00

MALAYSIAN DARK RED #EG148
Tender and delicious, violet-colored fruit are long and slender. This productive and tasty variety comes from the Southeast Asian country of Malaysia. A hard-to-find but very good variety that is perfect for frying. Pkt $2.50

MA-ZU PURPLE CHINESE #EG159
Delicious, sweet and tender describe the flavorful fruit of "Ma-Zu" eggplant. This variety bears deep purple fruit that are 8"-12" long and 2" in diameter. This favorite of Taiwanese farmers grows perfectly in warm areas and produces lots of fruit over a long period of time. Pkt $2.25

MELANZANE ROSSO DI ROTONDA #EG199 *New!*
(*S. aethiopicum*) 80 days Fruits are oblate, smooth and mature to a brilliant scarlet. Red eggplants are widely grown, but mostly in Africa and Asia. This one is the only red type traditionally grown in Italy, and it is renowned there! Rotonda is the town in southern Italy that is famous as the traditional source for this unusual type. It was probably introduced there in the late 19th century by veterans returning from colonial wars. Often exported as pickled eggplant. We first sampled this variety as a tasty relish, when we were traveling in Italy. Pkt (15 seeds) $3.00

MITOYO EG201 *New!*
Large fruits are oval to teardrop-shaped and nearly black. Flesh is very tender and sweet, it is even highly recommended for use without cooking! Fruits are also excellent baked or roasted, and are often used in pickling as well in their native Japan, were the variety was originally collected at a local market. Traditionally grown in the Mitoyo and Kanonji areas. One of the best tasting eggplants we have ever tried. Pkt (10 seeds) $2.50

NEW YORK IMPROVED #EG192 *New!*
75 days. Large black fruit produced on compact plants. The tasty flesh is good fried or baked. This heirloom was mentioned by Fearing Burr in his 1865 book. One of our oldest eggplant varieties! Pkt $2.50

NIPPLE FRUIT #EG135
(*Solanum mammosum*) This is one of the most amazing plants I have grown. Beautiful tall, thorny plants bear purple flowers, followed by long spikes of 3" yellow fruit that are curiously shaped, sort of like a cow's udder and glowing yellow-orange in color. These 2'-5' stems are sold for display in arrangements or alone. They fetch top prices at stores and are great for farmers' markets. I first saw these in Thailand several years ago being sold as potted plants along a road. The long-lasting, bitter fruit are not edible. Pkt $4.00

PANDORA STRIPED ROSE #EG129
A great market variety, teardrop-shaped fruit are a lovely lilac-rose color with thin white stripes. Strong, thornless plants give heavy yields; tender and delicious. Eye catcher. Pkt $2.50 *or 1/8 oz $6.00*

PING TUNG #EG109
70 days. A wonderful eggplant from Ping Tung, Taiwan. Fruits are purple and up to 18" long and 2" in diameter. This variety is so sweet and tender, superbly delicious! One of the best Chinese eggplants on the market. Pkt $2.50

PROSPEROSA #EG183
75 days. Massive fruits are nearly round to slightly teardrop shaped, and sometimes very slightly ribbed. Their rich dark purple exterior also glistens with a satiny greenish sheen—quite spectacular to see! The white flesh is as good as the fruit looks, being mild, tender, and slow to discolor when sliced; superb in parmagiana dishes. Yields all season long. Heirloom type grown for generations in Tuscany, in northwestern Italy. Pkt $2.50

RAYADA #EG178

An excellent introduction from the Puerto Rico Experiment Station at Rio Piedras. Created from a cross of a native white by an unknown parent, this variety has striped fruits about 5X3 inches, mainly purple but with white striping. What really sets this variety apart is its reputed resistance to the flea beetle, which for most of us is the major eggplant pest. Mild white fruit is sweet clear through. Pkt $2.50

RED CHINA #EG142

One of the most ornamental of all eggplants, the upright plants produce loads of small, flattened fruit that look similar to 'Jack-Be-Little' pumpkins. The fruit is a beautiful fiery-red color when mature. They have a slightly bitter taste which is milder when they are only slightly orange; great for Asian foods. The long-keeping fruit are perfect for fall displays. Was listed as 'Scarlet Chinese' in Vanderbilt's 1879 seed list. Pkt $2.25

RED RUFFLED #EG145

Also known as 'Hmong Red', this bitter-tasting Asian variety is used in Vietnamese cooking. The 2" fruits are flattened, ribbed and bright red in color. Used by florists and crafters as miniature pumpkins, which they closely resemble. One of the most beautiful eggplants we've ever seen. Pkt $2.50

RONDE DE VALENCE #EG162

Lovely, black fruit are almost perfectly round in shape and the size of a grapefruit, with deep purple color. A wonderful variety for stuffing, with great tasting, tender flesh. A traditional French heirloom named after the city of Valence, a quaint city on the Rhone River. Pkt $2.50

ROSA BIANCA #EG105

80 days. Colorful, light pink-lavender fruit with white shading. Rich, mild flesh is very popular with chefs and gardeners alike! No bitterness. A great variety for heirloom market growers. Grow the color that sells! Pkt $2.50

ROTONDA BIANCA SFUMATA DI ROSA

#EG116 120 days. This beautiful, round, white eggplant is shaded with rose-pink color. The lovely fruit grow to large sizes, making this one of the most striking types we sell! Excellent for market growers, this Italian heirloom is mild and delicious. Pkt $2.50 *or 1/8 oz $6.00*

ROSITA #EG179

80 days. Lovely 8"x4" neon, lavender-pink fruits have a mild, sweet, white flesh. The skin is tender, and not bitter. Produces excellent yields. This incredible heirloom was developed in Puerto Rico in the 1940's by the Puerto Rico Agric. Expt. Sta., Rio Piedras. One of our favorites every season. Pkt (10 seeds) $3.00

ROUND MAUVE #EG130

85 days. Round, 4" fruit are a lovely, deep mauve color; purple calyx. Plants are compact and have purple stems. They start producing very early. A very good specialty variety. Pkt $2.00

SYRIAN STUFFING #EG184

Another treasure received from our Syrian friend, Ragad Khorani. This one is used for stuffing, and the medium-sized, purple-black fruits are ideal for this use. Flavor is superb,

Malaysian Dark Red

Louisiana Long Green

Kamo

Stuffed Eggplant with Cauliflower & Green Curry

By Chef Quintin

INGREDIENTS

- Eggplant sliced in half and cored out
- 2 C of Cauliflower
- 2 heirloom tomatoes
- 1 Yellow bell pepper
- 3 kaffir lime leaves
- 2 T of green curry paste
- 1 T of fresh garlic
- 3 C of coconut milk
- 1 T fresh ginger
- 1 green chili roasted and peeled
- 1 T of olive oil
- 1 T of shredded lemongrass
- 1 C of fresh thai basil
- Sea Salt and Pepper to taste

PREPARATION

1. Salt eggplant and let sit. Then rinse with cold water and squeeze

2. Small chop all vegetables as well and the inside of the eggplant

3. Heat pan up with olive oil. Add garlic, ginger and all vegetables.

4. Deglaze pan with your coconut milk then fold in your curry.

5. Cook this for about 6 mins to incorporate flavors pull off heat.

6. Scoop the meat of this dish into the eggplant and bake at 350 for 18 minutes.

7. Finish dish by warming back up sauce and stirring in basil. This drench the top of the eggplant with the sauce. Garnish with Lime wedge.

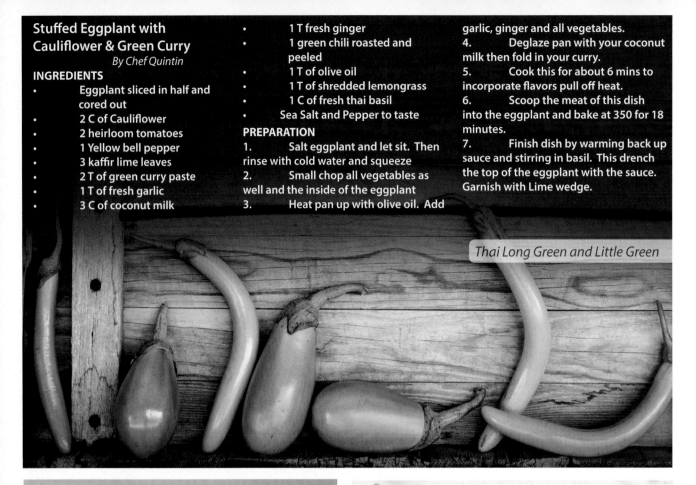

Thai Long Green and Little Green

Little Sailor

Syrian Stuffing

Thai White Ribbed

being rich and complex. Best harvested at 4-6 inches in length. Pkt (10 seeds) $2.50

TADIFI #EG180
80 days. Gorgeous little market variety, originally collected in the market at Aleppo, Syria, and furnished by our Syrian friend, Ragad Khorani. Striped fruits are purple and cream to green, reaching about 5 inches in length by 2-3 inches wide. Ragad says: "The flesh is very firm and creamy. It is the best when it is... cooked with butter or olive oil." We are very excited to offer this choice variety from a troubled land. Pkt $2.50

THAI CHAO PRAYA #EG166
Chao Praya is a Thai matti-gulla type eggplant that is vigorous and prolific. Fruit are round and creamy-green in color, 2-3 ounces in weight. Used in many dishes that are used in Thai kitchens and sold by food vendors on the city streets in Thailand. Pkt $2.00

THAI LAVENDER FROG EGG #EG186
80 days. Collected by the Gettles in central Thailand, where the natives refer to many colors of these small eggplant as "frog eggs." Tiny fruits are the size and form of a cherry tomato, lavender splashed with cream. Very robust flavor, and super high yielding! Pkt $2.75

THAI LONG GREEN (Green Elephant Tusk) #EG119
85 days. Very mild and sweet, the 10" to 12" long, very slender fruit are a beautiful light-lime green. One of the best-tasting eggplants; superb flavor and very tender. Good yields on 2' to 3' tall plants. This heirloom from Thailand is becoming popular with gourmet chefs. Pkt $2.00

THAI WHITE RIBBED #EG147
85 days. The most unique-looking of the Thai eggplants, these are pure white, flat and deeply ribbed; the flesh is mild and tasty. This was our first Thai variety listed in 1998. We are happy to have it back again, as it is a personal favorite of Jere's. Pkt $2.50

THAI YELLOW EGG #EG122
Famous in Thailand, the egg-sized fruit are picked when they are bright golden-yellow. They are used in many Thai dishes and as a garnish. A unique variety for specialty growers. Pkt $2.50

TSAKONIKI EG203 *New!*
80 days. Elongated fruits are slightly curved, run to about 7" long. Fruits are very beautiful, being purple with lovely white striping. The 2- to 3-foot plants are vigorous, sometimes a bit prickly; stems and flowers are purple. A treasure form Greece, were eggplants first entered cultivation in Europe. Pkt $2.50

TURKISH ORANGE #EG134
80 days. This beautiful heirloom comes from Turkey. The 3" round fruit are best cooked when they are green to light orange. This variety has very sweet and flavorful flesh. It imparts a strong, rich flavor to any dish. The small plants yield well. This variety is great for ethnic markets. Very ornamental-looking. Pkt $2.00

UDMALBET #EG104
90 days. A rare colorful eggplant from India. Egg-shaped fruit are light green, streaked in purple. Used in chutneys & curries; from a Tamil village. Pkt $2.00

UKRAINIAN BEAUTY #EG156
Big, beautiful, purple-black fruit are great for baking. This great variety comes from Ukraine and sets heavy yields on the 3'-4' tall bushy plants. We like large eggplants breaded and baked, then served with spaghetti sauce. Pkt $2.00

The garden suggests there might be a place where we can meet nature halfway.
-Michael Pollan

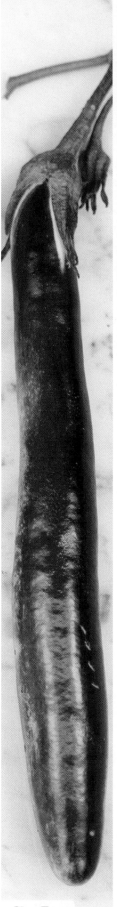

Ping Tung

Eggplant Cutlets
Yields 6 large servings!

1 large black beauty eggplant
Cut into 12-1/2" slices.

BATTER
1 cup veganaise mayonaise
1 teaspoon kosher salt
1 T Red Curry Paste
Mix well and set aside.

BREADING
6 cups Panko
1/2 cup nutritional yeast flakes
2 teaspoons onion powder
1 teaspoon sea salt
1/2 teaspoon garlic powder
1/4 teaspoon freshly ground black pepper
1/4 cup olive oil
Combine breading ingredients.

Preheat oven to 350. Grease a 10x15 inch sheet pan with non-stick spray. Place eggplant slice in batter and turn to coat both sides. Remove slice with a fork and set in breading mix, scoop crumbs over and around eggplant to cover completely and press lightly to coat sides and edges well. There should be no eggplant visible. Remove eggplant and place on baking sheet, repeat process with remaining slices. You might have a small amount of batter and breading left over. You can discard this or save for another time.

Bake eggplant cutlets for 25 minutes and remove from oven. Using a flat spatula carefully flip slices, then return to the oven and bake 20 minutes longer. Serve immediately with heirloom tomato sauce along with hot, buttered angel hair pasta.

Aswad

Foo Chow Round

Endive & Escarole

(Cichorium endivia) A long appreciated European delicacy, these crops add a lightly bitter piquancy to salads. All are best grown in rich soil, and cooler weather; in most of the country, this makes them best-suited to the fall garden. Grown in about the same way as lettuce.

BATAVIAN FULL HEART #EE101
AAS Winner 1934. Broad, thick, curled leaves; heart blanches white. A superb salad plant; tasty. Pkt (300 seeds) $1.50 *or 1 oz $4.00*

DE LOUVIERS #EE104
Leaves are very finely curled and deeply notched. Produces a good blanched and curled, yellow heart. This heirloom is high quality and tasty. In 1885 Vilmorin said, "Bulk for bulk, it yields a larger amount of useful produce." Pkt (300 seeds) $1.75

DE MEAUX #EE105
Broad, dark-green heads with creamy-white, blanched hearts that are heavenly in salads; the leaves are very notched. This pre-1885 French heirloom is best for fall plantings. Hard to find. Pkt (300 seeds) $1.75

FRISÉE ENDIVE #EE106
Also known as Curly Endive. Finely cut leaves add beauty and body to salads. Blanching, by tying the heads with a broad rubber band, yields a milder-tasting green. Lends a refined slightly bitter pop to salads. Pkt (300 seeds) $2.00

RICCIA CUOR D'ORO #EE107
(Golden Heart Endive) Early Frisee-type with deep-green outer leaves shading to a warm cream-color interior. Elaborate leaves are very deeply notched, or, as the Italians would say, 'molto fastigliata.' Blanching prior to harvest makes for a milder flavor and a more delicate color. Best grown as a fall crop. "Buon apetito!" Pkt (300 seeds) $2.00

Frisee

Fruit & Berries

Garden berries comprise a wide range of fruiting plants. The common thread is that they are distinct from tree fruits (more or less), don't take much space, and are quick to yield—most are grown as annuals and yield delicious harvest in only a few months from planting!

For this reason, seeds of many of these varieties were prized by settlers travelling to new homes. The treasured seeds would be sown into the very first gardens, usually even before a house had been finished! The family would then have at least some fruit that first season (and the second, and the third—it could take as long as five years before fruit trees would reach maturity!)

The garden berries can be used fresh, or made into sauces, pies or preserves. A typical old-time recipe for preserves couldn't be simpler, calling as it does for 2 pounds of ground cherries, a quart of sugar dissolved in a tiny bit of water, and the juice and rind of a lemon, all simmered together until the proper consistency is reached. Other garden berries could just as well be used.

Wonderberry

Otricoli Orange Berry

Solanum Berries

Here's another type of fruit that have long been useful, especially on new homesteads. The small black berries are a wonderful substitute for blueberries in muffins, pancakes, etc, and make superb sauces and pies as well. Though collectively known as garden huckleberries, they aren't true huckleberries (which are similar to blueberries). Instead, they are all relatives of the Deadly Nightshade, and confusion between poisonous and edible varieties has induced gardeners to be very reluctant to try eating them. However, the ones we offer are edible and are considered safe so long as the fruits have ripened to the point where all traces of green are absent. The plants are attractive, looking similar to pepper plants, and never need staking. They are grown like tomatoes or peppers (nightshade relatives--all!) and yield delicious berries very quickly from seed.

GARDEN HUCKLEBERRY #GR103
(*Solanum melanocerasum*) 75 days. Large, purple berries that are cooked and sweetened (do not eat raw); great in pies. Huge yields of fruit all summer long. Plant 14" apart. Strong tall plants do not have to be staked. Grow plants like peppers. Great for anyone wanting quick, easy berries and a huge yield. Originated in Africa. Pkt (35 seeds) $2.00

JALTOMATO #GR111
Used in Mexican cuisine, Jaltomatos are native to Central and South America. The one we offer has pea-sized purple berries that have a tart flavor. Only completely ripe fruit are to be eaten, as green berries and the rest of the plant may be poisonous. Fruits must be cooked and sweetened to obtain flavor. Used in relishes and jellies. Attractive plants are very prolific. Pkt (35 seeds) $2.75

OTRICOLI ORANGE BERRY #GR131 *New!*
(*Solanums nigrum*) 70 days. Here's a most unusual Nightshade plant, collected originally by the Gettles in Umbria, Italy, in the ancient roman site of Ocriculum. It was found growing along the Tiber river growing with the common black nightshade, (*S. nigrum*) Plants reach 2-3 feet tall, having typical nightshade leaves and white flowers. The small berries have a lot of visual interest being a bright orange—not at all the dark purple that you might expect. At maturity the plants are positively covered in clusters of brilliant orange! This species has been used as food for millenia, and we eat them here, but since this is a wild variety, we suggest eating them with caution, until you are positive you do not have sensitivities to them. (30 seeds) $2.50

WONDERBERRY #GR105
(*Solanum burbankii*) 75 days. Developed by Luther Burbank; tasty, small blue-purple fruit; good fresh or cooked. Small plants produce good yields in about 75 days. A historic heirloom that is easy to grow. Pkt (25 seeds)$2.50

Garden Huckleberry

Tamarillo

South American Solanum Fruit

Pepino

These varieties all hail from South America, where they enjoy a long growing season or even a completely frost-free environment, so they should be started early indoors, like tomatoes. (All are, in fact, closely related to eggplants and tomatoes!). Litchi Tomato is the quickest from seed, and is at its best in hot summer conditions. The remainder prefer cooler summer conditions, although we have ripened pepino and naranjilla outdoors here in Missouri. The plants are also very striking and attractive, and would be well worth growing for their ornamental appearance alone! All have been subjects for at least local markets, and are very useful delicious.

LITCHI TOMATO OR MORELLE DE BALBIS

#GR112   *(S. sisymbriifolium)* This was a favorite with customers who saw and sampled it in front of our store last summer. Large plants grow to 5', and are covered with thorns; sweet red fruit and large white flowers. Lovely to look at, but be careful with the thorns! We enjoyed the fruit all summer right from the plant. They're about the size of a cherry and taste like a cherry crossed with a tomato. A very pretty and attractive plant that originated in South America, but has been naturalized in many countries. Start plants as you would a tomato. Pkt (10 seeds) $3.00

NARANJILLA #GR104

(Solanum quitoense) A really unique fruit from the Andes; delicious sweet-and-sour taste, orange flavor; 2" fruit are round and yellow-orange in color, perfect for making delicious juice. In 1760, Mr. J. de Santa Gertrudis Siera called it "Nectar of the gods" and "the most delicious that I have tasted in the world." This plant takes at least 6 months to bear and is quite attractive as a potted plant. Pkt (10 seeds) $2.50

PEPINO MELON #GR117

(Solanum muricatum) One of our all time favorite fruit! This eggplant relative produces fruit that range in size from a chicken egg to a large goose egg, with a cream-colored rind that often has beautiful purple stripes. It has a sweet, mild flesh that is very melon-like. Used fresh or cooked. Beautiful, glossy ornamental plants require a fairly long season and are grown like eggplants. We had an abundant crop of these delectable fruit this past season here in Missouri. This fun plant can be grown indoors. Pepinos are popular in Peru, New Zealand and Australia and have just recently started to become common in US markets. This plant is native to the Andes Mountain region. Pkt (10 seeds) $3.00

TAMARILLO OR TREE TOMATO #GR118

(Cyphomandra betaceae) This fruit is extremely popular in Latin America and is native to the Andes Mountains of Peru. It is now becoming popular with gardeners in warm US regions, or as a greenhouse plant. Fast-growing plants grow to 10 feet and produce red, egg-shaped fruit that have a taste some what like tomatoes. Popular in Mexico for making drinks or boiling with sugar. Pkt (10 seeds) $3.00

Litchi Tomato

Husk Berries

All the Physalis types yield fruits loosely enclosed in papery husks (including the Tomatillo, which we list separately), and nearly all come from the New World. All are started just like tomatoes and are super easy to grow; they do not need to be staked! Few people realize that the Physalis varieties store extremely well, when kept in their protective husks, lasting for quite some time under refrigeration. They are used fresh or cooked, and are very juicy and sweet.

AUNT MOLLY'S GROUND CHERRY #GR132

New! 65 days. Polish heirloom variety has unusually fine flavor—very sweet with a nice hint of tartness. 1/2"-3/4" fruits are enclosed in a papery husk, drop from the ground when fully ripe. High pectin content makes this one choice for pies and preserves.   Pkt (50 seeds) $2.50

CHINESE LANTERN GIGANTEA #GR125

(Physalis franchetii) This lovely 2' perennial produces pretty seed pods, which are bright red-orange and look like glowing Chinese lanterns. Great as a fresh cut flower or dried for craft projects. So popular at farmers' markets, as everyone just loves these. This variety is extra large, and the berries inside the husk are edible when fully ripe; cook similar to a regular ground cherry. Fun to grow. Pkt $2.50

CAPE GOOSEBERRY #GR108

(Physalis peruviana) The cape gooseberry is native to Brazil and was grown in England by 1774. It was cultivated by settlers at the Cape of Good Hope before 1807. The delicious yellow-orange fruit grow inside paper-like husks that are easy to peel. They are great dipped in melted chocolate or made into pies and preserves. Pkt (50 seeds) $2.00

GROUND CHERRY (STRAWBERRY HUSK TOMATO) #GR101

70 days. Huge yields of tart-sweet berries. This is the common type used by the Pilgrims; excellent for pies, jams, and preserves of all kinds; also delicious fresh. The fruit grow inside a paper-like husk (the same as Tomatillos). Grow it the same as you would tomatoes. Pkt (50 seeds) $2.50

"I let no man drag me down so low as to make me hate him."
—BOOKER T. WASHINGTON

"That cannot be a true religion which needs carnal weapons to uphold it."
—ROGER WILLIAMS

Chinese Lantern Gigante

Aunt Molly's Ground Cherry

Ground Cherry (Strawberry Husk Tomato)

Tropical Fruit

The fruits in the list below are tropical or sub-tropical types and are suitable outdoors only in the warmest zones. Each variety has its unique quirks, and attention should be given to them before deciding to grow these fascinating types, which can challenge even experienced gardeners. But in frost-free or nearly frost-free environments, or in the greenhouse, these varieties can be successfully grown; they are fascinating, beautiful and just plain fun!

BANANA PASSION FRUIT #GR127

(Passiflora mollissima) Originating in Andean valleys, the Banana Passionfruit was domesticated shortly before the time of Columbus. Its vines, bearing large, deep pink flowers, may reach 20 feet, but in most of the US it must be grown in the greenhouse, as it can tolerate only the lightest occasional frost. Pendulous, elongated, yellow-skinned fruits have leathery skins outside, delicious pulp within. The aromatic, salmon-hued pulp is used in juices and desserts. (Seed cannot be shipped to Hawaii.) Pkt (10 seeds) $4.00

PASSIFLORA FOETIDA #FL224 *New!*

Tender perennial. Stunning when the two-inch, intricate, white- to lavender flowers are in bloom! Creeping vines climb with tendrils. Edible fruits are yellow to red, an inch or so in diameter, mild and pleasantly-flavored fruit. Stems and feathery bracts are covered with minute sticky hairs which trap insects, forestalling predation and possibly nourishing the plant! Native to subtropical Arizona, Texas and Florida, and throughout Central and South America and the Caribbean. Has been used medicinally in native cultures. Pkt (10 seeds) $4.00

DWARF COFFEE PLANT #GR126

(Coffea arabica nana) Tropical houseplant or greenhouse subject, eventually reaching 3-4 feet in height. Large, thin, glossy leaves are followed in due course by small, extremely fragrant, jasmine-scented, star-shaped flowers. These yield a yellow berry which contains the seeds, which when roasted are "coffee beans." These are fairly difficult to germinate. Pkt (10 seeds) $3.25

ORANGE MASTER POMEGRANATE #GR113

Here is an extra-dwarf pomegranate that's perfect for containers. Early-flowering plants are good for bonsai. Small, ornamental fruit. Will take light frosts, but should be grown indoors in cool climates. We have had a plant for years and are always amazed at the amount of flowers and fruit it produces. Easy to care for and requires less water than most plants. Pkt (10 seeds) $5.00

PINK BANANA #GR124

(Musa velutina) Lovely, small banana plants produce the most stunning, glowing, brilliant pink banana you will ever see. They are edible, but very seedy. Plants have large leaves that grow up to 24" long and add a wonderful tropical effect to your yard or patio. This species is relatively hardy, taking a few degrees of frost fairly well. Ripe fruit will start to split open when ready to eat. Showy and fun to grow! Can be hard to germinate, but is then easy to grow. Pkt (10 seeds) $4.00

Orange Master Pomegranate

Pink Banana

Passiflora Foetida

Banana Passion Fruit

Attila

Alexandria

Alpine Strawberries

Wild or alpine strawberries are native to Europe and have been appreciated since the Stone Age. The fruits are small compared to modern cultivated types, but the intense flavor tends to be very rich, and they are super sweet. Germination of the tiny seeds is actually easy in proper conditions. Growth may start out slow, as the seeds are so tiny, but the plants are very hardy. A harvest may be had the first year from an extra-early indoor sowing. Though they seldom make runners, your wild strawberries may be multiplied easily by dividing the plants in fall or spring. They also are ever-bearing, yielding throughout the season. The berries are very high in vitamin C and other antioxidants, and they taste so good! Alexandria Strawberry--Deep scarlet, egg-shaped fruits weigh two to three grams each. Everbearer that yields the first season from an early planting. A very productive alpine sort, sweet and flavorful.

ALEXANDRIA STRAWBERRY #GR221 *New! (Fragaria vesca)*
Deep scarlet, egg-shaped fruits weigh two to three grams each. Everbearer that yields the first season from an early planting. A very productive alpine sort, sweet and flavorful. Pkt (75 seeds) $2.50

ATTILA STRAWBERRY #GR220 *New! (Fragaria vesca)*
It's an alpine strawberry that makes runners! Ever-bearing type yielding fruit on mother plant and runners in as little as 4 months from sowing. The ability to increase and rejuvenate a planting from runners is a great advantage, and the potential multiplication is very quick. Aromatic fruits are small but very sweet. Pkt (25 seeds) $2.75

WHITE SOUL ALPINE STRAWBERRY #GR129 *(Fragaria vesca)*
An improved form of species Alpine Strawberry, White Soul reaches only to about 6 inches in height and yields small white to cream colored, aromatic fruits over a very long season. Similar to "Yellow Wonder". Pkt (75 seeds) $2.50

YELLOW WONDER WILD STRAWBERRY #GR122 *(Fragaria vesca)*
This cream-fruited variety is a favorite of many in Europe. The small fruit are very tasty and unique looking. Many prefer the taste of this yellow-fruited type to the more common red strawberry. These are served in only the finest restaurants and are easy to grow from seed! Pkt (75 seeds) $2.50

White Soul

GROWING GARLIC WITH AN ALTITUDE
Meet our garlic growers in New Mexico
We offer garlic on our website each summer

Ella with a nice braid of Chamisal Garlic

BOX CAR FARM

Avrum, Kristen, and their kids Ella and Silas Katz grow food with altitude at 8,100 feet. Boxcar Farm sits way up in the Sangre de Cristo mountains in Taos County in Northern New Mexico, where the family moved in 2006 to get closer to the source of the state's water – the acequias (ditches) and springs here carry fresh snowmelt straight off the 12,000 foot peaks in their backyard. Now certified organic, Box Car Farm has 10 acres in production – garlic, potatoes, onions, winter squash, root crops, greens, peas, beans, herbs – which are sold at farmer's markets, restaurants, grocery stores and to seed companies. Avrum and Kristen Katz started growing garlic together in the mid-1990s in Northern New Mexico, after becoming fascinated by the dozens of garlic varieties available. Kristen says she fell in love with Avrum when he gave her a big garlic braid the night of their first date. Soon, they got married and began collecting their own varieties – garlics that had naturalized ("gone wild") in Northern New Mexico , as well as garlic varieties collected from seed savers in other parts of the country that were too delicious to resist.

Because of our high-mountain climate, most of their garlic varieties do well in cold and moderate climates – anywhere it freezes in the winter. They grow mostly hardnecks, but the few choice softneck garlics they grow are good for colder regions where softnecks can sometime be hard to grow. www.boxcar-farm.com/

This year Baker Creek is offering five unique garlic varieties from Box Car Farm on our website, www.rareseeds.com

Music

Music is a popular Hardneck Porcelain variety -- big, fat, tasty cloves that store well into spring. The flavor on this is rich, a true Italian garlic that was brought to North America by an Italian gentleman by the last name of Music in the 1980s. In the spring of 2014, when all the other garlics had gone bad, Music garlic was still firm and very tasty. It does well anywhere it freezes in winter.

K's Backyard
This is a big, pearly-pink Softneck Artichoke variety that we found growing in an old Santa Fe garden in 1998. It originally had very small cloves the size of sunflower seeds and it is now our biggest softneck garlic. We have sent it to growers across the country and it seems to grow well in both coastal and cold regions – grower Paul Parma in Southern California said he'd never seen a garlic so huge. It has a rich, classic Italian flavor.

Chamisal
This Rocambole garlic came to the South West with the early Spanish settlers in the mountain valleys of northern New Mexico. We found this garlic growing wild (naturalized) along the "acequia" (irrigation ditch) in our small village at 8,000 ft in the Sangre de Cristo mountains. In 2001, the postmistress in Chamisal told us that garlic had been growing there since her grandfather was a boy. We went to look in early summer and found it covering several thousand square feet. Today, its bulbs reach up to 3 inches.

Sinnamahone
The story of Sinnamahone starts after receiving seeds in the early 2000s from a man who lived near the Sinnamahone River in rural Pennsylvania, where he said he got the seed from a "wild haired Sinnamahone Indian dude" who lived in the backwoods near there. We keep growing it because it is a beautiful Hardneck Rocambole with knock-your-socks off flavor – it is a big favorite of our customers at the Santa Fe farmers' market.

Rico's German Hardy
Our strain of this Hardneck Porcelain was first obtained from Seed Savers Exchange in 1990. It was grown in the Rocky Mountains for 12 years by our friends at a wilderness refuge, then passed along to us in 2002. It is absolutely huge, beautiful and tasty, very well adapted to colder regions, and bears single cloves that are as big as whole bulbs of some smaller varieties. It has a very strong garlic flavor.

AMYO FARMS
Jesse Daves and Sarah Montgomery run a market garden and CSA in Albuquerque, New Mexico called Amyo Farms. Their two children Henry(3yrs) and Emma Jean (1yr) are often seen playing in the fields, looking for strawberries, or "helping" at the market. Sarah's mom, Carole, grows flowers for market, and Jesse bother-in -law Andy, and long-time childhood friend Jack are also farmers at Amyo.

With Amyo Farms we are now down to 4,500 feet in a urban area and within the narrow fertile valley of the Rio Grande among the cottonwoods. Jesse and Sarah love to travel, often collecting seeds along the way to try on their farm. In 2003, they started a seed saving project in Guatemala with over 400 Maya families participating. They raise money for that project through their non-profit The Garden's Edge: www.thegardensedge.org

From the beginning of their journey, seeds and their story have inspired these two to explore the rich possibilities of a life tied to agriculture. Seeds offer inspiration and a promise of a bountiful future. They are very excited to be sharing the fruits of their labor with the community.

This year Baker Creek is offering three varieties from Amyo Farms on our website, www.rareseeds.com

Inchelium Red
A very popular and adaptable Softneck Artichoke garlic and a favorite for home gardeners and small growers.

Russian Giant
This variety can get huge! A Marble Purple Stripe Hardneck garlic with brilliant color and better than average keeping ability. Does great at farmers' markets and easy to clean. It has a mild flavor with large cloves that are excellent for roasting.

Moroccan Creole
Collected in 2009 from an open air market in the seaside town of Essaouira, Morocco. Creole variety with a lot of heat and good keeping ability. It came from the Moors to Spain. Hardneck variety that will produce a scape.

Moroccan Creole Garlic - We offer garlic only on our website.

Gourds

(Lagenaria siceraria unless stated otherwise)
20 seeds per pkt. Whether True Gourds, Angled Gourds or Edible Gourds, all of these squash-relatives are from the Old World originally, and all need similar conditions: a long season of hot weather, and abundant moisture in a rich soil. May be direct-sown into warm soil, or started indoors a few weeks early. The fruits will be straighter and more symmetrical if the long vines are trained up a trellis, but all may be allowed to sprawl along the ground; some may run 20 feet! The edible sorts are best harvested when young, tender, and mild-tasting.

BALI SUGAR TROUGH #GD127
This heirloom was collected on the Southeast Asian island of Bali, at a market there. Gourds are trough-shaped and measure 20" long by about 8" in diameter. Rare! (20 seeds) Pkt $2.50

BIG APPLE #GD115
The 8" fruit look just like giant apples! Very popular as crafts and fall displays; can be painted red or made into birdhouses. Unique and fun to grow; a sure sell at fall markets. Pkt $3.00

BIRDHOUSE GOURD #GD108
The popular gourd for making bottles, birdhouses and many other useful items. Fun to grow. Pkt $2.50

BULE GOURD #GD116
A rare French heirloom that is shaped like an 8" Big Apple gourd, but these are covered in attractive warts. They are very ornamental and make a good market item. Pkt $3.00

BUSHEL BASKET #GD111
Huge, round gourds, up to 24" across, can be used for all kinds of art work and as storage containers. Night flowering plants attract huge moths; very long vines. Fruit has a thick, hard shell. A best seller! Pkt $4.00 **or 1 oz $8.00**

DIPPER GOURD #GD117
These gourds have long handles and are just right for making water or feed dippers. Great for making arts and crafts. Pkt $2.75

GAKHAA #GD124
This variety was collected in the late 1980's in an oasis in Algeria, Northern Africa. The unique fruit are a thick, bowling pin shape and are an attractive green, with white spots. The fruit are great picked young and used like zucchini, or harvested at maturity and used as bottles or for craft projects. A rare North African heirloom that was sent to us by Bruno Defay of France. Pkt (10 seeds) $3.50

HAWAIIAN DANCE MASK #GD133
110 days. Uniquely-shaped fruits like a large flat bottom pear, about 10 inches tall and around 8 inches across at the base. Hawaiians used the gourd to make ritual helmets or "makini" prior to European contact. The small end of the gourd was removed, the large end hollowed out, eye openings cut, and the entire piece was decorated with fern fronds or sedge grass and white streamers. Each item had ritual significance, as the masks were worn at Makahiki, the annual festival honoring Lono, their deity of fertility and harvest. Pkt (10 seeds) $3.00

JAPANESE NEST EGG GOURD #GD104
(C. pepo) Highly popular in the 1800's, the gourds are the size and shape of a hen's egg and are white in color. They are used as nest eggs; often found growing wild here in the Ozarks. Pkt $2.00

MAYO BULE #GD128   A
favorite here, the pear-shaped, 1' long gourds are covered with large "warts," even when small. The mature fruits have very hard shells and make great containers. Productive vines are beautifully loaded with fruit. Collected in Sonora, Mexico. Rare and hard to find. Pkt (10 seeds) $2.50

ORANGE GOURD #GD105
(C. pepo) In 1885, Vilmorin wrote in *The Vegetable Garden*, "The fruit exactly resembles a ripe orange in size and color." We are pleased to offer this rare heirloom. Pkt $2.00

PERU SUGAR BOWL #GD129
Oblate to flattened tear-drop shaped gourds are produced in abundance on the vigorous vines. Fruits are about 5-6 inches wide and 4-5 inches long, Typical of the type used in the Huanta area of Peru, where renowned decorated gourds have been produced for centuries. Pkt (15 seeds) $3.00

SMALL SPOON #GD109
(C. pepo) Brightly-colored, orange and green striped small spoon-shaped gourds are excellent for fall decorations. Huge yields. Pkt $2.00

SPECKLED SWAN #GD103
Thick, dipper-shaped fruit that resemble swans with their necks curved; great for crafts. These large gourds have speckles when green. Unique. Pkt $2.50

TENNESSEE DANCING OR SPINNING GOURDS #GD101
(C. pepo) A tiny gourd just 2" long! They are bottle-shaped and green-and-white striped—turning tan when dry. This unique heirloom was sent to us by Mr. Junior G., of Primm Springs, Tennessee. They used to be popular there, and his Ma had said that when she was going to school, kids would bring 'em to play with. Dancing gourds spin just like a top. Pkt $2.50

VERRUQUESE DE MAURICE #GD131
Very unique, nearly cylindrical gourd often reaches 15 inches. Light green in the field, the fruits are outrageously warted—definitely in a class by themselves. Crafters will adore this one! Pkt (10 seeds) $2.75

Edible Gourds

(L. siceraria) Pick fruits when young and tender.

SERPENTE DI SICILIA #ED102
The popular Italian edible gourd. Long, slender fruit are a brilliant, light green color; very tender and delicious with a rich flavor. The Italians eat these steamed, sauteed, or stuffed and baked. Perfect for specialty markets. Pkt (20 seeds) $2.50

TAMBULI #ED105
This beautiful and tasty gourd is bright green in color, cylindrical in shape and with a distinguished neck and flat blossom end. It is strongly disease resistant. A great regional variety from the Phillippines. Pkt (10 seeds) $2.50

Mayo Bule Gourd

Small Spoon Gourd

Gakhaa Gourd

Bule Gourd

Verruquese de Maurice

Orange Gourd

Tennessee Dancing or Spinning Gourd

Hawaiian Dance Mask

Serpente Di Sicilia

Luffa Gourd
(ANGLED, VINING OKRA OR SPONGE GOURD)

DISHCLOTH or LUFFA #AG103
(*Luffa aegyptiaca*) Burpee's 1888 catalogue said, "A natural dishcloth, and a most admirable one. Many ladies prefer this dishcloth. The fruit grow about 2', and the vine is very ornamental, producing clusters of yellow blossoms, in pleasing contrast with the silvery-shaded, dark green foliage. In the North this variety requires starting in a hotbed. The dried interiors of these gourds have already become an article of commerce; grown in Florida, they are sold by Philadelphia and NY druggists." Pkt $2.50

BONANZA 141 #AG108
Long, ridged fruit are so delicious when lightly fried like okra or summer squash. Easy to grow and so ornamental. These make lovely large vines, yellow flowers and loads of fruit. Very resistant to insects and disease, can also be dried when fully matured and made into unique natural sponges! Collected in Thailand. Pkt (15 seeds) $3.00

Bonanza 141

Grains & Cover Crops

AUSTRIAN WINTER PEA #GS101
(*Pisum arvense*) Close relative of Garden or English peas, but this variety is grown as a cover crop. As hardy as Hairy Vetch and good as a nitrogen fixer, but more adapted to drier or alkaline soil. Matures a bit earlier in spring from a fall planting. Very attractive to deer. Can be sown in early spring in cooler climates. 1/4 lb $4.50

BLACK SEEDED SESAME #GS124
This black-seeded variety has tasty, nutty-flavored seeds that are popular in Thai cooking. It is also used to make healthy Black Sesame oil, which is popular in much of Asia and is a favorite oil of mine. Pkt $2.25

BUCKWHEAT #GS104
(*Fagopyrum esculentum*) Tender plant used as a warm-season cover crop. Plant anytime in warm weather; incorporate into soil when flowering begins (4-6 weeks). Not a nitrogen-fixer, but well known for adding organic matter to the soil. Can be planted and tilled under several times in a summer. Produces delicious and nutritious, edible seeds! 1/4 lb $5.50

CAMELINA OR FALSE FLAX #GS131
(*Camelina sativa*) Also known as Gold-of-Pleasure. Promising "new" plant for oil and biofuel that actually has been cultivated in Europe since the Bronze Age. Camelina also makes a great cover crop and livestock feed. A relative of mustard, Camilina establishes quickly, even in fairly dry, cool conditions. The seed is about 40% oil, which contains a high amount of healthful omega-3 fatty acid. A cutting-edge addition to sustainable agriculture. Pkt $2.00

CHUFFA #GS108
(*Cyperus esculentus*) This plant is also called Ground Almond or Earth Chestnut. The nutty, sweet tasting, small tubers are quite delicious and produced underground on perennial, grass-like plants. An important food crop in Asia Minor and Egypt since ancient times. This delicacy has been grown for thousands of years; only now is it starting to get popular in America. Pkt (25 small tubers) $3.00

CRIMSON CLOVER #GS136 *New!*
Annual. Also known as Italian Clover. Nitrogen-fixing legume often grown for livestock feed or wildlife forage, yet pretty enough for the flower garden! Crimson flower heads are great bee forage. Planted thickly, also makes a superior cover- or green manure crop, with its ability to smother out weeds and fix atmospheric nitrogen into the soil. This lovely, versatile plant should be much more widely grown! Pkt (1 oz) $3.00

FLAX #GS113
(*Linum usitatissimum*) True source of fibers that for thousands of years have been harvested and woven into linen. The seeds are a nutritious natural laxative and have been used to lower cholesterol. Stems up to 30" tall produce blue flowers from May to September. Annual. Pkt $1.50

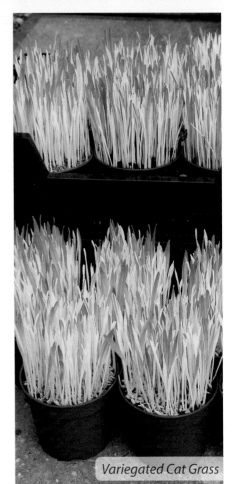

Variegated Cat Grass

Black Seeded Sesame, Flowering

HAIRY VETCH #GS105

(Vicia villosa) Plant spring or fall for nitrogen fixation and abundance of organic matter, even in acid soils. If mowed just as blooming commences, the plants die, leaving a natural mulch which can be left as-is for no-till planting or incorporated for soil improvement. Perennial if allowed to set seed. Hardy. 1/4 lb $4.50

MILLET, GERMAN FOXTAIL #GS107

(Setaria italica) Sow in spring or early summer. Used as a cover crop, hay or pasture. Chickens adore the small white seeds. Grows from 2-5 feet tall. Very drought-tolerant crop that is believed to have been used in China for nearly 5000 years, and grown in the US since 1849. 1/4 lb $5.00

QUINOA, CHERRY VANILLA #GS133

(Chenoppodium quinoa) 90-120 days. 3 to 5-foot tall plants are smothered in frothy masses of cream-to-pink flower heads. Dazzling enough for the most elegant border (or illicit, front-yard garden!) but eminently practical, like all quinoas, for greens or grain. Pkt $2.50

RAPE, DWARF ESSEX #GS102

(Brassica rapa) Robust member of the Brassica family. Puts large amounts of organic matter into soils; gives some control over nematodes. Sow late summer or very early spring, incorporate when flowering begins. Will grow slowly throughout the winter in Zone 7 south; not reliably hardy farther north. 1/4 lb $4.50

RICE CAROLINA GOLD #GS126

Considered the "grandfather" of long-grain rice culture in North America, according to the Carolina Gold Rice Foundation, who supplied our seed. This historic variety is believed to have originated from African and Indonesian sources, and appeared as a distinct variety in Charles Towne, Carolina Colony, by 1685. Carolina Gold really inaugurated commercial rice production in North America. Its long grains have superior texture, and a taste reminiscent of almonds and green tea. Although commercial production declined after the Civil War, this superior variety is known and loved to this day. We're excited to offer a genuine piece of early Americana! (Not for Northern gardeners, Carolina Gold is a long-season, true paddy rice requiring flooding for good cultivation, and support for the plants as they reach maturity.) Provided By The Carolina Gold Rice Foundation, Charleston, South Carolina. Pkt (1/2 oz) $2.50

SESAME, LIGHT SEEDED #GS106

(Sesamum indicum) Light-seeded. Cultivated in the Near East for at least 4,000 years. Plants grow to 5 feet in height. Makes an excellent cover crop or wildlife forage. Light-colored seeds are tasty and suitable for use in the kitchen. Controls harmful nematodes in some situations. Attractive flowers. 1 oz $3.00

VARIEGATED CAT GRASS #GS100

Barley (Hordeum Vulgare). Cats love a number of different grasses when they're in the mood for such things, but our barley is variegated in green and white stripes so it's a treat for the eye as well! A dish of grass for your feline companion can save a lot of wear and tear on your houseplants, and is much healthier for your cat as well. Pkt (275 seeds) $3.00

WHEAT, EMMER #GS134 *New!*

(Triticum dicoccum) We're so excited to be able to offer this "ancient wheat." Known only from archeological digs until the early 20th century, emmer wheat was found growing in isolated areas of the Middle East, Italy and Russia. The yields are lower than for modern, "improved" wheats, but it's superior in homestead gardens because of its disease resistance and its ability to yield on poor soils. Most importantly, the structure of this wheat's gluten is different from that of modern types, so it's often digestible by people with gluten sensitivity or wheat allergies! Sometimes called "Pharaoh's Wheat." Pkt (1 oz) $3.00

WHEAT, WHITE SONORA #GS135 *New!*

(Triticum aestivum) Here's another very old wheat, dating to the time before wheat was "improved." First brought to Arizona and the Southwest by Spanish missionaries in 1691, the "soft" grains are rounded and pale reddish in color. They make a stretchy dough that was instrumental in the development of the flour tortilla. White Sonora was the main variety available in the west, including California, up to the Civil War. This variety has recently been the object of a commercial resurgence in the Southwest, and is another type that is well tolerated by most people who suffer from celiac disease or wheat allergies. Drought tolerant, disease resistant, and highly adaptable. Pkt (1 oz) $3.00

Crimson Clover

Wheat Emmer

Pan Seared Baby Bok Choy

By Chef Quintin

Baby Bok Choy is delicious. The greens are tender and packed full of flavor and nutrients.

INGREDIENTS

6 baby bok choy
¼ cup of tamari
1 T of minced ginger
1 T of sesame oil
1 T of minced garlic
1 T of white sesame seeds
1 T of black sesame seeds
pinch of red chili flakes
1 T of honey

PREPARATION

1. Sliced bok choy in half

2. Place all ingredients in a bowl and pour over the bok choy

3. Heat a cast iron pan and drizzle a little sesame oil

4. Place cut side down in hot pan. Cook until golden brown. Pull and serve presentation side up.

5. Drizzle honey in pan with liquid that was reserved. Cook lightly and drizzle over bok choy.

134

Oriental Greens

200 seeds per packet. Various crops are offered here—all are traditional culinary types from Asia. Bok choy and Tatsoi are turnip relatives grown for their spatulate leaves and succulent petioles (stems) which are often white and very juicy. Mustards are grown for their thinner, often spicy leaves. Chinese cabbages and kale form tight heads, but of often quite unusual shapes compared to the usual Western ones. As a group, these types tend to be fairly early and tolerant to cooler weather.

CHINESE CABBAGE, WONG BOK #OR110
75 day. (Also known as Mandarin Cabbage) Large barrel-shaped heads occasionally reach 10 pounds, and of excellent quality; a very tender, productive heirloom from northern China. Best as a fall crop. Pkt (200 seeds) $2.25

CHINESE CABBAGE, HILTON #OR140 *New!*
70 days. Very easy to grow and made perfect heads in our Missouri gardens. Here's a superior Napa-type Chinese cabbage variety that has seldom been seen in the US. Medium-sized barrel-shaped heads are densely packed with crinkled, mild-tasting leaves. The preferred variety in the UK. Great raw or stir-fried, or in home-made kimchi! Pkt $3.00

CANTON BOK #OR124
The typical Nai-Pe-Tsai type pak choy, semi-upright plant produces thick, white stems and deep green leaves. Good for warm areas as it is heat tolerant. Pkt $2.00

CHINESE MUSTARD #OR134
This special selected Chinese mustard has thick large leaves. Spicy and delicious. We really enjoy these great greens. Pkt $2.00

CHINESE PAK CHOY #OR106
85 days. Long, white stems and dark green leaves; one of the most popular Chinese vegetables used in many Chinese dishes. Pkt $2.00

CHING CHANG BOK CHOY #OR127
This baby bok choy is a standard for quality. Small heads are harvested when just 5" tall; they are so tender and mild. The medium green plants are ready for harvest in 50 days. Perfect for marketing. Pkt $2.50 *or 1 oz $7.00*

GREEN LEAF GAILAN—CHINESE KALE
#OR133 Large, delicious stems and flower buds are cooked like broccoli but is easier to grow and thrives in much warmer weather. The texture is very tender and crisp, perfect for stir-fries, soups and more. A great variety for Asian markets. Give it a try! Pkt $1.50

EXTRA DWARF PAK CHOY #OR130
The perfect baby vegetable for marketing, this tiny pak choy is picked when just 2" tall! It has dark green, wrinkled leaves with thick, white petioles and can be used whole to make amazing salads and stir-fries! Very tender and delicious! Pkt $2.50 *or 1 oz $7.00*

JAPANESE GIANT RED MUSTARD #OR107
(*B. juncea*) Beautiful, large, Japanese type. Purple-red leaves with a delicious, strong, sharp, almost garlic-like, mustard flavor. Tasty stir-fried or boiled and makes a great pickling variety. Pkt $2.50 *or 1 oz $6.50*

Mizuna Lime Streaks and Red Streaks

Tatsoi

Green Leaf Gailan

Canton Bok Choy

Mizuna

Large Leaf Tong Ho

JIU TOU NIAO MUSTARD #OR120

(*B. juncea*) A wonderful leafy mustard that is an heirloom from South China. 16" tall plants have bright green serrated leaves that are tender and have excellent mustard flavor; great sauteed or in salads. A "Sher Li Hon" type of Chinese mustard. Pkt $2.00

KOMATSUMA TENDERGREEN #OR102

(*B. rapa*) Japanese mustard greens. Tasty, slightly spicy, mild flavor, great for stir-frying or salads. Good for hot or cold weather. Pkt $1.75

LARGE LEAF TONG HO #OR131

Also known as Shungiku or Garland Chrysanthemum. This variety produces large, smooth leaves that add tremendous flavor to stir-fries, soups and salads; great spicy, sweet, aromatic taste. It also produces lovely yellow flowers and is super easy to grow. Popular Chinese heirloom. Pkt $2.00

MICHIHLI CABBAGE #OR108

(*B. rapa*) 70 days. Big tall heads, widely grown in the Orient. Mild and tasty, very tender, great for stir-fry. Pkt $1.75

MIZUNA #OR101

(*B. rapa*) A delicious Japanese green; cook like spinach. Vigorous plant produces many thin stalks; very mild and tasty, early. Highly used in salad mixes. Pkt $1.75 *or 1 oz $4.00*

MIZUNA LIME STREAKS #OR135

45 days. Here's a different sort of mizuna: wide, very flat, ornately fringed leaves in clear bright green. Grows best in cooler weather, like other mizunas. Elegant in their own right, breathtaking when combined with Red Streaks mizuna. Makes micro-greens at 25 days. Pkt $2.25

MIZUNA RED STREAKS #OR136

45 days. The peppery foliage is almost like fine lace. Color runs green to purple-red. A splendid complement to Lime Streaks. Makes micro-greens at 25 days. Pkt $2.25

SAWTOOTH MUSTARD #OR138

(*Bassica juncea var. involutus*) Dark green leaves are very curly, tear-drop shaped and free of the prickles so often found on mustards. Plants are very upright, being specially selected for the baby greens market, and these may be harvested at 21 days. Or allow the leaves to grow larger, and enjoy their robust, spicy flavor at about 40 days. Pkt $2.25

SHANGHAI GREEN CHOY #OR126

A delicious baby type that is so much in demand with top Asian chefs. Compact plants are upright and have light green stems. They are extra tender and finely flavored. Pkt $2.50

TAINONG EMPEROR HEADING MUSTARD #OR128

A unique crop in America, this variety makes large, very crisp heads that are a medium green color and have a delicious flavor. Superb for pickling, frying and in soups. Pkt $2.50

TATSOI #OR103

(*B. rapa*) Superb mild flavor, a must for stir-frying and salads. Beautiful, small rosette heads; very popular at Asian markets. Plant after last frost to help prevent bolting. Pkt $1.75 *or 1 oz $4.00*

Salad Greens

200-600 seeds per pkt. A miscellany of crops is offered here. Each is unique; some are warm-growers, others revel in very cool weather. What they all have in common is their diversity of flavors and textures—too good to miss!

AURORA MIXED ORACH #OG124
A mix of radiant colors, all the more beautiful because the plants reach a nice size—very well suited to edible landscaping beds. Colors include red, gold, green, pink, carmine, and pure purple. Who says greens have to be green? This Frank Morton/Wild Garden Seed original is just plain fun! Pkt (40 seeds) $3.00

ARUGULA #OG106
(*Eruca sativa*) Delicious salad green has a spicy flavor; a rage in salads. I just love this green sprinkled on pizza and sandwiches. One of our most popular greens. Pkt $2.00 *or 1 oz $4.00 (d*

ARUGULA PRONTO #OG121
(*Eruca sativa*) Very serrated foliage, medium-green, which has quite a spicy taste. Unique in salads. A nice selection from Europe. Pkt $2.00

BLACK MUSTARD #OG118
(*Brassica nigra*) This black variety produces small dark seeds that are used as a spice; the spicy leaves are edible, too. It also makes tasty seedling sprouts. This plant is native to the Mediterranean where it has been grown for thousands of years. Many believe that black mustard seed is what Jesus spoke of in Matthew 13. Pkt $2.00

COLISH #OG127 *New!*
A leafy green from the highlands of Guatemala that grows well in cooler conditions; it is used in soups and stews; the yellow flowers are also edible in salads and are very attractive to bees. Pkt $2.50

CORN SALAD, DUTCH #OG104
(*Valerianella sp.*) This old-time favorite has a mild, nutty flavor. Tender leaves are excellent in salads or cooked. Pkt $1.25 *or 1 oz $4.00*

CORN SALAD OR MACHE, VERTE A COEUR PLEIN 2 #OG116
(*Valerianella sp.*) In 1885 France's Vilmorin said, "A very distinct variety, with short, roundish, smooth, half-erect, stiff leaves." The compact plants tend to be less productive than other types, but it is nicely flavored. Pkt $2.00

FRENCH DANDELION #HB215
(*Taraxacum officinale*) Perennial—This is a cultivated strain from a Dutch seedsman. Plants reach to 12 inches in height. Use the young leaves in salads, older leaves as boiled greens. Roots can be roasted and used in place of coffee, or lifted and forced during winter, like Belgian Endive. We're proud to offer this European strain of a traditional old favorite! Pkt (150 seeds) $2.00

GARDEN CRESS #OG101
(*Lepidium sativum*) Sweet and spicy tasting, perfect in salads. Ready for snacking in just 2 weeks. Pkt $1.50

GOLDEN PURSLANE #HB222
Annual, 35 days. The same upright habit and large, tender, succulent leaves as our green purslane, but this variety comes in a peppy, bright yellow green. So lovely in the garden or in your freshly picked salad! Purslane has the highest concentration of healthy omega-3 fats

Aurora Mixed Orach

Arugula

of any crop, and is rich in anti-oxidants as well. Leaves are sometimes pickled for storage. Pkt (500 seeds) $2.75

PURSLANE, GREEN #HB151
(*Portulaca oleracea*) Low, crawling plant produces tender stems and juicy leaves that are excellent added to salads. A popular green in Mexico that was favored by my Hispanic grandmother. Also used in herbal healing plans. Pkt (300 seeds) $2.00

GREEN WAVE MUSTARD #OG125   *New!*
50 days. (*Brassica juncea*) Curled and very frilly medium green leaves stay tender to a good size-- upright plants reach 2 feet in height. Stands long in the field, tolerates more heat than most, bolts very late; also very cold-hardy. Flavor is sharp: nice and spicy! A high-yielding type that makes a good crop in home or market gardens, and makes choice micro-greens. All-America Award winner in 1957. Pkt $2.00

MACHE COQUILLE DE LOUVIERS #OG123
Spoon-shaped leaves, very early and frost-tolerant variety. Mache is ideal for container- or pot cultivation as the plants are so compact and early; by sheltering the plants from the coldest winter conditions, a harvest may be had all winter long! Pkt (200 seeds) $2.50

MINER'S LETTUCE #OG119
(*Claytonia perfoliata*) This West Coast native appears abundantly there in the early spring. Succulent, mild-tasting leaves are not unlike spinach in texture, and saved many Gold Rush miners from scurvy. Enjoy it in salads or lightly steamed. Also makes a charming ground cover in the spring garden. Also known as Winter Purslane. Pkt $2.50

MUSTARD GREENS, SOUTHERN GIANT CURLED #OG110
(*B. juncea*) Large, upright plants with crumpled leaves that have a delicious mustard taste; slow to bolt, easy to grow. An old heirloom from the Southern US; makes a mighty swell mess of greens. Pkt $1.75 *or 1 oz $4.00*

RED ORACH #OG103
(*Atriplex hortensis*) 4'-10' tall and bright red. Beautiful and tasty addition to salads. Related to Lambs Quarters. Lovely! Pkt (150 seeds)$2.00 *or 1 oz $12.00*

PEPPER CRESS #OG113
(*Lepidium sativum*) Spicy, peppery taste, similar to water cress in flavor; ready for snacking in just 2 weeks. Can be grown on a windowsill; perfect in salads. Pkt $1.50 *or 1 oz $4.00*

SALAD BURNET #OG105
(*Sanguisorba minor*) Tasty in salads, great cucumber-like flavor. Pkt $1.25

WATERCRESS, AQUA LG. LEAF #OG122
(*Nasturtium officinale*) Large rounded leaves are succulent and pungent. A high-yielding strain for professional production, or for anyone who cherishes this unique crop. Best for autumn or spring planting. Pkt (250 seeds) $2.75

WILD ROCKET ARUGULA #OG107
(*Diplotaxis tenuifolia*) Has a more pungent taste than regular arugula; leaves are deeply lobed. An Italian favorite. Pkt $2.50

WRINKLED CRINKLED CRESS #OG111
(*Lepidium sativum*) A very crinkled and ruffled garden cress, attractive for salads and popular with chefs; quite flavorful. Pkt $2.00 *or 1 oz $4.00*

Red Orach

Grow Orach
French Spinach or Mountain Spinach (Atriplex hortensis)

This seldom-grown plant actually has been appreciated for reliable summer greens in the Mediterranean region where it is native, for at least 4000 years. Orach belongs to the same plant family as the well-known spinach and chard, and the less-famous lamb's quarters, all of which yield valuable greens in their own right. Orach's taste is similar to that of spinach. But orach has the great virtue of being tolerant to both drought and summer heat, unlike spinach which needs cool conditions. Orach also takes wind and salt spray, making it especially valuable to gardeners in maritime climates.

Fearing Burr, in his The Field and Garden Vegetables of America, wrote in 1863: "Orach is rarely found in the vegetable gardens of this country. The leaves have a pleasant, slightly acid taste, and, with the tender stalks, are used boiled in the same manner as Spinach or Sorrel, and are often mixed with the latter to reduce the acidity. The stalks are good only while the plants are young; but the larger leaves may be picked off in succession throughout the season, leaving the stalks and smaller leaves untouched, by which the latter will increase in size. The Orach thus procured is very tender, and much esteemed. A few plants will afford an abundant supply."

Another of orach's virtues is that it comes in colors, including the red orach, the leaves of which are a vibrant, jewel-tone red-violet. Use the leaves steamed or lightly stir-fried (they'll lose their brilliant red tone), or raw in salads and smoothies.

The plants may reach 4 feet in height in very favored locations and their gorgeous color makes them ornamental enough for the border and a slam-dunk in edible landscaping. They often self-sow, making them a most agreeable addition to modern gardens!

Add some of this healthful, colorful, crop to your garden and enjoy long-lasting greens.

Golden Purslane

Green Wave Mustard

Salad Blends

Delicious mixed greens are a joy to eat and can be grown nearly year-round in many places. Large packets contain 1,000 seeds

ROCKY TOP LETTUCE SALAD #SB103
Very Popular! Our improved formula blend is now better than ever! With more brightly colored and unique lettuces, it makes a flavorful and brilliant salad. A top-selling item for us; our customers just love it! Perfect for better markets or your home table. People love the rich, old-fashioned taste. Includes some non-listed rare varieties. Pkt $3.00 *or 1 oz $7.00*

EUROPEAN MESCLUN SALAD #SB101
Grow this mix of greens for one of the tastiest salads ever! Flavors range from sweet-mild to sour-hot-tangy, and colors come in red, purple, yellow, and green. Colorful lettuce, radicchio, arugula, endive, orach, mizuna, kale, mustard, corn salad, and more. A favorite with market growers. Pkt $3.00 *or 1 oz $6.50*

RED WING LETTUCE MIX #SB105
"The All Red Formula Mix." At last a lettuce mix that contains a wide range of the best brilliant red (and red-splashed) specialty types! Our growers love this beautiful mix and so do the chefs. Pkt $3.00 *or 1 oz $6.50*

SIAMESE DRAGON STIR-FRY MIX
#SB106 All the best Asian greens for stir-frying and steaming. A mix of many of the greens that I have enjoyed in Thailand. The rich flavor of these greens is incredible when lightly cooked and seasoned with garlic and Thai peppers. This formula mix is perfect for market growers. Also pick the greens in the "baby stage" for a tangy salad mix. We have been getting great comments from market growers about this mix. Pkt $3.00 *or 1 oz $6.50*

Kohlrabi

(Brassica oleracea) Here's a cabbage-relative with a difference: the main crop is the stem, which has been selected over the centuries to grow as an oblate sphere, about the size of an apple. Well grown, this stem is juicy and crisp, and tastes similar to a cabbage heart. The leaves are edible too, especially when young. This crop tolerates heat better than most cabbage relatives, and can be grown straight through the summer in most areas of the country.

DELICACY WHITE #KL105 *New!*
Beautiful, smooth globes are a lovely, light-green. They are quite uniforms and the flesh is tender and of high quality. These stay tender even as they mature. Pkt (400 seeds) $2.75

EARLY WHITE VIENNA #KL102
This old variety is about the same as the purple, except these have pale green skin; mild and tasty. Pkt (400 seeds) $1.50

EARLY PURPLE VIENNA #KL101
Delicious, cabbage-flavored bulbs that grow above ground. Purple skin and sweet, white flesh; good cooked or raw. Kohlrabi makes a real staple crop with high yields; cold hardy. A pre-1860 heirloom. Pkt (400 seeds) $1.50

SUPERSCHMELZ OR GIANT WHITE #KL103
60-70 days. Spectacular light green kohlrabi makes the largest bulb of any variety, up to 10 inches across, and weighing up to 10 LB! Yet the flesh is tender and never gets fibrous. Requires a very rich soil and plenty of space to reach gigantic proportions. Pkt (400 seeds) $2.75

Looking for more Rare Seeds?
Go online! www.rareseeds.com

Early White Vienna

Superschmelz or Giant White

Early Purple Vienna

Kale & Collards

(Brassica oleracea) 250 seeds per packet. Kale may be the hardiest of the cabbage kin. It excels in cold weather, tasting best after frost has kissed the tender, succulent leaves, and making moderate growth whenever there is even a slight warm spell. Start in containers indoors or direct seed in the garden in late June. May also be sown indoors for early spring planting. Kale thrives in rich soil, heavy on organic matter, and moisture-retentive but well drained.

BLUE CURLED SCOTCH #KA101
Compact plants yield tender, blue-green, crinkled leaves that are quite delicious; very cold-hardy, and rich in vitamin A. Pkt $2.25 or 1 oz $4.50

DWARF SIBERIAN #KA102
This tasty Russian variety produces leaves that are only slightly frilled and of top quality. 16" plants are very hardy and productive. Pkt $2.00

GEORGIA SOUTHERN (CREOLE) #OG109
A great old Southern favorite, pre-1880 heirloom. Has a good resistance to heat and cold. Sure, it's great for the South, but also good up North. Huge yield, a real producer, very tasty and flavorful. Pkt $2.00

MARROW STEM KALE #KA106
Winter-hardy kale grown for livestock feed or forage. May be cropped fall through spring in most climates. The main stalk of the plant is very large, succulent, and nutritious . Valuable, traditional alternative that has been neglected in conventional corn/soy agriculture. Pkt $2.25

FORAGE KALE PROTEOR #KA105
Medium height and superior leaf-to-stem ration make this kale superior to most garden varieties, at least when it comes to growing livestock feed. May be grazed, cut and fed, or ensiled or stored in clamps or the root cellar. Also may be planted in patches for feeding game. Extreme winter hardiness. Pkt $1.75

MORRIS HEADING COLLARDS #OG112
This variety is called "cabbage collards" by Southern old-timers because it makes loose heads that are dark green and slow to bolt. Tender leaves are very delicious. A popular heirloom that is fast-growing and productive. Pkt $1.75

NERO DI TOSCANA (Dinosaur or Lacinato Kale) #CB101
60 days. This loose-leafed "cabbage" dates back to the early 1800's at least. It has beautiful, deep black-green leaves that can be 24" long. They are heavily savoyed. This Italian heirloom is popular in Tuscany and central Italy for making fabulous soups and stews. One of the most beautiful and flavorful types you can grow. Pkt $2.50 *or 1 oz $6.00*

ORNAMENTAL FRINGED MIX #KA104
This lovely mix contains pretty shades of pink, purple, and white. Contrasts nicely with the deep green outer leaves. Also known as Flowering Kale, the plants look like huge frilly flowers. The leaves

Tronchuda Kale

Nero di Toscana Or Lacinato

Blue Curled Scotch Kale

-Kale Chips-

☐ 1 Pound bunch of fresh red or green kale, torn into bite sized pieces

☐ 3 Tablespoons extra virgin olive oil

☐ 2 Tablespoons raw apple cider vinegar or fresh lemon juice

☐ Course salt and black pepper to desired taste

☐ Optional herbs to desired taste

Preheat oven to 350 degrees F. Combine olive oil with vinegar or lemon juice and put into mister. Spread cleaned and washed kale onto parchment lined baking sheet in a single layer. Spray with olive oil/juice mixture to coat evenly. Sprinkle with sea salt and pepper to desired taste. Sprinkle with any other additional herbs as desired: rosemary, dill, garlic, etc. Bake for 12-13 minutes until crisp, watching carefully to not burn.

Scarlet kale

make a superb garnish and are good as cooked greens. Best grown as a fall plant because colors are more intense in cool weather. Pkt (100 seeds) $2.50

RUSSIAN RED or RAGGED JACK #KA103
50 days. Very tender and mild, a pre-1885 heirloom variety. Oak-type leaves have a red tinge, and stems are a purplish-red. One of our favorite kales. Great flavor. Pkt $2.50 *or 1 oz $4.50*

TRONCHUDA KALE #KA107
(Couve Tonchuda) or Portuguese Kale. A bit more heat tolerant than other kales, for a longer harvest period on either end of winter season. Leaves are large, flat, rounded, similar to collard, but very large and with very prominent white veins, earning some strains a variety name of "costata," meaning "ribbed." The leaves are more succulent and the flavor is more cabbage-like than other kales. The fleshy stems or petioles are enjoyed as well. Definitely an exciting addition to an already illustrious group! Pkt $2.50

SCARLET KALE #KA116 *New!*
A lovely curled "red" kale that produces lots of delicious, frilly leaves and takes on the chill of winter with stride! Pretty in the flower garden or on the plate. Rich in nutrition and flavor. Pkt (150 seeds) $2.75

VATES COLLARDS #OG108
75 days. In the 1950's, this strain was praised as a "new, dwarf strain," longstanding and heat-resistant, like all collards. Winter-hardy to the mid-Atlantic, producing a crop into very cold autumn weather. These make super healthy and delicious cooked greens. Pkt $2.50

Bulgarian Giant Leek

Leeks

By William Woys Weaver

If you are a fan of Agatha Christie murder stories, then surely you are familiar with her famed character Hercule Poirot. His last name is a pun, since it rhymes with poireau, French for leek, surely the most unlikely name for anyone aspiring to solve crimes! But a-ha! My little gray cells also tell me something about Christie and perhaps a wink and a brilliant idea that came to her over a warming bowl of leek soup. Who is to say this did not inspire her?

You cannot explore Belgian cookery (the homeland of Poirot) unless you also get to know leeks. I grow many varieties, have them in the ground all year around, and very glad of that fact when I price leeks at any supermarket. But what kind of selection do we find? Normally there is one bin of leeks. Let's see, Baker Creek offers five distinct varieties and I have nine more than that, and yes, each one has a unique flavor. But you have to sample them side by side in order to detect the subtle nuances.

My great-grandmother, Esther Hannum Hickman, studied at Mrs. Rorer's cooking school in Philadelphia in 1884-1885, and one of the first things she was taught, was the fine art of cooking leeks in white sauce. Her favorite variety was Musselburgh, a market leek developed in Scotland in the 1700s and still valued as one of the hardiest for overwintering in the ground. Don't forget that those leaves that you trim off the top of leeks are one of the best things to toss into the stock pot. They will give stock a delightful flavor, so don't waste them!

The Musselburgh leek has been grown for such a long time that it has produced a number of progeny, new sub-varieties selected out for special traits, like size, hardiness, or ability to stand up under heavy rains. One of the most popular of these is the sub-variety called Giant Musselburgh, which also goes by the names American Flag, Selected Musselburgh, and Scotch Flag. It is generally larger than the original Musselburgh strain, and seems to do better in our American climate. Regardless of which variety of leek you like, you should be starting your seed now (March to mid-April) so that the plants can get themselves well established before the heat of summer. It is important that they develop a good root system to help them overwinter, and if you have seeds left over try adding one or two tablespoonfuls to the next batch of bread you bake. They will give the bread a zippy onion flavor, just like Indian chapattis.

Leek

(Allium ampeloprasum) 400 seeds per pkt. Onion-relative that does require a long season, but is otherwise very easy to grow. Start the tiny seeds indoors in early spring, setting out anytime after the hard frosts are gone—seedlings can tolerate a few degrees of frost with no difficulty. Give leeks the richest possible soil. As the plants start to become really large, earth up soil or mulch, covering the stems, which then blanch or turn white, which is considered to improve the flavor. Mulched leeks do tolerate cooler autumn weather but should be lifted and stored before bitter cold arrives.

AUTUMN GIANT #LK106
Autumn Giant types are grown traditionally throughout Western Europe. Fine-flavored, mid-season variety for harvest through autumn. Leaves have a medium-green color; broad white shank is of medium length. Stands in winter in milder climates, harvest by December elsewhere. Pkt $2.00

BLEU DE SOLAISE #LK105
A 19th-century French leek with deep blue-green leaves that have a violet cast in cool weather. In cool weather, they excel, being very cold-hardy. This good-sized variety is finely flavored and a favorite of European gourmet gardeners and chefs, but hard to find in this country. Pkt $2.50

BULGARIAN GIANT #LK103
A long thin leek of the best quality; light green leaves. Fine autumn variety that is popular in Europe. Pkt $2.00 *or 1 oz $7.00*

CARENTAN #LK101
Long, thick (2" across), vigorous, and fast growing; delicate, deliciously mild flavor; great fresh or cooked. The Carentan leek was mentioned by Vilmorin in 1885. An old European favorite that is becoming rare. Very adaptable and yields are good. Pkt $2.25 *or 1 oz $7.00*

GIANT MUSSELBURGH #LK102
An heirloom that was introduced in 1834 near Edinburgh, Scotland. Large, very thick stems; tasty mild flavor. Grows well in most locations; perfect for home or market. This old favorite has huge size and is very winter hardy. Pkt $2.00

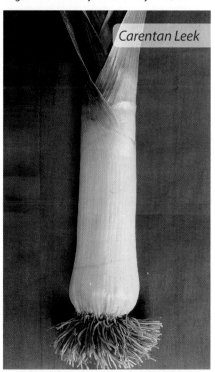

Carentan Leek

Lettuce

(Lactuca sativa) An Old World crop, appreciated since ancient times, that requires cooler temperatures to grow really well. Sow in place in the garden as early in spring as soil may be worked—seeds sprout and grow whenever mild weather predominates. Or start indoors and set out acclimated seedlings 2-4 weeks before last frost date. Succession plant lettuce for a continual crop, but avoid long days and heat of early-mid summer. May be grown right through the winter where the weather is mild, or under row cover, cold frames, etc. Lettuce is healthy and rich in Vitamins A & C. 250 seeds per pkt.

AMISH DEER TONGUE #LT125
50 days. Medium-green, triangular leaves are perfect for baby salad greens. It forms loose, upright heads and is slow to bolt. A popular variety with many heirloom growers. The old favorite of the Amish. Pkt $2.50

AUSTRALIAN YELLOW #LT152
50-60 days. A very bright yellow-green loose-leaf variety from Down Under. Heat tolerance and bolt resistance reported. Glossy, deeply savoyed leaves look like chartreuse seersucker! Pkt $2.25

BABY OAKLEAF #LT163
45 days. Selected out of Green Oakleaf, you get the same great medium-green coloration and deeply cut, oak-leaf form, only the plants are far more compact. Dense-foliaged habit; plants hold well even in warm weather. Performs brilliantly under cut-and-come-again management; great for pot- or container gardening! Pkt $2.50

BELEAH ROSE #LT169 *New!*
52 days. (Leaf type) Very frilly and shiny leaf type that is intensely ruby-red. It has to be one of the darkest lettuces around! The red color carries deeper down into the center than with many other good red varieties. Recommended for baby greens, or cut-and-come-again harvesting. Pkt $2.50

BIG BOSTON (Laitue Lorthois) #LT106
First offered in this country by Peter Henderson & Co. in 1890. Originally from France, it was renamed Big Boston by Henderson. A heading-type that is large, tender, and good for salads. Pkt $2.00

BLONDE DU CAZARD #LT135
An enormous French butterhead type; up to 12" across with big, wavy, green leaves. This lettuce has been grown in France for many years. Pkt (50 seeds) $2.00

BRONZE BEAUTY #LT149
40-50 days, leaf-type. Also known as Bronze Arrowhead. All-America Award winner for 1947, the year it was introduced by Germania Seed Company. Super-sweet leaves are blushed with medium bronze, mainly around the wavy leaf margins. Heat tolerant and slow to bolt. Spectacular and flavorful! Pkt $2.25

BRUNE D'HIVER #LT139

Flashy Butter Oak

Merlot

Flashy Butter Gem

Outredgeous

Compact, hardy, French butterhead-type lettuce that was introduced in 1855. Crunchy green leaves are blushed in reddish-brown color. Plants require little space when growing and are perfect for fall plantings. Hard to find in America. Pkt $2.00

BUTTERCRUNCH #LT155
65 days. Classic butterhead type was the standard for many years. Soft, buttery-textured leaves enclose a crisp, juicy, loose inner head of blanched, sweet-tasting leaves. Very heat-tolerant and slow to bolt, Buttercrunch stays mild long after others have turned bitter. Developed by George Raleigh, Cornell University, and an All America Selection for 1963. Pkt $2.25

BUTTER KING #LT154
65 days. The pale green leaves are soft and, yes, buttery; the heads are heavy and relatively compact, filled with tender inner leaves that are mellow, sweet and succulent. Slower to bolt and tolerates heat better than most butterhead (Bibb) types, making it especially valuable in the South, or wherever summer heat comes early or unpredictably. All America Selection in 1966; bred in Ottawa, Canada. Pkt $2.25

CELTUCE #LT147
A very unique lettuce. Grown for its celery-like stem that is tasty raw or cooked, the leaves can also be used as greens. High in vitamin C, introduced from China in the 1840's. Excellent! Pkt $2.00

CHADWICK'S RODAN #LT137
This variety was developed by the legendary Alan Chadwick, the English leader of the organic movement in the early 1970's. Green, loose-leaf heads are tinged in bright red. They are quite compact and perfect for small gardens. We are delighted to offer a historical lettuce that is also quite tasty. Pkt (50 seeds) $2.00

CIMMARON #LT122
65 days. Very nice, deep red, romaine-type heads; good resistance to bolting. Crisp, juicy texture and delicious flavor. This heirloom dates from the 18th century. Pkt $2.25

CRACOVIENSIS #LT136
A beautiful, tender and sweet leaf-lettuce with bright green leaves that are tipped in purple. This pre-1885 variety was referred to by Vilmorin as "Red Celtuce" as it is sometimes used for the bolting stem which is tender and light pink. Pkt $2.50

CRISP MINT #LT150
60-65 days. Romaine type. Large, succulent, mint-green outer leaves surround crystal-white hearts: mild, sweet and crunchy in flavor. Succulent heads to 10 inches in height are a standout in the salad garden. Pkt $2.50

DE PIERRE BENITE #LT141
A popular European crisphead lettuce with large, pale green, curled leaves; it is still grown commercially, although it is believed to pre-date 1885. Pkt $1.75

DEVIL'S EAR #LT146
50 days. Originally from Abundant Life Foundation. Very large, spreading, loose-leaf heads. Leaves are large, wavy-margined, suffused in burgundy. Nutty, crisp texture,

Garnet Rose

Australian Yellow

Forellenschluss

Ice Queen

Oak Leaf

bitter-free flavor. Slow to bolt, standing a very long time in the garden. Glorious! Pkt (50 seeds) $2.50

FLAME #LT113

60 days. A unique red leaf lettuce that is great for the new high-class markets. The color is intense crimson-red and is slow to bolt. Introduced in 1988. Pkt (50 Seeds) $2.50

FLASHY BUTTER GEM #LT160

70 days. Nearly full-sized Romaine type dappled in a lovely, deep crimson. Another "Flashy" introduction from Frank Morton, Shoulder to Shoulder Farm, this one is a high yielder, and also makes a great early baby Romaine. Very tender and delicious! Pkt (150 seeds) $3.00

FLASHY BUTTER OAK #LT157

55 days. Here's a newer lettuce introduction that combines crimson-red splashes with the leaf form of apple-green oak-leaf lettuce, and a butter-cos lettuce habit! It might sound mixed up but that's a good thing because "Flashy Butter Oak" combines superior taste, texture and form—truly at the forefront of today's open-pollinated breeding. This versatile variety excels equally whether harvested as baby greens, baby heads or at full maturity. The texture is silky, the taste is mild, juicy and sweet. A Frank Morton innovation. Pkt (150 seeds) $3.00

FORELLENSCHLUSS #LT104

60 days. Old Austrian heirloom; the name means "speckled like a trout." A superb, gorgeous romaine lettuce that is highly splashed in deep red. Very beautiful and tasty. Pkt $2.25 *or 1 oz $7.50*

GARNET ROSE #LT170 *New!*

74 days. (Romaine type) True bright garnet red and savoy leaves set this apart from some other red Romaine types. This one is red right through to the center. Scrumptious as a container subject, too! Pkt $2.50

GENTILINA #LT130

Lovely, bright green, frizzled, leafy heads that are very ruffled. Good resistance to bolting. Tender leaves are first rate in salads; an extra fine Italian variety. Pkt $2.00

GRANDPA ADMIRE'S #LT151

60 days. This heat-tolerant butterhead type has been lovingly preserved by descendants of Civil War veteran Grandpa George Admire, born in 1822. Forms large plants with large, loose heads; deeply crinkled leaves are gracefully splashed with bronze and are of very fine flavor! Originally a Seed Savers Exchange accession, donated to them in the 1970's by Chloe Lowry. Pkt $2.50

HENDERSON'S BLACK-SEEDED SIMPSON #LT108

60 days. Introduced in the 1870's by Peter Henderson & Co. Sweet and tender leaves, light yellow-green; very popular. Pkt $2.50 *or 1 oz $3.75*

ICEBERG #LT110

Compact, medium-large heads, very crisp. Introduced in 1894. The classic American lettuce. Low nutrition. Pkt $1.50

ICE QUEEN #LT166 *New!*

80 days. (also known as Reine des Glaces) A

Lollo di Vino

Lollo Rossa

Slo Bolt

wholly superior crisphead (iceberg) type, this French heirloom shows excellent tolerance to cold, and makes a great crop to plant extra early or late! The frilled outer leaves are mild enough to use for leaf-lettuce, or harvest as baby greens. With its darker green color and ever-so-slightly bitter interior, it's widely regarded as the best crisphead type around! Pkt $2.25

LAU'S POINTED LEAF #LT133
This variety was collected from Lau, a Chinese farmer in the highlands of Malaysia. It produces star-shaped plants with long, thin, bright-green pointed leaves. The flavor is sweet and very tasty. This variety was the fastest growing and most vigorous of the many lettuces grown in our 2006 trial. Pkt (50 seeds) $2.50

LITTLE GEM #LT116
50 days. Very small, green, romaine-type. One of the very best-tasting lettuces. A superb heat-tolerant variety that is sure to please! Pkt $2.25 *or 1 oz $5.00*

LOLLO BIONDA #LT143
One of the prettiest lime-green varieties I have seen; the shiny-green sister of Lollo Rosso. This variety also has extremely frizzy, crinkled and compact leaves. Tender and so tasty. A real standard in fresh European salads. Pkt $2.00

LOLLO DE VINO #LT159
56 days. Compact newer "lollo" type. Selected out of Merlot by Frank Morton, who noticed a particularly frilly individual. He saved seed from this and Lollo di Vino was born! Frank calls this a "distinctive little frizzlehead," and it definitely is! Very dark purple leaf type, with a very curly leaf margin. Dense, rounded plants. The variety's mildew resistance comes as a bonus, making this another spectacular new variety! Pkt (150 seeds) $3.00

LOLLO ROSSA #LT127
60 days. Very curled leaves are light green with stunning bright red edges. Mild and tasty. A most beautiful lettuce, superb for market. Pkt $2.50 *or 1 oz $7.50*

MASCARA #LT131
65 days. Wow! This lettuce is stunning with its Mascara-red, frilly, oak-shaped leaves that keep their color in warm weather. One of the brightest and most beautiful oak-shaped types on the market! Developed in Holland. Pkt (150 seeds) $2.25

MAY QUEEN #LT118
60 days. Early-maturing butterhead lettuce for the earliest spring plantings. Pale green heads are tinged with red, and the sweet, pale yellow hearts have a pink blush to them. A wonderful 19th-century heirloom. Pkt $2.00 *or 1 oz $5.00*

MERLOT #LT158
55 days. (Also known as "Galactic.") Reputed to be absolutely the darkest red lettuce in existence, which should make it tops for anthocyanin (anti-oxidant) content as well! Leaf lettuce with wavy to frilly leaf margins and very crisp, waxy leaves! Excellent bolt resistance, and good cold tolerance for a late fall to winter crop. Recommended as a cutting type for baby greens production or cut-and-come-again harvesting. We feel, along with our friend William Woys Weaver, that this variety is destined to become

a classic, and it certainly deserves it! Pkt (150 seeds) $3.00

MERVEILLE DES QUATRE SAISONS #LT107
48 days. A pre-1885 French heirloom; crisp and tender. The fine-flavored leaves have a reddish color. It is becoming popular again. Pkt $2.25 *or 1 oz $4.50*

MIGNONETTE BRONZE #LT111
60 days. Excellent for hot and tropical weather, slow to bolt; frilled leaves, bronze-green heads. A superb type for the hot parts of the country. This heirloom was introduced in 1898. Pkt $2.00

OAK LEAF #LT109
60 days. Introduced in 1771 by the French company Vilmorin. The tasty leaves are somewhat the same shape as an oak leaf; very hardy. Pkt $2.50

OUTREDGEOUS #LT148
Quite possibly the reddest lettuce variety known! Harvest as a leaf lettuce or allow to grow until the loose, Romaine-type heads develop—either way, it lends an "outrage" of red to salads or sandwiches. So pretty in the garden, too! Another Frank Morton selection. Pkt (100 seeds) $2.50

PABLO #LT162
70 days. Stunning Batavian type is lavishly splashed in vibrant bronze-purple. Lovely enough for the flower bed, or even as a subject for a still-life painting! Mild, crisp and juicy, and very slow to bolt. Batavian lettuces are heading types, and yield heads midway between the tight heads of a crisphead and the loose heads of a leaf type. Pkt $2.50 or 1 oz $7.50

PARRIS ISLAND COS #LT101
70 days. A tasty romaine-type. Uniform heads are pale cream-green inside, and the outside is dark green. Developed around 1949; named after Parris Island, off the East coast. Pkt $2.00

RED ROMAINE #LT115
Delicious, flavorful lettuce brings color and zest to salads. The red coloring develops best in cool weather. A good variety for specialty markets. Pkt $2.25 or 1 oz $6.50

ROUGE D'HIVER #LT105
60 days. Heirloom, red romaine-type from France. Listed in Vilmorin's Vegetable Garden Book from 1885. Red and green leaves; turns a deeper shade of red in cold weather. Pkt $2.00

ROUGE GRENOBLOISE #LT129
Beautiful red-tinted Batavian (Crisphead) lettuce; the heads have excellent flavor. Very cold-hardy and slow to bolt, these are vigorous-growing plants; great producers. This fine, old lettuce comes from France. Pkt $2.00

RUBIN #LT123
Very deep maroon, looseleaf heads. A stunning addition to the garden and salads, the leaves have frilled edges. Great for market growers; hardy. Pkt $2.50

SLO BOLT #LT167 *New!*
48 days--Ruffled, apple-green leaf type that does better than most lettuces under hot conditions--seldom bolts or becomes bitter. Introduced in 1946. For greenhouse or field

Cimmaron

Celtuce

growing, and an excellent variety for the South. Pkt $2.25

SPECKLED #LT103
45 days. Beautiful apple-green leaves speckled and splashed with deep red. Originally a Dutch variety brought from the Netherlands to Ontario, Canada by Mennonite immigrant Urias Martin in 1799. Used as a loose-leaf variety. Pkt $2.50

SUNSET #LT112
60 days. Super deep, beautiful red! A great variety for home and market growers alike. An excellent leaf-type that was introduced in 1987, but has since become rare. Pkt $2.00

TANGO #LT117
50 days. The leaves look like endive with their deeply-cut, crinkled appearance and dark green color. The tangy flavor makes this lettuce a winner in salads. Very uniform loose-leaf type. Pkt $2.00

TENNIS BALL #LT164
55 days. Rather loose heads are petite, 6-8 inches in diameter, Bibb or Butterhead type. This variety is documented to have been grown at Monticello by Thos. Jefferson, who noted: "it does not require so much care and attention" as other types. We offer the correct, black-seeded original strain. Listed in the Slow Foods Ark of Taste, and beloved by many about a century ago. Pkt $2.50

TOM THUMB #LT102
60 days. An heirloom lettuce that dates to the 1850's. It makes small cabbage-like green heads, only 3"-4" across. Very tasty, a winner for classy markets! Pkt $2.00

Beleah Rose

Speckled

Lau's Pointed Leaf

Melon

(Cucumis melo) We have heirloom melons that can mature in almost any climate. Try some of these sweet & juicy varieties this year and enjoy a taste trip into your past... enjoy the flavor! 25-50 seeds per pkt.

Rich Sweetness 132

AFGHAN HONEYDEW #OML120
This delicious melon is grown in the high mountain valleys, north of Kabul, Afghanistan. Recently brought back from that ancient country, it measures about 8" long and is football-shaped. The skin is netted and the flesh is green, crispy, and sweet. Pkt (15 seeds) $3.00

APPLE MELON #OML135 85 days. Adorable little tear-drop shaped melons just fit your hand. The cheerful golden-yellow-and green striped skin is thin like many Asian types; the fruit is eaten skin and all, like an apple. Our growers, the Gingerich family of Kentucky, first found this variety in Filadelfia in the Gran Chaco region of western Paraguay, in 1968. They grew it elsewhere in Paraguay and Belize for years before moving to Kentucky, where they have enjoyed it for several years. They and we are excited to pass this gem onto you! Pkt $3.00

ASHKAHABAD #OML131
80 days. A honeydew type that holds well after picking. The smooth skin is golden, the crisp flesh is green and has a rich, sweet flavor. A heavy producer of 8-10 lb fruits. Named for a city in Turkmenistan, in Central Asia, which is noted for its incredible diversity of indigenous melon types. Pkt (10 seeds) $2.75

Vert Grimpant

AMARILLO ORO #ML101
100 days. Beautiful, golden-yellow, oblong fruit grow to 15 lbs and have sweet, creamy-white flesh. A pre-1870 European heirloom winter type. Good shipper. Pkt $2.00

ANANAS #AML102
100 days. Sweet and juicy white flesh. A rare white muskmelon; fruit are around 5 lbs. An old 1800's heirloom. Pkt $2.50

ANANAS D'AMERIQUE A CHAIR VERT #AML110
Fragrant, incredibly delicious flesh that keeps getting rave reviews from our customers and is a favorite of our staff. This historic heirloom was grown by Thomas Jefferson in 1794. It was offered commercially in the USA in 1824, and it was illustrated in color in France in 1854 in the Vilmorin Album. This wonderful variey has become very rare. The fruit have netted skin and light green flesh that is firm, sweet, and highly perfumed. Productive plants can be trained up a trellis. Pkt $3.00 *or 1 oz $7.00*

BANANA #AML113
90 days. Banana-shaped fruit with smooth, yellow skin; and sweet, spicy, salmon-colored flesh. 16"-24" long, 5-8 lbs. It was listed in 1885 by J. H. Gregory's Catalogue, which said, *"When ripe it reminds one of a large, overgrown banana... It smells like one, having a remarkably powerful and delicious fragrance."* This is one of my all-time favorites, being very sweet and great for specialty markets. Pkt $2.50 *or 1 oz $6.00*

Valencia Winter

BARESE #ML128
Botanically a melon, like the Armenian cucumber, but with a completely different appearance: oblong smooth, spring green fruits have a downy surface.

Sweet, mild flavor, never bitter, burpless. This delicious heirloom originated in Bari, Italy. Pkt $2.25

BATEEKH SAMARRA #OML142

95 days. Oblong fruits are brownish-green and netted outside, lime green within. In our trials the flavor was an unusual, a very delicious, sweet-tart combination, with a distinct citrus taste. The name simply means "old melon from Samarra," which is a city in northern Iraq. Original seed was furnished by our friend, Iraqi seed collector Nael Aziz, who writes that this variety is known to have been grown in the Abbasid Period over one thousand years ago! Endangered due to war and America's aggressive promotion of patented seeds in Iraq. Pkt (10 seeds) $3.00

BIDWELL #AML147

95 days. This melon was grown by General John Bidwell, who received his seed stock from the USDA in 1869. He was a soldier in the Civil War and also became a US senator. He grew this melon in Chico, California. It produces massive fruits that weigh about 16 lbs each and are football-shaped. The orange flesh is sweet and creamy. Dr. Amy Goldman says "tastes like heavenly orange sherbet," in her book Melons for the Passionate Grower. $2.75

BOULE D'OR #ML106

(Golden Perfection) Very sweet, pale green flesh is just marvelous. Lovely yellow fruit have a unique, lacy netting, like a work of art. This was one of our top melons in our 2003 trials, truly incredible; my all-time favorite honeydew type. Sugary flesh is so flavorful and rich. This variety is a dream for market growers and will command high prices with gourmets and chefs alike! It was listed in Vilmorin's book, *The Vegetable Garden,* in 1885 but it is very rare now. Let's make this variety a market favorite again! Pkt $3.00

BURRELL'S JUMBO #AML127

80 days. Very delicious old variety from the D.V. Burrell Seed Co. An improved selection of Hale's Best, these melons have salmon-orange flesh that is very sweet; perfect for home or market. Pkt $1.50

CASABA—GOLDEN BEAUTY #OML113

110 days. A quality Casaba type. In 1927, Burrell's said it was the finest of Casabas. Very sweet white flesh, tough golden rind, and a good keeper. It can be stored well into the winter! Pkt $2.00

CAVAILLON ESPAGNOL #ML122

Large, oblong, green fruits are filled with delicious green flesh. A very rare and old melon, it was listed in 1893 in Haage & Schmidt's catalog in Erfurt, Germany, and also listed by the Vilmorin's of France earlier in the 1800's. A rare find that is rich and sweet. Pkt $2.50

CHARENTAIS #ML114

85 days. A famous superb heirloom French melon– super sweet and very fragrant. Light grey-green skin, smooth round 2-to 3-lb fruit, bright orange flesh. These are top sellers at high-dollar markets. This was my favorite melon in 2003. I just love the sweet flesh that is so firm. Pkt $2.50 *or 1 oz $7.00*

COLLECTIVE FARM WOMAN #OML110

80-85 days. This heirloom from Ukraine was

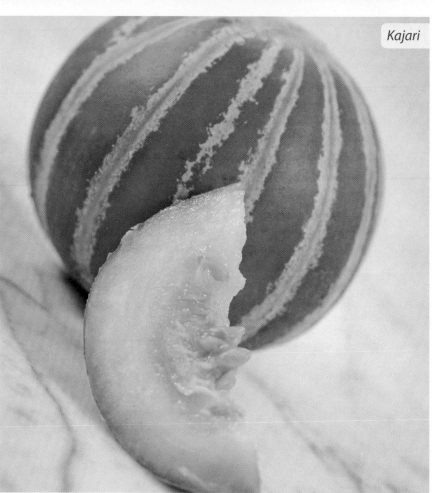

Kajari

Metki Dark Green Cucumber Melon

Melon Pie

Made with Mother Mary's Pie Melon. This is a favorite among diners at our vegetarian restaurant on our farm.

CRUST:
- ❑ ½ cup Earth Balance Natural Buttery Spread
- ❑ ¼ cup packed brown sugar
- ❑ 1¼ cups flour

Beat Earth Balance and brown sugar in mixer until fluffy. Add flour and mix thoroughly. Place in 9" pie pan and spread evenly over bottom and up sides of pan. Bake at 375 degrees for 10-12 minutes.

FILLING:
- ❑ ½ cup cane sugar
- ❑ 3 tablespoons organic cornstarch
- ❑ 2 tablespoons egg replacer—without water added
- ❑ 1½ cups Mother Mary's Pie Melon, cubed and liquified in blender
- ❑ ¼ cup water
- ❑ 3 tablespoons Earth Balance Natural Buttery Spread
- ❑ 1 teaspoon fresh, squeezed lemon juice

Stir together sugar and cornstarch in saucepan. Blend egg replacer, melon, and water; gradually stir into sugar and cornstarch mixture and cook over medium heat, stirring constantly until mixture thickens and begins to boil. Reduce heat and cook 1 minute longer. Remove from heat. Stir in Earth Balance and lemon juice. Pour into pie shell.

Sprinkle with toasted flaked coconut. After being allowed to cool, then refrigerate at least 1 hour before serving.

Enjoy this treat from the past!

Buy The Baker Creek Vegan Cookbook, published by Hyperion! See our book section.

Ananas d'Amerique a Chair Vert

Tigger

collected in 1993 by Seed Savers Exchange. Very popular on the peninsula of Krim in the Black Sea. Melons ripen to a yellowish gold, and the white flesh has a very high sugar content; a favorite among heirloom gardeners and market growers alike. Ripens early, even in Russia, and tolerates comparatively cool summers—known to do well in Canada. Pkt $2.50

CRANE #AML130

85 days. The famous California heirloom introduced in 1920 by Oliver Crane, whose family has been farming near Santa Rosa for six generations. Delicious Crenshaw-type melons have pale orange flesh that is very sweet and fine flavored; green-skinned rind with orange spots when ripe. Fruit are 4 lbs each. Pkt $2.50

CRENSHAW #AML107

105 days. Large melons with wonderful, sweet flavor! A family favorite; grows best in warm, dry climates. Fruit are oval-shaped and green-yellow; salmon pink flesh. Good yields of delicious melons. Pkt $2.00 *or 1 oz $5.00*

CRENSHAW BLANCO #AML128

110 days. An improved Crenshaw variety. Oval fruit are about 5 lbs each and have a creamy white rind when ripe; flesh is salmon pink, extra sweet, and of a very fine flavor. Great for specialty markets and shipping. Pkt (20 seeds) $2.50

D'ALGER #ML103

Another colorful ancient French Cantaloupe (possibly from Africa); it is definitely one of the oldest. Ribbed fruit are dark green (almost black) with silver splashes. As they get ripe, they turn yellow with near red splashes. The flesh is highly perfumed and very smooth and creamy, but the flavor tends to be bland. Compact vines; quality French seed from Bruno Defay. Pre-1800 Heirloom. Pkt $2.75

DELICE DE LA TABLE #ML118

A pre-1885 French heirloom that was listed in the French book The Vegetable Garden. The name of this beautiful old variety translated means "Delight of the Table". A very hard-to-find, almost unheard-of variety that is quite tasty. Pkt $3.00

DELICIOUS 51 #AML108

4-5 lbs, round-oval muskmelon, salmon-orange sweet flesh. A popular home garden variety; early. Pkt $2.50

EARLY FRAME PRESCOTT #ML110

80 days The Prescott melon that was grown in "Cold Frames" in the Europe of yesterday, hence the name. These are not the flat shape of our other Prescott's, but rather a roundish pumpkin shape with ribs, 2-3 lbs. each. Delightfully rich and sweet orange flesh. Pkt $2.75

EARLY HANOVER #AML132

75 days. Luscious, small 2 to 3-lb green-fleshed melons are bursting with sweetness. This was a famous melon at the turn of the 20th century and was introduced by T.W. Woods & Sons of Richmond, Virginia, in 1895. Pick just before the melons freely slip from the vines for best flavor. This is a great variety to add to your home garden or market stand; heavy yields. Pkt $2.50

EARLY SILVER LINE #OML116

75 days. Beautiful, oval, yellow fruit have lovely silver stripes and weigh 1-2 lbs. The white flesh is

Petit Gris de Rennes

Model

Emerald Gem

very crisp and sweet. This is a Korean type that was introduced by Burpee's and is one of the best. This one is a must for melon enthusiasts and specialty growers alike. Very productive and quite early, a good choice for the North and fun for kids to grow. Pkt $2.50

EDENS GEM (ROCKY FORD GREEN-FLESHED) #AML109
90 days. An old heirloom variety, from 1881. This old-timer is still a popular green flesh muskmelon, with a heavily-netted rind and smooth, sweet-flavored flesh. Fruits weigh 2-3 lbs. A good keeper; has firm flesh. From Colorado. Pkt $2.00

EDISTO 47 #AML106
90 days. Deep salmon-colored flesh; fine flavor and hard rind; 4½ lbs. Excellent for hot, humid conditions; great for home gardens or market. Pkt $1.50

EMERALD GEM #AML120
85 days. An heirloom introduced by Burpee's in 1886. It was very popular for years, but now it has become rare. The fruit have green rinds and luscious, sweet, orange flesh; 2½ lbs each. Pkt $2.50

ESCONDIDO GOLD #AML158
Huge fruit have grown up to 18 lbs, oblong with bright yellow rind. Flesh is soft, sweet and very fragrant; these are known for great taste. At one time this was a popular market melon at several of California's markets. Pkt $2.50

GOLDEN JENNY #AML133
An outstanding golden meated version of Jenny Lind", developed by long time friend and the late, master seed saver, Merl Neidens. Short vines just go wild producing these succulent, sweet 2 lb. beauties. Give this one a try at upscale markets. Early and productive. Pkt $2.50 or 1 oz $6.50

GOLDEN CRISPY #OML133
Commercial variety that was discontinued in the early 1980's. Small, oblong to pear-shaped fruits weigh about a half-pound. Smooth golden skin enclose incredibly sweet, uniquely aromatic white flesh. We're excited to re-introduce this worthwhile variety that was almost lost. Pkt. $3.00 or 1 oz $7.50

GOLDEN HONEYMOON #AML119
92 days A honeydew melon with a brilliant, gold rind and delicious green flesh; unique flavor. Two weeks earlier than regular Honeydew; excellent yields. Will rarely sunburn; a great keeper, unique and rare! Pkt $2.50

GOLDEN SWEET #OML101
This early melon has gorgeous, lemon-colored rinds and small size. The flesh is white, crisp and good. An easy to grow variety from Taiwan. Pkt (10 seeds) $2.50

GREEN MACHINE #AML134
85 days. Vigorous, compact vines produce green-fleshed 2-lb melons at an incredible rate! This delicious, sweet variety is really amazing! A true improvement in melons bred by the late, Merl Neidens, a master of heritage gardening and plant selection. His varieties always receive rave reviews from our customers. Superb taste. Pkt 3.00

GREEN NUTMEG #AML114
85 days. Fearing Burr said in 1863, *"The Nutmeg Melon has long been in cultivation, and is almost everywhere to be found in the vegetable garden... It is of most delicious excellence... one of the best."* It is

Ashkahabad

Mother Mary's Pie Melon

a medium-sized green-fleshed melon that has a heavily-netted skin and rich, sweet, delicious flesh; heavy aroma. Pkt $2.50

HALE'S BEST 45 #AML101
85 days. A popular heirloom developed around 1920 by a Japanese market grower in California. Sweet, smooth, orange flesh. A good flavored muskmelon. Pkt $2.00

HA'OGEN #OML150 *New!*
75-80 days (Also known as Israel Melon) An excellent-tasting, early melon. Commonly thought to have originated in Israel, where its name means "anchor" but may have actually originated in Hungary. Flavorful green flesh; good yields of nearly round, 3-4 lb fruits; a beautiful melon! Very fragrant. A long-time favorite of the Gettle family. Pkt $2.50

HEALY'S PRIDE #AML153
A big, pretty, oblong melon with musky-sweet orange flesh; Heavily netted and up to 15 lbs in size. This melon was developed by E.J. Healy of St. Francisville, IL. It is a great melon for most of the Midwest and was introduced in 1952. High-quality flesh with a great taste makes for some great eating. Pkt $2.25

HEARTS OF GOLD #AML115
85 days. An orange fleshed muskmelon dating back to around 1890. Quality 2-3 lb. netted fruit with firm, sweet, tasty flesh; one of the first "modern type" melons. It was once very popular. Pkt $2.50

HERO OF LOCKINGE #ML120
80 days. Small, round, one-pound fruits have delectable, creamy-white flesh that is full of flavor and sweetness. This English heirloom was introduced in 1881 by Sutton's Seeds, but it was named for Lord Wantage of Lockinge, founder of the British Red Cross, and was developed at the family estate at Lockinge Park. A favorite! Pkt (15 seeds) $3.00

HONEYDEW - ORANGE FLESH #AML104
98 days. Light green, smooth skin; orange flesh. An orange-fleshed version of the regular Honeydew; tasty. Pkt $2.50 *or 1 oz $5.00*

HONEYDEW - TAM DEW #AML103
100 days. Beautiful, ivory-green fruit, deep green; very sweet flesh, with classic Honeydew flavor! A superb variety. Pkt $2.50

HONEY ROCK #AML105
80 days. An early heirloom melon; 3-4 lbs. Thick, sweet, firm deep salmon-colored flesh; good yields of quality fruit. An AAS winner for 1933. Good size for an early melon. Pkt $1.75 *or 1 oz $5.00*

INEYA #OML125 *New!*
80 days. A variety from the former Soviet Union that we are very pleased to offer! Uniform, 6-to 8- inch fruit in a smooth-skinned, hard, golden rind have white to very pale cream-colored flesh, crunchy yet juicy. The flavor is positively outstanding, like a honeydew in flavor with overtones of mulberry or banana. Pkt $2.50

INDIAN CREAM COBRA #OML134
Here's a really unusual variety from Australia, with a distinctive flavor and aroma. The elongated fruits are smooth-skinned; the skin splits and peels back when the fruits are fully ripe. Some say this resembles a Cobra's hood! The flesh is pinkish and unusually dry, and is often used to flavor homemade ice cream Down Under. Pkt $3.50

Thai Golden Round

Afghan Honeydew

Plum Granny

IROQUOIS #AML125

85 days. Large 5 to 7-lb fruit, thick deep-orange flesh, of good quality. This melon is very good for the Midwest and Northeast. Developed by Dr. Munger of Cornell University, 1944. Pkt $2.00

JENNY LIND #AML117

80 days. This fine melon dates back to the 1840's and was sold by many of the seed companies of that day. It was named for the famous singer, Jenny Lind, "The Swedish Nightingale." This wonderful 1- to 2-lb turban-shaped melon is very sweet and has light green, delicious flesh. It is becoming popular again with those who try it! Pkt $2.50

KAJARI #JS235 *New!*

This amazing early Indian melon was collected by Joseph Simcox. The fruit are a brillian copper-red and are striped in green and cream, making this an extremely unusual and beautiful melon. The pale green flesh is sweet, aromatic and slightly musky in taste. Joe believes that this melon originated in the Punjab, and Joe spent more than 8 years trying to find seeds of this extremely interesting variety. Vine produces lots of 2 lb fruit. Pkt (15 seeds) $4.50

MANGO MELON OR VINE PEACH #OML115

The 3" fruit are the size of a peach, with a yellow rind and bland white flesh. This variety was very popular in Victorian times for making sweet pickles, pies, and preserves. Developed in China and introduced into America in the 1880s. In the Orient this type of melon is pickled. Pkt $2.50

METKI DARK GREEN SERPENT MELON (ARMENIAN) #OML104

65 days. An ancient heirloom, introduced from Armenia into Italy as far back as the 1400's. It is a melon, but is used like a cucumber; picked small (18" or less), it is very mild and tasty, but the fruits can grow to over 3' long! Easy to grow, and good yields; it should be planted in more gardens. Pkt $2.50

METKI PAINTED SERPENT MELON #OML105

Very long fruit with dark green and pale green stripes and excellent flavor; a rare Armenian-type cucumber that is actually a melon; very unique and is a great selling item at farmers markets everywhere. Pkt $2.50

METKI WHITE SERPENT MELON #OML106

The light green Armenian cucumber that is botanically a melon; sweeter and crisper than regular cukes, pick when under 18" for best taste. Delicious and easy to grow. Try selling all three colors of our Metki Serpents at your specialty market for a real sensation! Pkt $2.50

MINNESOTA MIDGET #AML140

70 days. This very small, very early heirloom was introduced in Minnesota in 1948. They have sweet, orange flesh, measure just 4" across, and are perfect miniature versions of the "Classic Muskmelon." Compact 3'-4' vines produce good yields. I fondly remember these as the only melons our family could get to ripen in Charlo, Montana, about 20-some-years ago. Pkt $2.50

MISSOURI GOLD #AML150

A very old heirloom from Southern Missouri, which has been in one Missouri family since Civil War times. This variety was given to an Illinois seed corn grower in the 1970s, who has preserved it ever since. This is a very rare variety, with 2-3 lb fruit, sweet, orange flesh and good yields. A real old-time hillbilly variety that we are very pleased to offer. Pkt $3.00

The Pear Melon with David Leroy Kaiser

Ha'Ogen

MODEL #ML132 *New!*

75 days. Globular fruits are lightly netted. The green flesh is thick, very aromatic and sweet. Choice variety from a Polish seedsman. Personal melons at about one to two pounds each. Extra fancy looking! Pkt $3.00

MOTHER MARY'S PIE MELON #AML162

A favorite in our Vegan Restaurant. Here's a really different little melon! Tart little fruits are about softball sized or slightly smaller, weighing to about 6 ounces. Smooth, occasionally netted bright yellow-orange skin contains the white flesh. The fruit is fragrant, tangy and moderately sweet. Original seed was preserved by W.R. Lorence, whose Minnesota grandmother, a century ago, made pies from a combination of this melon and apples. Our cooks turn these into incredible pies, crisps and cakes. Enjoy wonderful melon flavor in your summer baking and preserves! Pkt $3.00

NEW MELON #OML139

Small, round to slightly tear-drop shaped melons with smooth skin of pale green. The juicy flesh within is yellow to white. A Japanese specialty type developed in the 1950's; beloved for its fragrance and its sweet taste. Pkt $2.75

NOIR DES CARMES #ML109

80 days. A beautiful and rare heirloom from France, the famous "Black Rock" melon preserved by the Carmelite monks. It was mentioned by Mawe & Abercrombie in 1787. Nearly black in color, the fruit turns orange as it ripens. They are deeply ribbed and have smooth skin. The flesh is orange in color, thick, flavorful, and perfumed. Excellent and unusual. The fruit weigh about 3-6 lbs each. Pkt $2.75

OBUS OR KROUMIR #ML111

90 days. Another of the true French cantaloupes that we have obtained from France's best collectors. This one was developed from "Noir des Carmes" and was mentioned by Vilmorin in 1904. The fruit are generally oblong in shape. Dark green rinds get golden as the fruit ripens. These are very sweet and have orange flesh; 4-8 lb. in weight. Rare. Pkt $3.00

OKA MELON (BIZARD ISLAND STRAIN) #AML154

A popular melon in Canada's Montreal region in the 1920's and 1930's. It was grown in Montreal's rich soil before disappearing from catalogs, only to be discovered many years later, still being grown on Bizard Island in Quebec. Developed about 1912 by a Trappist monk at La Trappe, Quebec. In 1932 Dupuy & Ferguson, seedsmen and nurserymen of Montreal, said *"The colour is a beautiful cream, with a bright salmon flesh that is very thick and well netted. The most delicious, sweet and juicy melon. It is of strong habit, a fine setter. The Oka melon is the result of years of patient and intelligent selection from the product of Montreal Market crossed with a red-fleshed variety."* Indeed it is very sweet and flavorful, being a good melon for the North. Pkt $2.50

OLD GREEK #ML124

90 days. This unusual melon came to the US with Greek immigrants in the early 20th century, who settled in Utah to work mining jobs there. Slightly oblong, netted fruits vary quite a bit in size, attaining 10 lbs in really good conditions. The orange flesh is very sweet. Ripe fruits keep fairly well. Pkt $3.00

OLD TIME TENNESSEE #AML142

An old favorite of mine. Produces huge, oblong

Zatta

Minnesota Midget

Schoons Hardshell

melons that weigh 12-14 lbs and have a deeply creased rind. Their orange flesh is superior, being loaded with unique fruity undertones and a sweetness not often found in modern melons. High sugar content. Fragile melons are not good keepers but are winners with gourmet foodies. This old Tennessee heirloom was almost lost to modern gardens. Pkt $3.00

Noir des Carmes

ORAN'S MELON #AML136
85 days. A local heirloom from the Missouri Ozarks that has been grown by the Oran Ball family for over 55 years. Large 6 to 8-lb fruit are netted and ribbed, the flesh is a rich orange color, and the flavor is very good. Excellent for the Midwest region. Pkt $2.50

ORLINABEL #ML121
Rare, Charentais-type melon having green flesh and attractive yellow tracery on the skin. The slightly elongated fruits are very sweet, reaching 2-3 pounds, and the vines are very productive. Apparently selected in 1973 and reputed to carry some fusarium wilt tolerance. Pkt $3.00

PEAR #AML145
90 days. Football-shaped fruit have wonderfully fragrant, sweet orange flesh that has a delicate flavor. This heirloom from the Northwest pre-dates 1900. Pkt (15 seeds) $2.50

PETIT GRIS DE RENNES #ML104
85 days. Dense, 2-lb fruit have orange flesh that is superbly sweet, flavorful, and perfumed. This variety is early and well adapted to cool climates. The fruit weigh around 2 lbs and have a grey-green rind. This fine French variety is of the best quality and is the favorite melon of the French melon expert and author Bruno Defay. Rare in the USA. One of our most-requested market melons, specialty growers love them because they command top prices! We continue to receive rave reviews about this melon, which is surely one of the best Charentais types. Pkt $3.50 *or 1 oz $9.00*

Indian Cream Cobra

PIEL DE SAPO (TOAD SKIN) #ML113
110 days. Oval, 8"-long fruit, and skin that's mottled green and yellow, somewhat like a toad's skin. Sweet, white flesh has a very good taste; one of the earlier maturing winter melons, but still rather late. Very rare; from Spain. Pkt $2.50

PLANTER'S JUMBO #AML126
85 days. Thick, sweet, orange flesh; fruit are over 4 lbs. A good variety for drought or heavy rainfall. Popular market melon, makes a good shipper. Pkt $1.75

PLUM GRANNY or QUEEN ANNE'S POCKET #OML114
75 days. Beautiful, ornamental fruit are yellow with deep orange stripes and only 2"-3" long! They are grown for their wonderful fragrance! These melons were very popular in Victorian gardens and have been our most requested melon. Bland flavor. Pkt $2.50

PRESCOTT FOND BLANC #ML102
70 days. The most unique and beautiful French melon we sell! The fruit is 4-9 lbs, very flattened and ribbed, with warts and bumps. Melons have grey-green skin turning straw color; flesh is salmon-orange. Once one of the best-known melons, it was mentioned in the 1860's, but it likely is much older. The flavor is very rich if picked at perfection, and the fragrance is heavenly. This is a favorite melon of mine, almost unheard of in this country. Pkt $3.00

Charentais

Apple Melon

Tendral Verde Tardif

Jake's

PRIDE OF WISCONSIN #AML135

An old fashioned Wisconsin heirloom that was grown for the Milwaukee markets in the 1920's. large fruit are oblong and have soft, sweet, juicy orange flesh, real muskmelon taste. Pkt $2.50

RAMPICANTE ZUCCHERINO #ML126

80 days. The name means *"climbing sugar melon."* Traditionally grown on trellis or other support, but may be left to creep along the soil's surface. Fruits run 2 to 2 ½ lbs. Sweet salmon-to-orange flesh. A fine Italian heirloom that is quite delicious. Pkt $2.75

RICH SWEETNESS 132 #OML126

Incredible little melons from the former Soviet Union. The fruit are a beautiful red, striped with golden yellow and weigh only about ¼ lb! The flesh is pure white and quite sweet. These have a very refreshing taste and are very fragrant. They are perfect for single servings. These little melons are so much fun and great for children's gardens. The vines are very productive and produced all season long. One of the best new varieties we've discovered in the last few years. Try a few of these delicious little melons in your home or market garden. Pkt $3.00

RIDDLE #OML127

Unique little melons weigh about 1 lb and are mostly egg-shaped. They vary in color from white to caramel-brown and green. Flesh is white, sweet and flavorful. A fun little variety that have some variation in fruit shape. Developed in the former Soviet Union. Pkt (15 seeds) $2.00

RUGOSO DI COSENZA #ML108

A beautiful "Amarillo Oro"-type melon from Italy. It is a good late-season market variety, with sugary-sweet white flesh and a bright-golden rind with ridges; hard to find here. Pkt $2.00

SAKATA'S SWEET #OML102

85 days. A favorite Asian variety of Dr. Amy Goldman, author of *Melons for the Passionate Grower*. These small 3"-4" round melons are very sweet with a high sugar content. Oriental varieties open a whole new dimension to melons as they are amazingly different. Crisp and crunchy; they have edible skins. Their small size and light, golden rind make them very attractive. This fine Japanese variety was developed by Sakata's Seed Co., of Yokohama. This is a must for marketing. They are in high demand by melon lovers and command top prices! Rare and colorful. Pkt $2.50

SCHOON'S HARDSHELL #AML129

Very large fruit have a hard, heavy and deeply ribbed rind; a very good shipper or home garden variety; salmon flesh is very flavorful, spicy and unique. A New York heirloom that is a favorite of melon expert Dr. Amy Goldman. Pkt $2.00

SIERRA GOLD #AML116

85 days Well netted, 3-lb. Fruit with thick, salmon-colored flesh; sweet and of superb flavor. An excellent home- and market variety. Resistant to powdery mildew. Pkt $2.00

SLEEPING BEAUTY #AML156

Developed by Merlyn Niedens in the late 1990's. This variety produces lots of small, sweet melons that have succulent orange flesh. Flattened fruit are netted and have yellow tan colored rinds. Compact vines are ideal for small gardens, and those who grow in raised beds. Pkt $2.50

SMALL PERSIAN #OML112

110 days. Rare, old-time melon with a sweet, bright orange flesh and a dark green rind. Distinctive flavor! The Persian melon has been offered in America for nearly 200 years but traces it's origins to ancient Persia (Iran). Pkt $2.00

Golden Crispy

Bateekh Samara, A one thousand year -old Iraqi treasure that is nearly extinct.

SWAN LAKE   #OML124

A small and beautiful honeydew type. This variety has superb, sweet melting flesh that ranges in color from white to pale salmon. Attractive fruit are perfect for marketing, or for the home gardener who wants a great 2-3 lb melon. Pretty, smooth yellow skin. Pkt $2.50

TENDRAL VERDE TARDIF #ML117

One of our favorite varieties in our 2012 trials. Oblong melons with a dark green rind and sweet white flesh, that is of excellent quality. A popular winter melon variety in Europe, but rare here. Very late. Pkt $2.00

THAI GOLDEN ROUND #OML121

The plants are extremely productive and did well here in our climate. The big 6-lb fruit look like glowing orange pumpkins. One of the most unusual and attractive melons we've ever grown. The green flesh is sweet and melting and has a very unique tropical taste, somewhat un-melon like in flavor. This variety adds a whole new category of melons to the US and is sure to be a favorite of gardeners who love diversity. Pkt (10 seeds) $2.00

TIGGER #OML107

90 days. The most amazing looking melon we have grown. The fruit are vibrant yellow with brilliant fire-red, zigzag stripes (a few fruit may be solid yellow), simply beautiful! They are also the most fragrant melons we have tried, with a rich, sweet, intoxicating aroma that will fill a room. The white flesh gets sweeter in dry climates, mild tasting. Small in size, the fruits weigh up to 1 lb. The vigorous plants yield heavily, even in dry conditions. This heirloom came from an Armenian market located in a mountain valley. Pkt (15 seeds) $3.00, *or 1 oz $10.00*

TIP TOP #AML112

90 days. Introduced by A.W. Livingston Seed Co. in 1892. This variety was discovered in a field of market melons by a gentleman, named Frank Miller of Lancaster County, Pennsylvania and he sent it to Livingstons. Salmon-orange flesh is sweet and spicy. Pkt $3.00

UZBEK SWEETNESS #OML132

An early melon coming from Uzbekistan. The golden skin is nearly smooth, with only a hint of netting; no discernible ribbing; pure white, sugary-sweet flesh. Size runs from about 4 lb to an occasional 10 lb fruit. Pkt (10 Seeds) $2.50

VALENCIA WINTER MELON #ML115

An old-time melon listed by American seedsmen in the 1830's but probably goes back much further; believed to come from Italy. Can keep four months into the winter. Very sweet cream-colored flesh, dark green skin; rare and delicious. Pkt $2.50

VERT GRIMPANT (GREEN CLIMBING) #ML116

A very old, green-fleshed French melon; can easily be grown on a trellis because the fruits are small, 1-2 lbs. Fruit is slightly oblong, and the flesh is crisp and juicy. Makes a great cooking melon; keeps well. A very rare heirloom; French grown seed. Pkt $2.50

YELLOW CANARY #ML105

100 days. An elongated-shaped melon with a deep yellow rind. Flesh is light green & very sweet and tasty. A favorite! Good yields. Pkt $2.00

ZATTA #ML125

80-85 days. Traditional variety of Italy, where it is called "Brutto ma Buono." The name translates to "ugly but good," but it looks beautiful to us: 4-lbs. ribbed fruits in green to yellow. The flavor of the orange flesh is very sweet and rich. This melon was first described by Castelvetro in 1614; believed to have been grown by Thomas Jefferson as "Massa". Pkt (10 seeds) $3.00

Prescott Fond Blanc

Boule d'Or

Green Machine

Delice de la Table

Crane

162

Golden Sweet

Rugoso di Cosenza

Uzbek Sweetness

Hale's Best

Sakata's Sweet

Tam Dew Honeydew

Emerald Gem

Jelly Melon

KIWANO or AFRICAN HORNED CUCUMBER #JM101
(*Cucumis metuliferus*) Very unusual fruit with spiny "horns." The green-yellow skin turns a bright deep orange when ready to harvest, and the pulp inside the fruit resembles lime green Jell-O. The fruit has a sweet-sour, banana-lime-tropical fruit taste; good juiced and sweetened, delicious with yogurt. This fruit is showing up quite often in US markets. Native to Africa, it is hardy and easy to grow; can be grown just about anywhere you can grow melons. Beautiful vine and fruit! Tiny seed. Pkt (10 seeds) $3.00

Jelly Melon

Cassabanana

CASSABANANA or MELOCOTON #MC101
(*Sicana odorifera*) Wow, this is exciting! I saw this crop along the roadside in Guatemala. The fruit were brilliant flaming red, and about 2' long—one of the most beautiful things I had ever seen! They have bright orange flesh that is sweet and is used in drinks, jellies and other desserts; it has a unique tropical fruit taste. The fruit are fragrant and keep for a long period, like squash, making this a hot item for fall sales for pumpkin growers. Huge vines can grow to 50' and are quite ornamental, but they do require a very long season and are mostly grown in Florida and the Deep South. Here in southern Missouri the fruit almost ripened, but we ran short of days. This plant was first mentioned in Europe in 1658 as a popular plant in Peru. We are happy to have located a small supply of seed. Pkt (10 seeds) $4.00

Cassabanana

Bitter Melon
20 seeds per pkt.

GREEN SKIN #BM108
(*Momordica charantia*) 90 days .This Indian variety produces nice-sized, 8-inch green-skinned, curiously bumpy fruit. The plants yield well and are attractive in the landscape, having deeply cut leaves, bright yellow flowers and developing fruits—very effective on trellises and arbors! Bitter melon is a traditional staple in much of Asia; local cuisines appreciate the mildly bitter taste in soups and curries. As a bonus, the pulp surrounding the seeds turns brilliant scarlet at full maturity, and its sweet taste is also utilized in its native lands. Bitter melon is recognized for its value in blood-sugar regulation among diabetics. Pkt $1.50

Green Skin Bitter Melon

Snake Melons

LONG EX SNAKE #SM102
This medium-sized snake melon produces beautiful 12-20" fruit that are green with white stripes and snake-like. At maturity they turn bright red inside and out. Lovely vining plants grow well in warm summers, and produce well. Pick young fruit, slice, and add to flavorful curries, soups and stir-fries. A fun and easy-to-grow melon. Pkt (10 seeds) $3.00

Long Ex Snake Melon

Wax Melons
25 seeds per packet.

CANTON GIANT #WX104
The famous giant variety that is very popular in South China. Large, long fruit can grow to 40 lbs! They have mild, tasty, white flesh and a deep green rind. A real ethnic treasure that is hard to find. Pkt $3.00

Okra

(Abelmoschus esculentus) 30-75 seeds per packet. This African native and staple of the Deep South really thrives on heat! Slaves from Angola called okra "ngumbo" which became gumbo, a popular name for several okra dishes to this day. Does best when direct-sown into warm soil, but can be started earlier indoors and transplanted, so long as the young plants aren't allowed to become root bound. Soil for okra need not be especially rich; plants are drought tolerant but produce more with adequate moisture. Keeping pods picked encourages further production.

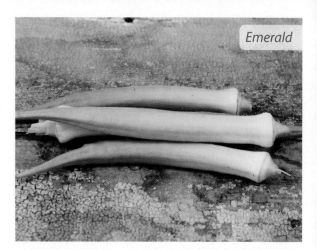

Emerald

ALABAMA RED #OK132
A delicious heirloom from Alabama, this variety has fat, red pods that are great fried or in gumbo! One of our most popular varieties, it is unique and rare. Pkt $2.50

BECK'S BIG BUCK HORN #OK139 *New!*
Fast-growing plants reach the modest size of about 5 feet in height, yielding tons of plump, tender ribbed pods all season long! This okra is a German heirloom, originating in this country via Malcolm and Delphine Beck of Comal County near San Antonio, Texas. When the Becks bought their farm in 1968, they noticed mature plants of this okra growing in the prior owner's garden, and the Becks planted some of the seed the following season. It turned out that the variety was originally smuggled out of Germany by one of the neighbors. Has sometimes been dubbed "snapping okra" because of the ease with which the remarkably tender pods can be snapped off the stalks for harvest. Pkt $2.75

Burgundy

BOWLING RED #OK120
Lovely plants that grow 7'-8' tall and have deep red stems. The great-tasting pods are long and thin, being quite tender even when longer than most. This heirloom has been grown by the Bowling family of Virginia since at least the 1920's. Pkt $2.25

BURGUNDY #OK102
55 days. Pods are a beautiful, deep red, and stems are also red. Very tender and delicious. Ornamental; tasty. Pkt $2.50 *or 1 oz $6.00*

GRANDMA EDNA'S CHEROKEE LONG POD #OK138 65 days.
This okra has been in Melba Beasley's family for seven generations. It can be traced back to her grandmother, Edna, a Cherokee gardener who passed seed along to her descendants. Melba writes: "Grandma really wanted us to remember our heritage in numerous things she passed on to us. This seed was really important to her." This variety makes very large plants, spreading several feet wide and eight feet high, and Melba recommends a step ladder to pick them! Pkt $2.75

CLEMSON SPINELESS #OK103
60 days. Plant is spineless; tasty green pods, best picked small. Developed in 1939. Still a standard in many home gardens. Pkt $1.75 *or 1 oz $4.00*

Louisiana 16" Long Pod

EAGLE PASS #OK133
From the area around Carrizo Springs and Eagle Pass, Texas. Productive plants are a favorite of the local farmer who grows this variety. A great okra that is less slimy than others; big pods are tender and delicious. Pkt $2.00

EDNA SLATON'S CANDELABRA #OK135
Graceful, branching plants, reaching shoulder height, give great yields of 12-inch cowhorn-type pods, which remain tender even after reaching a large size! The prickly pods are a pretty, pale green. Performed well in the hot and dry conditions of summer 2011, when others failed. Originated in Georgia. Pkt (20 seeds) $2.75

EMERALD #OK105
58 days. A Campbell Soup Co. variety from 1950; early, round and smooth, deep-green tasty pods; high quality and early, tall plants. Pkt $2.50

GOLD COAST #OK136
Spineless pods are light green and often reach 6" in length while remaining tender. Compact plants to about 5 feet tall are very well branched, producing plenty of sweet, tender pods. A bit later than some types; very drought tolerant. Throw in resistance to root-knot nematode and you've got a great variety for the Deep South. Recommended! Pkt $2.50

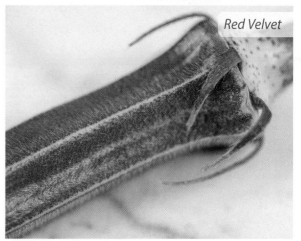

Red Velvet

HILL COUNTRY HEIRLOOM RED #OK112
Fat pods are very tender and full of good "Okree" flavor that is so popular in the hill regions of eastern Texas. The pods are reddish green in color, and the plants have red stems, very productive and high quality. Pkt $3.00

JIMMY T OKRA #OK107
The plants are of medium height, having two types of pods: one smooth and the other ribbed. Pods are 8-12" long; very productive. It was grown by Jimmy T. Morris in the 1940's and 1950's in the Elizabethtown and Hodgenville, KY, area. Pkt $2.00

Jing Orange

Pink Okra

www.rareseeds.com

JING ORANGE #OK126

60 days Lovely pods are a deep reddish orange and are quite colorful. This Asian variety produces lots of flavorful 6"-8" pods early, even in dry conditions. An exciting new variety that is unique and beautiful. One of the most tender we grow. Pkt (10 seeds) $2.75

LOUISIANA 16-INCH LONG POD #OK127

Large, branching plants produce huge yields of truly giant pods, up to 16 inches long! This heirloom comes from Evangeline Parish, where it has been grown for a very long time. Sent to us by Cajun and Creole seed collector Kurt Bridges, who says the plants often get "big like a fir tree" in Louisiana. Pods stay tender for longer than most, but should still be picked young. We loved this variety! Pkt (15 seeds) $2.50

MILSAP WHITE #OK122

Seed for this variety was sent to us by Will Sawyer, who received the seed from a lady in Copperhill, Tennessee, who had been growing this long-time favorite of her late mother. Pale green pods are quite tasty, and smallish plants are very productive. A great Tennessee heirloom. Pkt $2.00

PERKINS LONG POD #OK108

Very green, extra-large pods are tender and delicious, the perfect okra for canning and gumbo. Vigorous and productive plants are 5' in height; an old favorite. Pkt $2.00

PINK OKRA #OK141 *New!*

(Abelmoschus moschatus) Here is something different and charming! Petite little plants with deeply lobed dark green leaves are smothered in vibrant pink, five-petaled flowers, each with a snow-white center! Attracts hordes of bees and butterflies. Plants reach to 3 feet, sometimes more in favored locations. This plant is variously described as an okra or a hibiscus (they are closely related anyway), but it does produce a small edible pod. Flowering may be prolonged by frequently removing spent blooms. Self-sows generously, may be perennial in mild climates. Pkt (15 seeds) $2.75

RED VELVET #OK137

70 days. Stems and pods are a deep, rich burgundy to scarlet. Pretty enough for the flower beds, and a stunning choice for edible landscaping. Plants top out at about 4 to 5 feet. The pods are slightly ribbed or fluted; tender and delicious harvested at 3-5 inches in length. Pkt $2.75

ROBERIE #OK131

This okra has been grown for 100 years by the Roberie family in St Landry Parish, Louisiana. A good producer of medium-sized green pods that are produced over a long season. Pkt (25 seeds) $2.50

SILVER QUEEN #OK140

65 days. Pale green to nearly white cowhorn pods are unusual and striking—the color is almost like the heart of an Iceberg lettuce! Lightly ribbed pods reach 7 inches in length and are great in gumbos and curries; harvest slightly smaller for deep-fried okra. Plants are moderate in size (for an okra) and typically measure 6-7 feet. Pkt $3.00

STAR OF DAVID #OK106

70 days. Israeli variety. Short, very thick pods are quite delicious. The pods are twice as fat around as most okra. Pkt $2.50

STELLEY   #OK134

Louisiana variety originally collected in St. Landry Parish, Louisiana, at the heart of Cajun heritage and culture, where it was found growing near an old, abandoned homestead nearly 50 years ago. The plants are fairly compact, reaching 5-6 feet in height, and are super productive! The pods stay tender to 6"-7" in length. Original seed was furnished by our friend, collector Kurt Bridges. Pkt (20 seeds) $2.50

STEWART'S ZEEBEST #OK123

This spineless okra produces tasty, extra tender, green pods that are round and not ribbed. Tall, branching plants set heavy yields of this great heirloom. Pkt $2.75

Clemson Spineless

Eagle Pass

Bowling Red

Onion

(Allium cepa) 300+ seeds per packet. A very ancient Old World crop—records exist telling how many onions were allocated to the laborers building the pyramids, and they were a basic ration to Greek hoplites. Long-day onions tend to do best in the North and short-day types do best in the South; the dividing line is at about the 35th parallel. Onions grow best in mellow soil, rich and possessing much organic matter. The tiny seeds are usually started indoors, although they may be direct sown if conditions and timing are suitable. Spring-planted onions are started about 9-12 weeks prior to setting out, which may be several weeks before the last frost date. When setting onion plants in their final location, allow about 6-8 inches from their neighbors, if in beds; or 4 inches if in rows, spacing rows at least a foot apart. Apply a heavy mulch to control weeds, as onions will not grow large in competition with weeds. Harvest onions when the green tops begin to fall over; cure several weeks and store at cool room temperature.

AILSA CRAIG #ON122
Long day. Very well-known globe-shaped heirloom onion that reaches really huge size—5 lbs is rather common! The skin is a pale yellow and the flesh is relatively mild and sweet, so is recommended for fresh use—not a storage type. Introduced in 1887 by David Murray, gardener for the Marquis of Ailsa, at Culzean Castle in Maybole, South Ayrshire, Scotland. Pkt $2.50

AUGUSTA #ON132 *New!*
(Long-day type) Oblong yellow-skinned variety for fresh eating. The flesh is creamy-white. Roots come in fairly small, averaging about 4 ounces. Not a storage type. Pkt $2.50

AUSTRALIAN BROWN #ON101
Intermediate day. Introduced in 1897 by W. Atlee Burpee. This variety produces extra fine large bulbs that have superb flavor! The yellow-brown roots are a standard on our farm for their sureness to produce quality. Pkt $2.50

BRONZE D'AMPOSTA #ON115
Intermediate day. Attractive reddish-bronze onions are good-sized and sweet. A great variety for fresh eating, as it is not too hot tasting. A decent keeper in storage and a good overall red type. Named for the small city of Amposta, Spain. Pkt $2.00

BRUNSWICK #ON120
Long-day type. First offered in 1870, Brunswick is a deep red-to-purple flattened type. Usually very mild and sweet, it nevertheless stores very well. Pkt $2.25

CRIMSON FOREST-BUNCHING #ON110
(Allium fistulosum) Beautiful, brilliant red stalks, flavorful and tasty. Very unique and colorful, a bulbing type. Pkt (250 seeds) $2.00 *or 1 oz $9.00*

FLAT OF ITALY #ON104
Intermediate day. Beautiful red "cipollini"-type, flat gourmet onions from Italy. They are bright red in color and very flat, perfect for fresh eating or cooking. This is a very old Italian variety that

Noordhollandse Bloedrode

Martina

Ishikura

Onion Soup

By William Woys Weaver

The classic French onion for soup is the one the French call Jaune paille des vertus otherwise known as Brown Spanish and introduced in 1793. Other good soup onions in the Baker Creek catalog are Alisa Craig (developed in Scotland and introduced in 1887), Australian Brown (1897) and Yellow Flat Dutch (1888). Of course, you can make onion soup from just about any onion you want, but if you're after that rich buttery flavor with huge depth and character, go for the heirlooms. When raised organically, they take up all sorts of vital minerals from the soil, and that is part of the secret of their good flavor. I am now going to share with you my favorite onion soup recipe, which only takes about 30 minutes to prepare. Company coming on short notice? Here is your starter course to launch the dinner! It's even better when reheated the next day.

Soupe à l'oignon
Yield: Serves 4 to 6
1 and a half pounds of onions, preferably Brown Spanish
3 tablespoons butter
1 tablespoon olive oil
1 tablespoon brown sugar
1 and a half quarts well-flavored beef stock or bouillon
salt and pepper to taste

Cut the onions in half lengthwise, then slice paper-thin to make half-rings. Heat the butter and oil in a deep stewing pan and when the butter begins to foam, add the onions. Stir to coat the onions with the oil mixture, then add the sugar, stirring it as well. Cover and sweat the onions over a medium-low heat for about 10 minutes, or until soft and beginning to turn color. Add the stock and season with salt and pepper. Cover and simmer gently for about 20 to 30 minutes then serve. For variation, you can brown some slices of crusty bread in butter and then float them on top of the soup liberally sprinkled with grated cheese.

was mentioned by Vilmorin in 1885. A good choice for fresh market. Early. Pkt $2.50

HE SHI KO-BUNCHING #ON111
(Allium fistulosum) An heirloom Japanese, perennial bunching onion. Stalks grow and divide from the base. Mild and tasty. These are an essential ingredient in both Oriental and American foods. A non-bulbing white type. Pkt $2.00 *or 1 oz $6.50*

ISHIKURA #ON125
(Allium fistulosum) Popular and traditional Japanese variety for sukiyaki, soup and salads. Reaches enormous proportions (to 2½ feet tall, one inch across) while remaining tender and scallion-like. Never forms a bulb. Earth-up as for leeks to produce long white shanks. Very nice variety that we are excited to offer! Pkt $2.50

MARTINA #ON131 *New!*
(Short day) Early "yellow" type having ivory flesh and brown skin. Roots are round to slightly flattened. Recommended for spring planting in the south; worth a try for a late summer-fall crop at northern latitudes. A popular European variety. These do well here in Missouri as spring crop. Pkt $2.50

NOORDHOLLANDSE BLOEDRODE
#ON119 (Dutch Red) Long day. The name translates as North Holland Blood Red, and these beauties are indeed a lovely, shiny ox-blood red. Large, slightly flattened onions are very pungent, which makes them good keepers in spite of their rather thick neck. They can also be grown for scallions, as they often are in Holland. A good variety for Northern gardeners. Pkt $2.50

RED CREOLE #ON112
Short day. This onion is great for the South and is a good keeper. Hard, flat bulbs have spicy, red flesh. A good cooking onion or in salads. Pkt $2.50

RED OF FLORENCE #ON103
Long day. Oblong-shaped, bright red onions, great for planting spring or fall, seem to do well in many areas. They are very mild and sweet, great for salads and pickling! A delicious Italian heirloom. Very rare. Pkt $2.50 *or 1 oz $7.50*

SOUTHPORT RED GLOBE #ON124
Long day, 120 days. First released in 1873, and still one of the best. Firm fleshed, medium sized, globe-shaped, deep red roots are one of the best keepers of any red onion. Carries some resistance to fusarium rot. Truly a top-notch producer for the North! Pkt $2.50

SOUTHPORT WHITE GLOBE #ON126
AKA "Silver Ball" and "White Rocca." A long day onion for the Northern States. This onion has a handsome globe-shaped bulb. It grows to a large size with pure white skin and flesh of mild flavor. Seedsman Thomas Griswold once wrote that this was the "best white onion for market," and Southport is still one of the best white keepers available today. This Connecticut heirloom was named after the town of Southport and grown along Connecticut's Mill River. Onions were exported by the millions from this agricultural epicenter also known as the "Onion Capital." The Civil War increased the demand all the more because pickled onions were used to keep scurvy at bay. May be used to produce scallions, requiring only about 65 days. Pkt $2.25

STUTTGARTER #ON116
Long day. A tasty old favorite that sets medium-large, yellow onions with a good, pungent flavor. This variety is among the best keepers and produces well. Plant some of these for winter eating and store them clear through to next spring. Pkt $2.50

TOKYO LONG WHITE-BUNCHING #ON109
(Allium fistulosum) An old-favorite Japanese bunching-type, looks like a long slender leek. Sweet and mild flavor, tasty. Pkt (400 seeds) $1.75

TROPEANA LUNGA #ON108
Intermediate day. Long, tall bulbs are unique and popular with Mediterranean chefs. Harvest this gorgeous onion in mid-summer for your own delight, or sell this winner for top prices at market. They are a lovely shade of red. This heirloom from Tropea is rare in America. Pkt $2.50 *or 1 oz $8.00*

WETHERSFIELD RED #ON127
Long day. This variety dates to the 1700's. Popular from New York to Bermuda and it brought much wealth to the onion growers of the New England, as well as to the Yankee traders who sold ship-loads of it. The 1856 Comstock-Ferre catalog states, "It is the kind mostly grown at Wethersfield. It grows to large size, deep red, thick, approaching to round shape, fine-grained, pleasant flavored, and very productive. It ripens in September, and keeps well." It is a slightly flattened, deep blood-red onion of renowned quality. A true piece of horticultural Americana that deserves to be more widely grown. Pkt $2.50

YELLOW FLAT DUTCH #ON121
Long day. An onion by this name was offered in 1888 by RH Allen Seed Company, who wrote: "A good variety; mild flavored; large, and keeps well." This is a long day type that is fine for kitchen use. We offer imported Dutch seed. Pkt $2.25

YELLOW OF PARMA #ON105
Long day. Large, golden onions are oblong globe-shaped. This late onion makes an excellent keeper; a rare and hard-to-find Italian variety. Pkt $2.50 *or 1 oz $7.00*

ZEBRUNE SHALLOT #ON129 *New!*
(Cuisse de Poulet du Poitou) Gorgeous heirloom French eschalion or "banana" type shallot yields plump, long, torpedo-shaped bulbs. Bulbs are brown tinged with pink. The flesh is very mild and sweet, and large yields may be had starting the first year from an early planting. Excellent keeping quality makes these gourmet shallots useful over a very long season! $3.00

"No other human occupation opens so wide a field for the profitable and agreeable combination of labor with cultivated thought, as agriculture."
—ABRAHAM LINCOLN

Parsnip

(Pastinaca sativa) Northern European relative of the carrot. Parsnip roots are long, white, and, after a hard frost or two, mild and sweet. Sow in early spring in most areas, as seed germinates best in cool weather, and is slow to germinate even under the best conditions. Traditionally, gardeners would plant the seed rather thickly, just barely covering, and sow some radish seeds in the row. The radishes sprout quickly, marking the row's location while the parsnips are germinating; the radishes mature quickly and are pulled, leaving the row to the parsnips, which require the whole season. Plant parsnips in rich and very deeply worked soil, and allow plenty of space—8-12 inches apart is ideal. May be stored right in the garden all winter, or until the soil freezes. Old-fashioned crop that really deserves to be included in today's gardens.

HALF LONG GUERNSEY   #PR103

The Guernsey variety was the most popular parsnip of the 19th century. Introduced prior to the 1850's, this variety is medium-long, and has thick shoulders and smooth white skin. Flavorful flesh gets even sweeter after a good frost in autumn. In 1898, Nebraska Seed Company of Omaha said, "As name indicates, not as long as the Hollow Crown. Quality very sweet and delicate". We are glad to bring you this great old treasure. Pkt (400 seeds) $2.50

HARRIS MODEL #PR102

Delicious, tender, white, 12" roots have a sweet flavor; refined in appearance. Great boiled, fried, or used in "Parsnip Bread." A good producer and popular variety. Pkt (600 seeds) $2.00

HOLLOW CROWN #PR101

Tasty, white, long roots, sweet flavor. Harvest after frost; a standard in all fall gardens. A popular variety in the 1820s. Pkt (600 seeds) $2.00

Hollow Crown

Whipped Parsnip and Fig
By Chef Quintin

In a pinch this recipe is a quick and easy way to feed your little ones. We wind up eating half before it even gets to the jar stage!

INGREDIENTS
- 4 parsnips (wax free)
- 1 pint of fresh figs
- 2 C of organic apple juice
- 1 t of lemon zest
- Pinch of salt
- 2 T of olive oil (extra virgin)

PREPARATION
1.   Peel parsnips and place on pan. Roast in oven at 350 until fork tender
2.   Take stem off Figs and place in blender or robo coupe
3.   Add the rest of ingredients.
4.   Add parsnips and blend until very smooth.
5.   Chill and enjoy!

Garden Peas

(Pisum sativum) Whether grown for green peas, or for edible pods, garden peas are all grown the same way. They should be planted in earliest spring or even in late winter, as soon as soil can be worked. They require a very mellow soil, as the roots are shallow and not especially vigorous. Plant about 1" deep. Most types require support—a trellis, fence, etc. (Bush types are really short vines, and will support each other when planted fairly close together.) The trick is to get them going early enough to take a crop before late spring weather turns really warm, as heat shuts the plants down. Pick edible podded types frequently, as they are best before the pods become tough. 75-125 seeds per pkt.

ALASKA #GP101

50-60 days. Very early, great for short-season areas; good yields of delicious soup peas. An heirloom from 1880. Pkt $2.25

BLUE PODDED BLAUWSCHOKKERS #GP107

A beautiful and ornamental pea that produces lovely purple-blue pods that can be harvested young and used as a snow-pea, or let mature and shell for fine soup peas. This unique type dates back hundreds of years in Europe, and is still popular in parts of Europe and Canada. It also produces lovely purple flowers! Fun to grow and good to eat, the perfect crop for kids and those who like color. Pkt $2.75

DESIREE DWARF BLAUWSCHOKKERS #GP108

Stunning violet-blue pods are produced on lovely little bush plants that do not require staking. The delicious peas are perfect for soups and stews, or the pods can be picked small and these can be used as a snow pea. A great addition from Holland. Pkt (75 seeds) $3.00

IMPROVED MAESTRO #GP109   60 days.

Heavy crops of 4-to 5-inch pods are produced on plants that seldom reach 3 feet in height, do not require staking. Peas are medium-sized, very sweet, and good for freezing, and the pods often contain up to 12 peas each. Tolerant to a number of common pea diseases. Pkt $2.50

KELVEDON WONDER #GP112 *New!*

75 days. (also known as First Early) Super-early dwarf variety reaches only about 18" tall, requiring no staking. Highly recommended for successional sowings; also a great variety for container planting or cold-frame growing. Produces heavy crops of sweet, small peas, often eight per pod; typically yields two fat pods per node. Resistant to pea wilt and downy mildew. Pkt $2.75

LAXTON'S PROGRESS No. 9 #GP105

An old-time pea introduced in 1908. High-yielding and tasty, this pea does better than many in warmer weather. The tightly-filled pods are easy to shell, and compact vines are a good choice for small gardens. Pkt $2.25

Tom Thumb

LINCOLN #GP104

An old-time pea introduced in 1908. High-yielding and tasty, this pea does better than many in warmer weather. The tightly-filled pods are easy to shell, and compact vines are a good choice for small gardens. Pkt $2.00

LITTLE MARVEL #GP102

60 days. Vigorous bush plants, heavy yields, and fine-flavored peas. A great home garden variety. An heirloom from 1908. Pkt $2.25 *or 1/2 lb $5.50*

TALL TELEPHONE #GP106

Long vines reach up to 6 feet with support, and large pods yield 8-10 peas each. The peas are large in size, being sweet and tender. This popular garden favorite was introduced in 1881 and is still a standard with many. Pkt $2.25 *or 1/2 lb $5.50*

TOM THUMB #GP110 *New!*

50-55 days. Tom Thumb is absolutely the best pea variety for container planting! Reaching only 8 to 9 inches in height, it's grown mainly as a shelling type, but the pods are also sweet, tender and delicious when harvested very young. This variety excels when tucked into small spaces around the garden, and for cold frame production very early or very late in the season. This unusual heirloom originated in England and was first introduced in the US by Landreth Seeds, Philadelphia, in 1854. Even more frost tolerant than most other pea varieties, and, naturally, it requires no staking! Pkt (75 seeds) $3.00

WANDO #GP103

This pea was introduced in 1943 and is a great pea for the South, being somewhat heat resistant and can be planted later than most peas. Medium-sized peas are great fresh or frozen. Pkt $2.25

Snow & Snap Peas

CAROUBY DE MAUSSANE #SN111

65 days. This time-honored variety produces some of the largest pods we've ever seen in snow peas—often reaching 5-6" in length! The robust plants vine to 5 feet. The bicolored flowers, borne in pairs, are pink and burgundy, maturing through purple to nearly sky blue, distinctive and pretty enough to merit a spot in the border. The succulent pods are of robust flavor and vary somewhat from plant to plant, which makes this variety all the more interesting in stir-fries and salads. Originated in Maussane, near Avignon in southern France. Pkt $2.75

CASCADIA #SN112

65 days. A snap pea with unusually thick-walled pods. Pods are at their peak at about 3" long, and have sweet, wrinkled little peas in them at that time. So crisp and juicy! The plants require no staking, since they reach only about 30" in height. A newer variety that has some disease resistance, a distinct improvement over Sugar Ann. Bred by Jim Baggett of OSU especially for the Northwest. Pkt $2.50

CORNE DE BELIER #SN109

A delicious French snow pea that pre-dates 1860! Wonderful, gourmet flavored, large, flat pods are perfect for steaming, sauteeing and nibbling on fresh from the patch. A historic variety that is finally available in America. Creamy-white

Golden Sweet

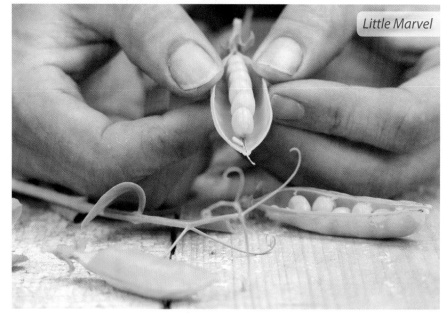

Little Marvel

Desireee

blooms. Pkt $2.50

DWARF GREY SUGAR #SN113

60 days. The pods are plump, fleshy and very tender when harvested young. In 1856, the Comstock, Ferre and Co catalog said: "About 3 feet high, and of very strong growth. Pods, long, and slightly curved. Containing mostly seven peas, which show in relief along the pods. They are usually cooked in the pods like snap beans. Of excellent quality, but rather late, and only a moderate bearer." This variety produces 2 to 3 inch pods as well as a bonus of delicious green foliage and lavender red flowers that are pretty and tasty in salads. Pkt $2.25

DE GRACE #SN110

A lovely dwarf variety that was grown in America before 1836, and likely much longer ago in Europe. This variety has been extinct to the North American seed trade for more than 20 years, so we are happy to bring back this great pea. The pods are medium sized and sweetly flavored, crisp and tender. The vines produce over a long season and are more frost hardy than many modern varieties. Pkt $2.75

GOLDEN SWEET #SN104

More than a novelty, this variety produces flat pods that are a beautiful, bright lemon-yellow, great in stir-fries. Tall 6' vines with purple flowers. Collected from a market in India; rare and tasty. Pkt $2.75

MAMMOTH MELTING SUGAR #SN102

70 days. Large, sweet-flavored pods; tall, 4' plants. Needs cool weather to give good yields. Pods are tasty stir-fried or in salads. Pick before the peas inside start to get large. An heirloom variety that has been popular for many years. Pkt $2.50

OREGON SUGAR POD II #SN105

Large, thick, 4.5" pods are superbly tender and delicious. This is my favorite snow pea-type. Bush plants are high yielding and stay compact. Developed by Dr. James Baggett, of Oregon State Univ. A winner. Pkt $2.50 *or 1/2 lb $5.50*

SUGAR ANN #SN107

An early, edible-pod pea ideal for small gardens. Its short, bushy vines do not need support, and it produces about 10 days earlier than other snap peas. Delicious pods are a joy sauteed, fresh or steamed. An AAS winner from 1984. Pkt $2.50 *or 1/2 lb $5.50*

SUGAR SNAP #SN106

This is the wonderfully sweet, edible-pod pea so popular with consumers and gardeners. The delicious, tender pods are great raw (eaten before you ever leave the garden), stir-fried, or in salads. They also freeze very well. An AAS winner from 1979. Pkt $2.50 *or 1/2 lb $5.00*

No occupation is so delightful to me as the culture of the earth, and no culture comparable to that of the garden.

-Thomas Jefferson

Kelvedon Wonder

Wando

Mammoth Melting Sugar

Hot Pepper

(Casicum annuum, C. baccatum, C. frutescens) Native to the Americas, peppers come in thousands of varieties, many unusual flavors, and all shapes and sizes. Heirloom peppers are often more flavorful than the modern-types, and most give huge yields. They are one of the easiest crops to grow, and are not much bothered by pests. All types of peppers are frost-tender, and are usually started indoors several weeks before the last frost date, although they may be direct-seeded in gardens in long-season climates. Set transplants out after warm weather has really settled. Peppers prefer rich and moist soil and full sun, although they will tolerate some shade, and some, especially C. frutescens, actually prefer a break from hot summer sun. Most types can be used green or ripe, and hot types tend to become more pungent when fully ripened in hotter conditions. 25 seeds per packet.

ANAHEIM #HPP103
80 days. Delicious mildly-hot flavor, excellent for roasting or frying; good yields of very large chili peppers. Pkt $2.50

BHUT JOLOKIA #HPP171
100-120 days from transplant. Also known as Ghost Pepper, Naga Morich. Legendary variety, one of the world's hottest peppers, if not the hottest, with readings in excess of 1,000,000 Scoville units! Bhut Jolokia starts out slow but eventually makes tall plants, exceeding 4 ft in favored locations. The thin-walled, wrinkled, pointed fruits reach 2-3" in length, ripening mostly to red. Pkt (10 seeds) $3.00

BLACK HUNGARIAN #HPP101
75 days. Unique, black-colored fruit that are the shape of a Jalapeno. They are mildly hot and have a delicious flavor. The tall plants have beautiful purple flowers that make this variety very ornamental. Rare and colorful! Pkt $2.50

CARIBBEAN RED HABANERO #HPP133
For those who like it hot! These can be twice as spicy as the common orange habanero, so use caution as you enjoy the incredible warmth and rich, smoky-citrus taste of these lantern-shaped 2" fruit. Very ornamental, as well as perfect for spicing up a pot of chili or making killer hot sauce. A heavy producer, so you will have plenty of extras for farmers market. Pkt $2.50

CAYENNE LONG THIN #HPP117
Slender, long peppers turn bright red and are very hot. The 2' plants are vigorous and quite productive. Very popular for drying and using as a spice; also used medicinally. This heirloom has been popular for many years. Pkt $2.25

CHIMAYO #HPP190 *New!*
80 days. Legendary, thin-walled drying type from northern New Mexico. Uniquely complex flavor have earned this a small but faithful following. So singular that it is offered as a unique type in local markets, and was well known throughout the Southwest in the late 1800s. Heat is typically very mild. Ripens green to red, and dries a distinct deep red color. Rare

Chocolate Habanero

Chimayo

Lemon Drop

Craig's Grande Jalapeno

Trinidad Scorpion "World Record Breaker"

and very special! Pkt Pkt (15 seeds) $3.00

CHINESE FIVE COLOR #HPP121
Screaming-hot little peppers turn a rainbow of vibrant colors, from purple, cream, yellow, orange to red as they ripen. Need I say ornamental? The plants are great for containers inside. Just pick a few any time to liven up your salsa. Pkt (15 seeds) $2.50

CHOCOLATE HABANERO #HPP136
So beautiful. The chocolate-brown, lantern shaped fruit are about 2" long, and so ornamental! But don't let the color fool you; these are not candy, but rather flaming-hot fruit that carry a massive 300,000 Scoville units of heat! Hot pepper enthusiasts love the heat and flavor that these chocolate fruit are packed with, but be careful and use in moderation. Pkt $2.50

CRAIG'S GRANDE JALAPENO #HPP150
A big, fat jalapeno that is perfect for making lots of salsa. Perfect for anyone who loves jalapenos. It has thick, flavorful, hot flesh. Developed at Redwood City Seeds. We love this one! Pkt $2.50

DATIL #HPP191
(Capsicum chinense) 100 days. Blazing hot, blunt little 3.5-inch fruits ripen to a brilliant orange-yellow. The heat is vicious, being comparable to habanero types, but the flavor is more complex, sweeter and more fruity. Renowned pepper originating from St. Augustine, Florida. Local legend says they were brought there from Spain, where they do enjoy a following in Minorca. However, they may also have originated in Chile. Pkt $2.75

ESTACENO CHILE #HPP194 *New!*
80 days. A genuine Northern New Mexico chili, a family heirloom of our grower, Jeff Martinez, whose family had it from at least the time of his great-great grandfather. Pods are thin walled and hot; size varies, up to 10". Use green in chili verde or salsa, or dry them to dark red for chili powder. Named for the Espanola Valley village of Estaca. Pkt $2.75

FISH PEPPER #HPP122
80 days. An African-American heirloom popular in the Philadelphia/Baltimore region. A pre-1947 variety that was used in fish and shellfish cookery. The color of the fruit range from green, orange, brown, white and red, being spicy and hot. What really makes this pepper stand out is its wonderful foliage, as the 2' tall plants have stunning white and green mottled leaves, which makes this variety superb for ornamental and edible landscaping. Pkt (25 seeds) $2.75

FILIUS BLUE #HPP143
A wonderful, ornamental pepper. These compact plants have a wonderful bluish tinge and produce lovely, small violet-blue fruit that are quite hot. Production is heavy, thus creating a stunning display of color that can't be missed! Perfect for ornamental landscaping or in pots. So pretty. Pkt $2.50

FRIARS HAT #HPP202 *New!*
100 days. (Capsicum baccatum) Widely known as Chapeu de Frade, which is Portuguese for the English name. Robust plants commonly reach 3-4 feet tall, and to 6 feet in ideal locations. Pendulous fruits are oddly shaped, somehow

Mustard Habanero

Purple Jalapeno

Rezha Macedonian

Green Curry Paste

By Chef Quintin

This recipe require some muscle. Use a mortar and pestle to make authentically. In Thailand curry paste is made from a wide variety of herbs, so the recipe below is just a general guide, feel free to add other ingredients, if you like!

INGREDIENTS

1 tablespoon sliced cilantro roots
1 tablespoon coriander
1/2 tablespoon cumin
1 1/2 tablespoons galangal
1/4 cup garlic
1 Kaffir Lime
3-4 tablespoons sliced lemongrass
1/2 teaspoon peppercorns
1 tablespoon salt
1/2 cup sliced shallots
1 teaspoon soy sauce
10-15 Green Thai Chili Peppers

PREPARATION

1. Toast coriander, peppercorns and cumin in a pan until light brown. You'll hear the crackling sound when they're ready. Let the spices cool so they will grind easily.
2. Slice shallots, lemongrass, galangal and cilantro roots into small pieces. I use one lemongrass stalk.
3. Slice thinly or grate the kaffir lime zest, about 1 tablespoon. They will grind into fine paste with smaller fibers.
5. Grind the spices into powder. Add lemongrass and galangal into the mortar. Grind them into rough fibers.
6. Add salt, garlic, kaffir lime zest,cilantro roots and soy sauce next. Add fresh green chili peppers and leaves next.
7. Pound until the mixture turn into a fine paste so that you can't recognize individual ingredients.

(Now, add some coconut milk and veggies with a tablespoon or so, of this curry paste and cook into a delightfully warming dish.)

reminiscent of a Renaissance hat or a cathedral bell. Mild to medium heat with a unique spicy taste that is quite delicious. Very ornamental and rare.   Pkt $3.00

GOAT HORN HOT #HPP139
This variety is great! Grows well in containers, and produces lots of extra-hot, long, horn-shaped fruit that are perfect for pickling or in any dish. Productive and easy to grow. A popular hot pepper in Asia. Pkt $2.00

GOLDEN CAYENNE #HPP183 *New!*
70 days. Typical long, slightly twisting cayenne type fruits, sometimes slightly hotter than red cayenne, and also a bit larger at 4-6 inches long. The fruits start out green, ripen to golden-yellow, developing their most intense heat only at full maturity. Compact plants to 2 feet tall. Pkt $2.50

HINKELHATZ #HPP198 *New!*
85 days--Small, hot peppers are shaped like a chicken's heart, which is just what the name means. This historic variety has been cultivated by the Pennsylvania Dutch since at least as early as the 1880s. Wedge-shaped fruits are 1- to 2 inches long, about 3/4 inch wide. They start out green, ripening in time to glossy deep red. The Mennonite community uses them in their signature pickles, or for pepper vinegar.   Pkt $2.75

HUNGARIAN HOT WAX #HPP125
70 days. A Hungarian heirloom that is excellent for short season areas, very popular for canning and pickling. Medium to very hot fruit are light yellow in color; sets fruit over a long season. Pkt $1.75

INDIA JWALA or INDIAN FINGER HOT #HPP140
The long, slender fruit are wrinkled, and about as long as a finger. This variety is extra-hot, and very popular in its native India, where it is used in much of India's flavorful food. The very productive plants produce fruit that start out light green and then turn red when fully mature. A good pepper that dries nicely. Pkt $2.50

LEMON YELLOW HABANERO #HPP134
A lovely lemon-colored member of the habanero family, this ornamental variety is quite colorful when the plants are loaded down with yellow fruit! A great eating variety that carries plenty of heat and flavor for most any dish. It makes a lovely lemon-colored hot sauce. This Caribbean favorite is very hot, so use a little caution as you enjoy with your friends. Pkt $2.25

LEMON DROP #HPP172
(*C. chinense*) 100 days. Seasoning pepper from Peru ripens to a clear lemon yellow, sometimes with a dark purple blush. The flavor is a very clean, uncomplicated, slightly citrus-y heat. 2-foot plants are covered with the thin-walled, conical fruits which reach 2-3 inches in length, with very few seeds. Pkt $2.50

LEUTSCHAUER PAPRIKA #HPP129
A lovely drying pepper that comes from Matrafured, Hungary. It has been grown there since the 1800's when it was brought from Leutschau (Slovakia). The medium-hot paprikas have great flavor, are terrific for drying, and

Bhut Jolokia

Fish Pepper

Thai Burapa

Chinese Five Color

make a delicious spicy powder. Very rare! Pkt $2.50

LONG PURPLE CAYENNE #HPP120
Very spicy pods are lovely bright purple in color, making them quite unique and colorful. The tall plants are just covered with dark fruit; great for hot sauce, chili and soup. Nice enough for the flower beds. Pkt $2.50

MAULE'S RED HOT #HPP189 *New!*
70 days. Also known as "Lady Finger." High-yielding plants are very productive, even in short-season climates. Glossy red, 10- to 12-inch Cayenne-type fruits, and of similar heat. A fine sort for picante sauce or drying. Originally introduced by William Maule Seed Company of Philadelphia, in 1912. Pkt $2.50

MUSTARD HABANERO #HPP170
95-100 days. Outrageously colorful habanero-type fruits start out a very light green blushed with purple, and ripen to a unique mustard color and finally to fiery orange, with plants bearing fruits of all colors simultaneously. Originated in the fields of our friend James Weaver, Kutztown, PA, where it appeared as an off-type of some more conventional variety. The result is a stable and very singular new variety. Super hot, like most habaneros. Pkt $3.00

OSTRA-CYKLON #HPP200 *New!*
80 days. Gorgeous, blood-red Polish paprika type—thin-walled for easy drying and just a tiny bit of heat. Compact, productive plants make good yields of 4 ½" long by 1 ½" wide fruits, which ripen to a deep red. Superb for making dark red Polish paprika, should make a good frying type as well. Pkt $2.75

PASILLA BAJIO #HPP105
78 days. Mild-sweet-hot, fruit is dark green, turning brown as it ripens. This pepper is used in Mexican "mole" sauces; tasty. Pkt $2.25

PEACH HABANERO #HPP179
90 days. Typical bullet-shaped slightly wrinkled habanero type fruits, but with a difference: this variety ripens to a clear bright salmon color. Amazingly beautiful and richly flavored. Hot, hot, HOT!! Pkt $2.75

PIMIENTO DE PADRON #HPP168
These small-fruited peppers originated in Galicia, northwest Spain, where the bite-sized green fruits are sauteed in olive oil and served with coarse-ground sea salt in tapas bars across the country. Most of the peppers are relatively mild, but an occasional unpredictable hot one led a New York times writer to call eating the dish a game of "Spanish Roulette!" Also fine for pickled peppers; the heat increases as they ripen to red. An authentic regional variety. Pkt (15 seeds) $2.75

POBLANO #HPP184
75 days. One of the most popular chilis in Mexico! 3- to 6-inch heart-shaped fruits are usually of gentle heat, at around 2000 scovilles. Used green, after roasting and peeling, it is the classic pepper for chili rellenos. Dried, the fruits turn a rich dark red-brown and may be ground into an authentic red chili powder. Plants reach 2 feet or so and require a long season. Pkt $2.25

POLOSTRA-ROKITA #HPP201 *New!*

70 days. Large thick-walled fruits are of medium heat. Ripens to deep red color. Medium heat, at 30,000 to 50,000 scovilles. Fruits are about the size of Anaheim. Very productive. Used in green or red stage. Pkt $2.50

PURPLE JALAPENO #HPP118

75 Days. A large Jalapeno pepper that turns deep purple before maturing to red. Great, mild Jalapeno flavor; great for salsa and other Mexican foods. Plants both productive and ornamental. Pkt $2.50 *or 1/4 oz $7.00*

REZHA MACEDONIAN #HPP197 *New!*

80 days. The name means "engraved;" another local name, Vezeni Piperki, means "embroidered". Both names refer to the curious lines on the skins of tapering, long, thin peppers. The fruits, which range from mild to sometimes very pungent, are to be seen hanging in great clusters, drying in Macedonian warm late autumn sun. The traditional farmers save seed from the hot fruits which also show the most pronounced striations. Our foundation Seed was donated by schoolchildren from the villages of Kalugeritsa and Zleovo. Pkt (10 seeds) $2.50

RING OF FIRE #HPP187

60 day. Newer variety that's an improvement over Cayenne. Similar type and similar heat (around 50,000 scovilles) but earlier and more productive. Very smooth, bright red 4-inch pods are excellent for drying. The name says it all! Pkt $2.50

ROOSTER SPUR #HPP188

95 days. Very hot and very attractive! 2-inch peppers ripen to fire-engine red, mostly held vertically above the foliage. Use fresh for seasoning or dry for chili powder, flakes, etc. Very hot and very flavorful. Pkt $2.50

SANTA FE GRANDE #HPP119

Spicy, 4" peppers, glowing gold in color and quite warm; makes pretty pickles and salsa. Ornamental plants give heavy yields over the entire summer, making this a perfect choice for home or market gardens. Introduced in 1965. Yummy! Pkt $2.00

SCOTCH BONNET YELLOW #HPP161

Attractive, golden-yellow, squat little peppers with a shocking heat and superb fruit-like flavor. They also have a wonderful, unique aroma. A standard in Caribbean cooking. Wonderful, but very spicy—please use caution. Pkt $2.50

SERRANO TAMPEQUINO #HPP102

75 days. Large plant bears club-shaped fruit; very hot and pungent, distinctive flavor. Pkt $2.50

TABASCO PEPPER #HPP106

(*C. frutescens*) 90 days. This famous heirloom was introduced into Louisiana in 1848 and became the main ingredient in Tabasco Pepper Sauce. This pepper is very hot and has a delicious flavor. The plants grow up to 4' tall and are covered with small, thin peppers. Needs a warm summer or can be grown as a potted plant. Fruit ripen from green to orange, then red. Pkt $2.50

Black Hungarian

Rezha Macedonian

Peach Habanero

Poblano

Golden Cayenne

Maule's Red Hot

TAM JALAPEÑO #HPP104
70 days. A very tasty, mild Jalapeno-type, with the same delicious flavor but a lot less heat. Great yields. Pkt $2.50 *or 1/4 oz $7.00*

THAI BURAPA #HPP127
Fiery little red, pointed peppers are popular in Thailand for flavoring many dishes. Loads of fruit are produced late on tall, bushy plants. The flesh is thin, making these great for drying for use in winter; an attractive variety that is perfect for Asian cooking. Pkt $2.50

THAI RED CHILLI #HPP107
90 days. The hot heirloom chili from Thailand, these peppers are used in almost every dish in old Siam. Small, pointed fruit are easy to dry, bright red in color. The Thais love the pungent heat. Ornamental plants are loaded with fruit. Pure Thai seed. Pkt $2.50

THAI YELLOW CHILLI #HPP109
The golden-yellow version of the Thai pepper. Fruit is also very hot and flavorful. Used less than the red chili, these are still seen in almost every market in Thailand. Beautiful. Seed collected in Thailand. Pkt $2.50

TRINIDAD SCORPION #HPP178 *New!*
90 days. New record holder for heat—the hottest chili on the planet! Wrinkled, lantern-shaped fruits ripen to a searing red-orange. Named as the world's hottest pepper by the New Mexico Chile Institute, edging out the previous record holder, Bhut Jolokia, although some authorities dispute this. Trinidad Scorpion averaged at 1.2 million Scovilles. Who needs pepper spray? Pkt (10 seeds) $3.00

TUNISIAN BAKLOUTI #HPP132
The traditional pepper of Tunisia, a small country on the famed Barbary Coast that was once considered the "bread basket" of the Roman Empire. Large red, tapering pods have a wonderful hot flavor, but tend to get more mild with cooking. Delicious flavor that is perfect with couscous, and other wonderful North African dishes that are making me hungry as I type! Pkt $3.00

WHITE HABANERO #HPP110 *New!*
Small bushy plants yield loads of these 1"-2" creamy-white, bullet-shaped fruit. This Caribbean variety is a favorite for its smoky, fruity taste and extreme heat. Ornamental and unique. Pkt $2.50

"A highwayman is as much a robber when he plunders in a gang as when single; and a nation that makes an unjust war is only a great gang"

—BENJAMIN FRANKLIN

Sweet Pepper

(Capsicum annuum) 25 seeds per packet. See hot pepper listing for more details.

ARROZ CON POLLO #PP169 *New!*
80 days. Originated in eastern Cuba. Another Caribbean "seasoning pepper!" Looks like a habanero but remove the seeds and there is no heat, just delicious flavor. Two or three will season a whole quart of dry beans when cooked. Plants have high yields, best harvested orange to red. For an authentic Cuban recipe, sautee with onion, garlic, annato, and add with fresh chopped cilantro to a pot of beans. Pkt $2.50

BULGARIAN RATUND #PP159 *New!*
75 days. Slightly wrinkled, sheep-nose type pepper, on plants reaching to about 2 feet in height. Very thick-walled emerald-green fruits ripen red, reach about 3.5 inches in diameter by 2.5 inches long, making them nice and blocky. Productive even in the Northern states. Foundation seed furnished by Bulgarian collector Hristo Hristov. Pkt (15 seeds) $2.50

BULLNOSE #PP124 *New!*
75 days. The original Bull Nose pepper was popular in early America and was grown by Thomas Jefferson. They are still grown at Monticello today. This is one of the first medium-large "bell"-type peppers, although this strain may be larger than the strain grown by Mr. Jefferson and are more likely dating back to the Bull Nose of mid-to-late 1800s. Delicious good-sized fruit are great in salads or for cooking. Pkt (10 seeds) $2.50

CALIFORNIA WONDER #PP106
70 days. An excellent green bell pepper; nice size and very good yield; a popular old-time variety. Pkt. $2.50 *or 1/4 oz $7.00*

CANARY BELL #PP191 *New!*
70 days. Superior sweet pepper, medium-sized, thick-walled green fruits ripening to bright yellow color. Sets early and produces all summer. Superb in salads, and a premier type for grilling. Exceptional flavor, very productive two-foot plants. Resistance to Tobacco Mosaic Virus. Pkt $2.75

CHOCOLATE BEAUTY #PP172 *New!*
70 days. Blocky, medium to large, green, 3-4 lobed fruits ripen to a rich chocolate-brown. The green fruits are good, but they are spectacular when fully ripe--crisp, juicy, and very sweet! Productive enough to make a good variety for market growers, and so early! Pkt $2.75

CHERVENA CHUSKA #PP186 *New!*
85 days. Also known as Chervena Chujski. Very wide shoulders on these wedge-shaped, thick-walled deep-red fruits. Bulgarian heirloom traditionally used for roasting, but fine for fresh use as well. Robust plants. Flesh of these six-inch long fruits is very, very sweet. Pkt $2.50

CORNO DI TORO GIALLO #PP112
The traditional favorite in Italy. Long, 8" tapered, bull-horn-shaped golden-yellow peppers are sweet and spicy. They are great fresh or roasted. Large plants yield well. Among the best peppers you can grow and so delicious. Pure Italian seed. Pkt $2.50 *or 1/4 oz $7.00*

Yellow Miniature Bell

Chocolate Miniature Bell

Red Mini Bell

Jimmy Nardello

White Lakes

Sweet Chocolate

CORNO DI TORO ROSSO #PP113

Same as the Corno Di Toro Giallo, but fruits are a deep glowing red. These are wonderful fresh, & for roasting and frying. Great for market growers & home gardeners alike. Pure Italian seed. Pkt $2.50 *or 1/4 oz $7.00*

CRIOLLA DE COCINA #PP168

I first received seed for this great pepper 15 years ago, so I am so excited to get it into the catalog! This small pepper was collected in 1988 in Nicaragua from a farmer. It produces small 4" peppers that are fragrant and richly flavored; these have strong pepper flavor making them perfect for a variety of dishes. Fruit is very wrinkled & unique looking. Pkt (10 seeds) $2.50

DOUX D'ESPAGNE OR SPANISH MAMMOTH

#PP138 This variety was introduced before 1860. In the 1880's, this pepper was shipped to the large markets in Paris from warmer areas like Algeria and Valencia. In the 19th century the 6-7" long fruit were among the largest offered, and popular with cooks. It produces long, cone-shaped peppers that are perfect for frying and salads. They are sweet and flavorful, but hardly ever offered in America. A good-producing pepper that is reported to be disease resistant. Pkt $2.25

EMERALD GIANT #PP109

78 days. Large, blocky bells have thick, sweet flesh. Dark green fruit turn red when ripe. Vigorous plants give heavy yields. A good variety for the South. Developed in 1963. Pkt $2.50 *or 1/4 oz $7.00*

ETIUDA #PP175 *New!*

75 days. One of the best peppers we ever tasted, it is sugary sweet when ripe. Blocky, thick-walled orange fruits are crisp, very sweet and juicy. These mandarin-orange bells can reach up to a half-pound in weight, and are lavishly produced on tall plants. Originally a Polish commercial variety, Etiuda is equally at home under row cover, in the greenhouse or out in the garden. Lovely and very choice! Pkt $3.00 *or 1/4 oz $12.00*

FRIARIELLO DI NAPOLI #PP163

This is the famous frying pepper of Naples, Italy. This heirloom produces small, long, cone-shaped peppers that are fried or pickled and are known for their sweet, distinctive flavor. The plants are very productive, so you will get plenty of delicious fruit all summer. Pkt $2.50

GEORGESCU CHOCOLATE #PP158

80 days. A fine pepper of Romanian origin. Green fruits mature dark salmon-pink to a rich chocolate-brown in a fairly short season. Compact plants produce an elongated bell-type fruit to 5 inches long, blunt on the blossom end and not quite a bull's horn shape. Very pretty! Seeds were originally supplied to us by Bulgarian collector Hristo Hristov. Pkt (10 seeds) $2.50

GOLDEN CAL WONDER #PP108

78 days. Colorful golden bells that are very sweet and tasty. Gold peppers are superb for fresh eating, great for kitchen or market gardens. The productive plants produce early & are good for the North. Pkt $2.50

GOLDEN MARCONI #PP127

80 days. A late Italian pepper with beautiful, big, yellow, 7" tapering fruit. Very sweet; great for frying or fresh. This wonderful heirloom is so delicious and mild; a great variety for market. Pkt $2.50 *or 1/4 oz $7.00*

Horizon Bell

Melrose

Oda

Paradicsom Alaku Sarga Szentes

Golden Cal Wonder

HORIZON BELL #PP187 *New!*

73 days--Plants produce excellent yields of brilliant orange-yellow bell peppers. Blocky, four-inch fruits are thick-walled, ripening from medium green to orange-yellow at maturity. Sweet and flavorful gourmet pepper for salads, stuffing and more! Pkt $2.75

ITALIAN PEPPERONCINI #PP111

A popular, thin, little pickling pepper, this heirloom comes from southern Italy. The 3"-5" fruit has a superb flavor and just a little heat. Small plants. Pkt $2.50

JIMMY NARDELLO ITALIAN #PP143
A customer favorite!

This fine Italian pepper was grown each year by Giuseppe and Angella Nardiello at their garden in the village of Ruoti, in Southern Italy. In 1887 they set sail with their one-year-old daughter Anna for a new life in the USA. When they reached these shores, they settled and gardened in Naugatuck, Connecticut, and grew this same pepper that was named for their fourth son Jimmy. This long, thin-skinned frying pepper dries easily and has such a rich flavor that this variety has been placed in "The Ark of Taste" by the Slow Food organization. Ripens to a deep red, is very prolific, and does well in most areas. Pkt $2.50 *or 1/4 oz $7.50*

KING OF THE NORTH #PP131

68 days. Early, good-sized peppers of a heavy yielding habit. The variety thrives in the cooler summer weather so prevalent in New England, and yields crisp bells, green ripening to red, right up until frost. Pkt $2.50

LILAC BELL #PP188 *New!*

75 days. Fruits are a stunning medium lilac-purple. Crisp, juicy, and sweet! What a lovely addition to a relish tray! Medium-sized fruits start out yellow-green, ripen to purple, finally to red. Pkt $2.75

LIPSTICK #PP151

70 days. A delicious pepper with 4" long tapered, pimiento type fruit that are super sweet. This fine pepper is early and ripens well in the North. A flavorful favorite with thick, red flesh. Pkt $2.50

MARTA POLKA #PP199 *New!*

75 days. Large, elongated bells ripen to golden yellow. Plants are very compact, but very productive nonetheless. Tolerates adverse growing conditions. Great choice for low-tunnel growing, early- and late-season, or container planting. Very popular Polish variety that should be a hit over here as well! Pkt $2.50

MIDNIGHT DREAMS BELL #PP189 *New!*

75 days. Blocky four-lobed bells are the most amazing ebony-black we have seed in a pepper, amazing looking! The glistening, gem-like fruits are unusually thick walled, crisp and mild. Produced abundantly on compact plants that are very sturdy. A new favorite! $3.00

MINIATURE CHOCOLATE BELL #PP181

New! 90 days. Small, perfectly-formed bells are the color of milk chocolate. Stocky plants are amazingly productive! Lucina Cress shared this family-held heirloom from Ohio, where she stuffed these cute little peppers with cabbage, pickled and canned them. Great for salads. Pkt $2.50

MINIATURE YELLOW BELL #PP180
New! 90 days. 2-inch long, miniature bells in cheery, sunny yellow are great in salads, for canning or stuffing. Compact, stocky plants are covered in sweet, slightly tapered, well-flavored fruits. Heirloom type from Ohio. Pkt $2.50

MELROSE #PP152
This is a superb heirloom frying pepper, brought from Italy years ago. The 4" fruit turn brilliant-red and start producing very early, with flavor that is rich, flavorful, and very sweet. Great fried or fresh, a true Italian that seems to have been widely grown in the Chicago area. We have had many requests for this pepper. Pkt $2.50

ODA #PP190 *New!*
70 days. Very strong, compact plants cranks out tapered, pointed bells from early summer on. The fruits are the loveliest shade of plum purple, ripening to a lustrous red-brown. Crisp, juicy, thick-walled fruits are very sweet. The short stature make it a great choice for cloche- or low-tunnel production. Pkt $2.75

ORANGE BELL #PP137
Super sweet, brilliant orange fruit are blocky and good-sized with thick flesh that is flavorful and among the best tasting of all peppers. Plants produce large yields of this most magnificent pepper. Pkt (20 seeds) $2.75

OZARK GIANT #PP154
What a pepper! This variety produces huge, long bell peppers that have delicious, thick flesh. They start out green and turn bright red. Very productive plants and great flavor will make this old Ozarks variety a favorite. Pkt $2.50

PARADICSOM ALAKU SARGA SZENTES PEPPER #PP160
80 days. One of the truly great Hungarian peppers. Yellow, flat, ribbed, pumpkin-shaped fruit have the tremendous flavor that peppers from Hungary are famous for. The flesh is very thick, crisp and juicy. This rare variety was collected at a farmers' market in Matrafured, Hungary, but developed at Szentes, Hungary. A winning variety. Pkt $2.00 *or 1/4 oz $7.00*

PEPERONE DI CUNEO #PP173
78 days. Tomato shaped sweet peppers in red and yellow. Very productive, thick-walled and fine-flavored. From seed collected by Jere on his 2012 Italian trip. This variety was first mentioned in the 1915 "Market Bulletin" from the town of Cuneo, Italy. This is the local pepper of Cuneo, where it is still grown on a small scale to this day. We loved snacking on these as they have a most amazing, sweet pepper flavor. Very productive in our Missouri gardens. Pkt $2.50

PURPLE BEAUTY #PP121
75 days. Purple peppers are always a favorite, as they are so colorful. This variety produces loads of beautiful bells on compact, bush plants. Crisp texture and mild sweet flavor make this one popular with everyone. I even believe Peter picked a peck of these purple peppers, and I don't blame him. Pkt $2.50

QUADRATO D'ASTI GIALLO #PP103
80 days. The giant yellow Quadrato bell pepper has huge fruit that are a favorite here.

Topepo Rosso

Criolla de Cocina

Doux d'Espagne

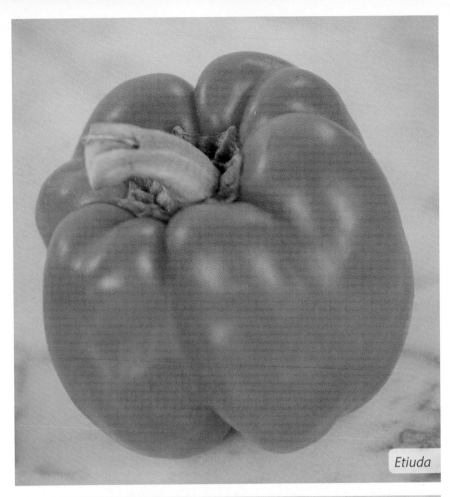

Etiuda

The largest variety we have grown, beautiful and blocky, with very thick walls. The flavor is outstanding—sweet and rich! One of the best varieties for marketing, this Italian gem gives very heavy yields. This superb pepper is a real winner! Pkt $2.50 *or 1/4 oz $7.00*

QUADRATO D'ASTI ROSSO #PP102

80 days. Very thick, brilliant red flesh that has a delicious rich-sweet taste. One of the largest red bells, it is excellent for frying, salads, or stuffing. Producing large yields, this beautiful variety is the perfect pepper for home and market growers. Very popular with many fine markets in Italy. Superb! Pkt $2.50 *or 1/4 oz $7.00*

RED CHEESE PEPPER #PP119

80 days. Candy-sweet, round, flat, 3" pimento-type peppers that have thick red flesh. Used to color and flavor cheese; great for stuffing or fresh eating. So good they're almost addicting. Productive plants. Pkt $2.50 *or 1/4 oz $7.00*

RED MARCONI #PP107

80 days. A late Italian pepper that yields big, 7" long, tapering fruit; very sweet, great for frying or fresh! Pkt $2.50

RED MINI BELL #PP120

60 days. Oh, so cute! Tiny, red bell peppers are only about 1-1/2" tall and wide; they have thick red flesh that is very sweet. 2'-tall plants produce loads of these little winners, and early, too. Great for stuffing. Pkt $2.75

SHEEPNOSE PIMENTO #PP171

70 days. Gorgeous cheese-type sweet pepper, ripening from green to red. The fruits are round, oblate, and stylishly ribbed—so pretty in the garden or on your table! Thick walled, crisp and juicy fruits keep an extraordinarily long time when refrigerated. An Ohio heirloom, so you know it's a great performer in northern climates. Pkt $2.75

SHISHITO #PP144

A favorite old Japanese variety which produces 3" long, slightly wrinkled fruit that are perfect for making tempura and other traditional recipes. Fruit is emerald green in color; mildly flavored with just a bit of spice. It really is superb. It is the standard with many chefs. Pkt $2.75

SIGARETTA DE BERGAMO #PP165

We offer here the esteemed "Cigarette Pepper" of Bergamo, Italy. The long, slender cigarette-shaped fruit are highly popular in salads, due to their taste. It is also perfect for pickling and frying. A delcious, hard-to-find variety. Pkt $2.50

SWEET CHOCOLATE #PP126

75 days. I love the flavor of this rich, chocolate-brown pepper. The flesh is cola-red color, very sweet and delicious. The medium-sized semi-bell-shaped fruit ripen very early, making this variety perfect for the North (or anyone who loves early peppers). Great in salads. Pkt $2.75

SWEET RED STUFFING #PP130

The brilliant red-colored version of our heirloom stuffing peppers which were given to us by an Amish grower. The seed was passed down from her grandmother. Very productive plants, producing tiny bell-shaped peppers about 1-2" across. Pkt $2.75

Midnight Dreams

Lilac Bell

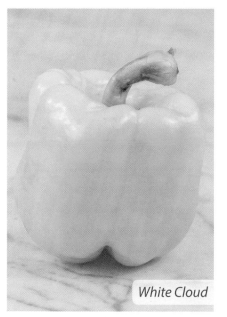

White Cloud

Canary Bell

Chocolate Beauty

SWEET YELLOW STUFFING #PP129

This amazing little pepper comes to us from an Amish grower. The seed was passed down to her from her grandmother, whom she fondly remembers growing these peppers in the 1950's in Lancaster, Pennsylvania. The very productive plants produce the cutest little mini bell-shaped peppers, only 1"-2" across! Used to make wonderful stuffed and pickled peppers! Pkt $2.75

SYRIAN THREE SIDED PEPPER #PP176

New! 80 days. Large fruits are about 6-8 inches long and as large around as a coffee cup. Fruits are three sided just like name says. Ripens to a deep oxblood red. Taste is super-sweet but ocassionally, there is heat in the skin. Very productive in our trials. Another gift from our Syrian friend, Raghad Gorani. This Syrian heirloom made a big hit in our kitchens last summer as they have excellent flavor. Pkt$2.50

TOPEPO ROSSO #PP101

This Italian heirloom produces tasty, blood-red, round, pimento-type peppers that are very sweet. The flesh is very thick and crisp. Short, compact plants produce huge yields; great fresh or cooked. A wonderful specialty variety that has many uses. Pkt $2.50

VIOLET SPARKLE #PP167 *New!*

75 days. Pointed, wedge-shaped fruits are purple streaked with pale yellow. We originally received a few seeds of this variety from a Russian seed trader. Ripens red. Very lovely and delicious, sweet, crisp and thick-walled. One of the finest and prettiest peppers we have tried! Pkt $3.00

WHITE CLOUD #PP122 *New!*

70 days. Ivory bell-shaped fruits start out pale ivory, ripening in due course to fiery red-orange. Sweet, mild flesh. Compact plants are great in containers! Pkt $2.75

WHITE LAKES #PP161

Very generous producer of dainty, somewhat pointed peppers. The young fruits take on an ivory or cream color very early, eventually ripening to a stunning red-orange. Originally a Russian variety deserving of much wider recognition. Delicious, productive, and beautiful. Pkt $2.50

YELLOW MONSTER #PP156 *New!*

90 days. Gigantic, behemoth elongated yellow bell peppers can grow 8 inches long by 4 inches wide! These impressive fruits are really sweet, meaty and wonderful, so pretty after they turn from green to bright sunshine-yellow. These are great fresh, fried or roasted, so you will be happy the plants produce plenty of these colossal beauties. Pkt (10 seeds) $2.75

"Permanent good can never be the outcome of untruth and violence."
—MAHATMA GANDHI

King of the North

Violet Sparkle

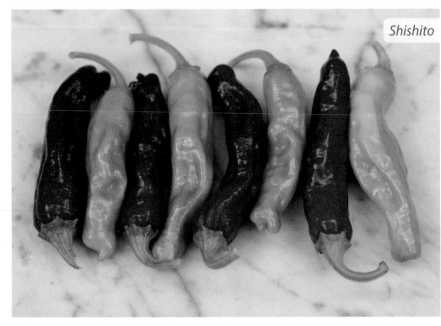

Shishito

Castelfranco

Rossa di Treviso

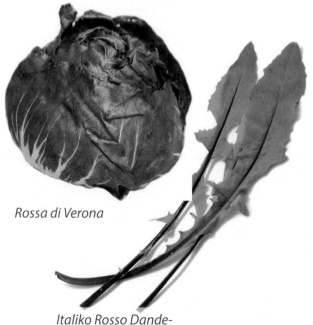

Rossa di Verona

Italiko Rosso Dande-

Radicchio & Chicory

(Chicorium intybus) These are used like lettuce to make beautiful and tasty salads, and some are good cooked. Most require cool weather and shorter days of autumn to head up and reach their most brilliant coloration, and so are mainly grown as fall crops. We offer quality Italian seed. 250 seeds per packet.

RED RADICCHIO

CASTELFRANCO #RC102

An improved selection of this beautiful, old Italian heirloom, the round heads are cream-colored and splashed with wine red. This colorful variety is becoming a rage in salads. A high-dollar crop for market growers. Very popular in Italy! Pkt $2.00

ROSSA DI TREVISO #RC101

A famous radicchio from Treviso, Italy. We offer an improved selection. Makes a long, slender bunch of leaves; turns deep brilliant red in cool weather. A must for all colorful and tasty salads! Pkt $1.50 *or 1 oz $6.00*

ROSSA DI VERONA #RC103

(Red Ball of Verona) Dark wine-red, round, medium-sized heads. We are happy to offer this great Italian selection. Pkt $1.50

VARIEGATA DI CHIOGGIA "RUBIS" #RC104

Beautiful, large, round-headed radicchio; brilliant red-and-white color. From the old Italian fishing town of Chioggia. A popular Italian variety. Pkt $1.50

SUGAR LOAF CHICORY

SUGAR LOAF #RC105

This green cos-type Italian specialty has a mild taste and beautiful, large heads. Fall planted; great for home or market. Pkt $1.50

ITALIAN DANDELIONS

CATALOGNA PUNTARELLE DANDELION #RC107

(Punatrelle a Foglia Stretta) Popular in Italy, hardy and excellent for early spring greens; great cooked like asparagus. This strain has very long, slender, Dandelion-like leaves. Pick small for Mesclun salads. Pkt $1.50 *or 1 oz $7.50*

ITALIKO ROSSO DANDELION #RC106

Beautiful, bright red stems and deep green leaves make this variety a winner! Baby leaves add great tangy flavor to salads, or good as a cooked green. We offer true Italian seeds for this heirloom. Pkt $1.50 *or 1 oz $7.50*

BELGIAN ENDIVE

WITLOOF DI BRUXELLES #RC108

We offer a select strain of "Witloof" or Belgian endive. This chicory is planted in the garden in spring, then dug and forced to grow in a cool, dark place, to make the delicious "Chicon heads" that command high prices at market. Very Tasty. Pkt $1.50

GRUMOLO CHICORY

GRUMOLO BIONDO "GOLDEN" #RC109

Small rosette head with rounded, thick, golden-green leaves. This is a popular baby salad item in Italy; best for cool-season growing. We offer quality Italian seed. An heirloom from the Piedmont region, very hardy. Pkt $1.50

GRUMOLO ROSSA DI VERONA "AIDA" #RC110

We are able this year to offer the exciting red-leaved Grumolo. Use these like mini-lettuce in specialty salads; perfect when mixed with the "Golden Grumolo." This variety needs cool weather to produce red leaves. Always in demand with fine chefs. Pkt $1.50

Radish

(Rhaphanus sativus) Cabbage relatives that come originally from Asia. Radishes are at their best in cooler weather, but will take more heat than most cabbage relatives. Salad-types are quick to mature, often in 28-35 days, and should be succession planted every 2-3 weeks from early spring well into fall, to keep a continual harvest. Winter or storage types take longer (60-75 days), and should be planted in mid to late summer for harvest in the fall. These are used and stored similar to the more familiar turnip. All types are grown in ordinary garden soil, worked deeply enough to accommodate whatever roots are expected. (Daikon types may grow a foot or more in length!) Adequate moisture, correct thinning and weed control are all that's required to grow this easy crop! 200-500 seeds per packet

BARTENDER #RD136
40 days. Hefty long tapering roots reach 9 inches long and 1 ¼ inches diameter. The snappy color is a bright, clear cherry red—very chic! The pink flesh is firm, crisp and pungent. A heavy yielder even under hot and humid conditions. Pkt $2.25

CANDELA DI FUOCO #RD134
(Candle of Fire) 35 days. Similar to Long Scarlet and several historic varieties that have appeared over the years, but this one is an imported Italian strain. Intensely ruby-red tapered roots with consistently firm and mild white flesh. Roots can reach 10 inches in length! This variety can be crowded quite closely in the bed or row, as the roots are so slim. Pkt $2.50

CHINA ROSE #RD104
One of the oldest types of radish. A very hardy fall/winter variety. Roots are about 5" long and a rose color. Pkt $2.50

CHINESE GREEN LUOBO (QINGLUOBO) #RD119
A popular radish from northern China, the tasty flesh is bright green. Very unique and colorful, they are shaped like Daikons. These only grow well in cool weather; great for fall planting. An old Chinese standard. Rare. Pkt $2.25

CHINESE RED MEAT #RD114
The colorful "Beauty Heart" radish of historic China has 4" round roots with white-and-green skin, but the magic is in their rose-red center, which is so sweet, crisp, and delicious. A good radish to add color to salads and stir-fries; must be grown in cool weather and does best when fall planted. Sometimes called "Watermelon Radish" at market. Pkt (100 seeds) $2.75

CHINESE WHITE WINTER #RD105
7"-8" long, white winter radish, with a blunt tip; crisp, solid flesh. Good raw or cooked. Tasty. Pkt $1.75

CRIMSON GIANT #RD137 *New!*
45 days. Very large spring radish, great in salads, relish trays and more. Roots are round, deep crimson outside, crisp and snow-white within.

Chinese Red Meat and Chinese Green Luobo

Rat's Tail

Runder Schwarzer Winter

Reaches to 4-5" in diameter without getting hollow, pithy or hot. This very choice variety has been around for at least a century. Pkt $1.75

DE 18 JOURS #RD138 *New!*
18 days. Old French variety gives unbelievably rapid yields! The name translates as "of eighteen days," and this radish will yield roots in 18 days, under ideal conditions! Round to cylindrical roots are red with white tips; flesh is crisp and juicy. A French breakfast type, often grown under glass for off-season production. Pkt $2.00

EARLY SCARLET GLOBE #RD111
22 days. The classic round red radish. Crisp white flesh is mild and tasty. Has better warm weather tolerance than many. Pkt $1.75 *or 1 oz $5.00*

FLAMBOYANT #RD139 *New!*
28 days. Plump, barrel-shaped roots, reaching to 4" long, are rosy-pink to scarlet outside with white tips. White flesh is crisp, juicy and mild. A favorite in Europe, and a popular market variety in southern France,but rarely seen in this country. Pkt $2.00

FORMOSA GIANT LUO BUO #RD127
90 days. An old favorite in Taiwan that used to be called Formosa. Big, fat oval-shaped roots weigh about 2-3 lbs. They are crisp and have an excellent, sweet taste. Very good in soup. Pkt $2.00

FRENCH BREAKFAST #RD108
A pre-1885 French heirloom; mild, spicy flavor with a red top and a white bottom. An attractive gourmet variety. Pkt $2.00 *or 1 oz $5.00*

GERMAN GIANT #RD116
Very large, round red radish that was collected in Germany. These keep their fine quality even when large. This heirloom is very popular with the Amish. Mild and tasty. Pkt $2.00 *or 1 oz $5.00*

GIANT OF SICILY #RD118
Large, 2", round, summer radishes are bright red in color, with great taste and good quality. We offer pure Italian seed for this heirloom from Sicily. Pkt $2.00 *or 1 oz $5.00*

HELIOS #RD125
So unique! This bright yellow, olive-shaped radish is truly one of the most beautiful radishes I've ever grown. This heirloom came from Alzbeta Kovacova-Pecarova of Kosice, Czechoslovakia. A favorite spring radish that really adds color. Pkt $2.75

JAPANESE MINOWASE DAIKON #RD112
Popular old Japanese favorite, the giant white roots grow to 24" long and 3" wide. Sweet and very crisp, this radish is a delight pickled, stir-fried, steamed, or raw. Pkt $2.00 *or 1 oz $5.00*

JUTRZENKA #RD140 *New!*
30 days. Nearly round roots are an unusual rose-pink color--lovely in salads, on relish trays and more. Makes nice mild, sweet roots. Pkt $2.25

LEDA #RD141 *New!*
28 days. Plump cylindrical to egg-shaped radishes, snow-white inside and out! Very choice European variety. Pkt $2.00

LONG BLACK SPANISH #RD102
(Noir Gros Long D'Hiver) Long, 9" black roots have pure white flesh that is crisp and

Violet de Gournay

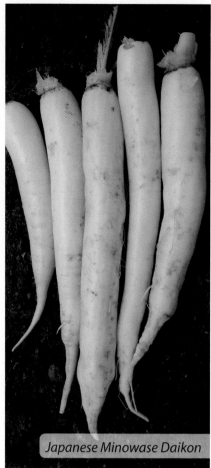
Japanese Minowase Daikon

Jutrzenka

Saxa II   Plum Purple   Pink Beauty

Leda

Zlata

pungent. This long version of Black Spanish is much harder to find than the round. Great for fall plantings. This is a very old European heirloom. Pkt $2.00

LONG SCARLET #RD107
A pre-1870's heirloom, long and slender, bright red radish. It is fast becoming rare. Flesh is tender, crisp and mild. Pkt $2.00

MALAGA #RD142 *New!*
35 days. Round roots are a very unusual color--deep plum purple/violet, so pretty in contrast with the snow-white flesh! Mild roots stay firm and crisp over a long season. We are very excited to offer choice Polish variety. Pkt $2.50

MISATO ROSE #RD133
This variety produces 3-4" roots and is recommended for fall sowing. Skin runs from light pink to green, but it is the flesh that is the real treat, being bright pink, sweet, spicy and flavorful. Unusually large, dark green leaves set this variety apart. Pkt (125 seeds) $2.50

MIYASHIGE DAIKON #RD132
A delicious, white Daikon type radish from Japan. These long white roots grow to 15" or more! Mild and very crisp; perfect fresh in salads, or for making wonderful pickles. These are planted in late summer and harvested in fall and early winter. Pkt (200 seeds) $2.50

MUNCHENER BIER #RD124
A famous German heirloom radish that is popular in much of northern Europe, 4" white roots have a pungent, crisp flesh that is sliced onto bread or served with pretzels. It also produces tender seed pods that are tasty pickled or added to salads. Pkt $1.75

NATIONAL 2 #RD131
Quarter-sized, round red roots have a nice white tip. A popular type at European markets. These are early, crisp and have a nice, mild flavor. Colorful and attractive looking. Pkt $2.00

OPOLANKA #RD143 *New!*
28 days. Oblong scarlet roots with white tips. Mild, crisp roots are very pretty in salads. Great for cropping early and late under glass or row cover, or grow outdoors all season. Choice Polish form of the old French Breakfast type. Pkt $2.00

PINK BEAUTY #RD109
29 days. A beautiful, round, pink radish that has become hard to find. It is sweet and tasty. Popular at specialty markets, a must for all radish growers! Wonderful and unique. Pkt $2.50 *or 1 oz $5.00*

PINK SUMMERCICLE #RD135
30 days. Lovely, carrot-shaped roots are in the most lovely shade of bubblegum pink! They are crisp and of good quality. Fun to grow. Pkt $2.75

PURPLE PLUM #RD122
28 days. Here is one lovely radish, with its bright purple skin that makes this one of the most colorful varieties for marketing. 1½" globes have sweet, crisp, white flesh which does not get pithy. Pkt $2.50 *or 1 oz $5.00*

RAT'S TAIL #RD126
This amazing edible-podded radish variety produces loads of tender, large seed pods that add a delicious flavor to salads and stir-fries.

They are also superb when pickled. An old Asian heirloom that was grown in US gardens in the 1860s, this real gourmet treat was a favorite last summer. Pkt $2.50

ROUND BLACK SPANISH #RD101
(Noir Gros Rond D'hiver) Large 5" winter type, probably grown since the 16th century or before. Deep, near-black skin and snowy-white flesh; will keep all winter in good conditions. Fine, fairly hot flavor; good raw or cooked. Pkt $2.00

RUNDER SCHWARZER WINTER #RD144
New!
65 days. Round, coarse-skinned winter radish is very dark, almost black with white flesh. A variety of similar name was listed in a 1904 Vilmorin publication as being distinct from Round Black Spanish. Pkt $2.50

SAXA 2 #RD130
Popular European radish that matures in just 18 days; wow, they are quick! The earliest radish we have grown. Bright red, smooth, round, perfect globes are crisp and delicious. Pretty and productive. Ready when tops are just 4" tall! Pkt $2.50

SCARLET TURNIP WHITE TIP (SPARKLER)
#RD113 Very handsome, round, bright scarlet color with a white tip. Sweet and juicy; an heirloom from the 1880's. Pkt $1.75

VIOLET DE GOURNAY #RD129
This French heirloom can grow 10" long and has deep violet-purple skin and pungent white flesh that is great for cooking, pickling or grated raw in salads. It is a fall/winter radish that is generally planted in summer or fall and harvested in early winter. Sometimes these can be spring sown in northern areas with great results. Introduced prior to 1885. Pkt $2.25

WHITE HAILSTONE #RD106
An early, old-time, white spring radish, this one is superb! Simply the best tasting radish we have tried, and many of our customers agree. Very mild and crisp. Pkt $1.75

WHITE ICICLE #RD123
Slender, 6", ice-white roots have crisp flesh and fine flavor, mild and fine quality. This pre-1865 heirloom is still popular with home and market growers alike. Easy to grow. Pkt $1.50

WARTA #RD145 *New!*
35 days. Polish variety that is getting a lot of attention. Carmine red, white-tipped, oblong roots stay mild, crisp and firm. Pkt $2.00

ZLATA #RD146 *New!*
30 days. The name means "gold" in Czech, and the silky, russeted yellow roots look like orbs of pale gold. This variety is fairly spicy--Europeans love it! Resists splitting and bolting; excellent bunching type, and the young leaves are especially nice for greens. Pkt $2.50

> "Wisdom is better than weapons of war..." —
> **ECCLESIASTES 9:18**

Early Scarlet Globe

Malaga

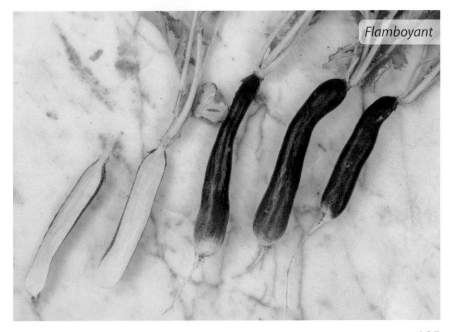
Flamboyant

Roselle (Hibiscus sabdariffa) 15 seeds per packet.

THAI RED ROSELLE #RS101

A super plant for making cranberry-flavored bright red beverages, jelly, pie, and tea. Much is grown in Asia, tropical America and the Mideast, as the flavor is wonderful. A tasty sauce can be made by boiling and sweetening the fleshy calyxes. The leaves are also used to make a drink. The plant is red and very beautiful. Start very early indoors, unless you live in the far South. Citrus-flavored flowers are delicious on frozen desserts. This plant has too many uses to name here. Pkt $3.00

Rhubarb

(Rheum rhabarbum) Central Asian native that has been grown in Europe for centuries, for medicinal and food use. At its best in cooler summers with cold winters, but can be grown in warmer climates with some afternoon shade. Seeds are started indoors or outside in a nursery bed, and transplanted to their final location. Mature rhubarb plants are quite large, so space them at lest 2 feet apart. Requires rich soil and ample moisture. Harvest the succulent stalks starting the second year. 25 seeds per packet

VICTORIAN #RH101

(Perennial) This variety was offered in 1856. Thick stalks are popular for making delicious pies, cobblers and preserves. This variety can be harvested starting as soon as the second season. Rhubarb is very popular in Canada and the northern U.S. Do not eat the leaves as they contain poisonous oxalic acid. Pkt $2.75

GLASKIN'S PERPETUAL #RH103 *New!*

This English heirloom has for generations enjoyed a well-deserved place in American gardens. The thick stalks are bitter-free, deep red at the base and shading to green toward the leaf. Started indoors very early, a light harvest is possible the first year with heavy yield each year thereafter. Hardy throughout the continental US, prefers areas with cooler summer weather. Pkt $2.75

Glaskin's Perpetual

Thai Red Roselle

Rosellade (Roselle "Lemonade")

Ingredients:

Approximately 1 bunch of finely chopped roselle leaves and stems

1 quart of water; boiling
2 quarts of water;room temp.
2 tsp. spearmint (optional)
1/4 c. honey (optional)

Pour the boiling water over the chopped roselle and spearmint (if you are using it) in a pitcher or bowl; steep 10-15 minutes, stirring occasionally if necessary.

Strain off the leaves and stems and stir in the honey (if you are using it); and then add the room temp water.

Pour over ice if desired and serve.

From Customer Clara Stone

Rutabagas

(Brassica napus) Cabbage relative grown for its roots, which are similar to turnips but larger, sweeter and milder. Requires a longer season, 90-120 days, but can tolerate cool temperatures as it matures, and is at its best harvested in late autumn. Sow about 90 days prior to expected fall frost, in rich, deeply worked soil of average fertility. Thin to about 8-12 inches apart, control weeds and keep moist. The leaves of some varieties make passable greens when harvested young. 400 seeds per packet.

AMERICAN PURPLE TOP #RT101

Very tasty, mild, and sweet; great cooked or raw. Bright yellow flesh; top quality. A pre-1920 heirloom, a great fall vegetable. Pkt $2.50

COLLET VERT #RT104

Finely flavored old standard that has a bright green top and yellow bottom, making these roots unique and colorful. Popular in France since the 19th century, it still holds a place with many gourmets and gardeners who love its rich taste. Pkt $2.50

JOAN #RT107

90-100 days. Roots are uniform with very smooth and pleasing shape. Flesh is dense,

American Purple Top

crisp, and mild, having a delicate and very sweet flavor, particularly after being kissed by light frost. A refined version of American Purple Top, that has some tolerance to Club Root, a disease that often afflicts brassicas. Pkt (125 seeds) $2.00

LAURENTIAN #RT102

An improved "Purple Top" rutabaga, its delicious yellow roots are great fried or baked; sweet, and so tasty. Very uniform and makes a good market type. Pkt $1.50 *or 1 oz $4.00*

NADMORSKA #RT105

90 days. A superior rutabaga, apparently first introduced from Lithuania by the Seed Ambassadors, and first offered by us a couple of seasons back. The golden-fleshed roots are large, having apple-green tops and the balance in cream. The shape is more upright or bottle-like. Here's a monument to the world-wide sharing of premium, open-pollinated vegetable varieties! Pkt (125 seeds) $2.50

SWEDE ØSTGOTA #RT108

75 days. Early maturing Scandinavian variety is ideal for fall harvest from a late-summer planting. Roots start out round, and are very good for bunching. But if allowed to grow, they eventually become large and slightly flattened. Green shoulders give way to white bottoms, very free of side roots and blemishes. The flesh is fine-grained, very white and sweet. Excellent storage qualities make Østgota excellent for market! Pkt (100 seeds) $2.50

WILHELMSBURGER #RT106

(German Green Top) 90 days. Historic old rutabaga variety that has been the preferred market type in Northern Europe for many years. Roots are large and white-skinned, with the top of the root being an unusual green. The crisp golden flesh is fine-textured, free of bitterness or coarse fiber. Ours is a selection of Wilhelmsburger Hartmann, from 1935, and was originally bred in Germany. Pkt (100 seeds) $2.50

Salsify

(Tragopogon porrifolius) A European favorite known in Roman times and cultivated since at least the Thirteenth Century. Sow ½" deep in very early spring, keeping moist until seedlings emerge. Needs at least 6" spacing, full sun, only ordinary garden soil, but this must be finely worked and free from rocks to produce straight roots. Lift and store mature roots in autumn. If left until the second spring, young shoots may be harvested and used like asparagus. Eventually forms attractive purple blooms on 3-ft stems.

SALSIFY MAMMOTH SANDWICH ISLAND
#SF101 Heirloom, native of Europe. Tasty in soups and stews, or cooked alone. Plant in spring, dig in fall; a non-sweet parsnip-like root. This variety dates back to the 1800s. Young plants look like grass. Pkt (125 seeds) $2.00

SCORZONERA DUPLEX RUSSIAN GIANT
#SF103 *New!* A popular European variety that has flavorful black roots that are extra long. Much like salsify, but Scorzonera has dark roots. This old-fashioned vegetable is great harvested in the fall after frost. A favorite variety with chefs. These have a delicious sweet taste. Pkt (125 seeds) $2.50

Sorghum

(Sorghum bicolor) Sorghum is one of Africa's greatest contributions to the world's agricultural diversity and is a traditional crop in the South. Adaptable and drought tolerant, sorghum varieties exist that provide grain, sweet syrup, animal fodder, or sometimes, more than one crop from a single planting! The main requirement for sorghum is heat—plant the seeds about ½" deep a couple of weeks after spring frosts are over and soil is really warm. Ordinary garden soil and moisture are sufficient to get a crop, although sorghum may be more productive under better conditions. Seeds are ripe at about the same time as sugar content of the stalks reaches maximum. 50 seeds per pkt.

BLACK AMBER #SR107
100 days. One of the oldest cane sorghums still on the market, named for its shiny black seeds. The 6-8 foot stalks make a delicious golden sorghum syrup. We are happy to offer this sorghum that was a standard in early America and is still used today. Pkt $3.00

BROOM CORN MULTI-COLORED #SR102
The multi-colored tassels are so popular for fall decorations. Colors include red, gold, burgundy, black, bronze, and more! Broom Corn can also be used to make brooms. Pkt $3.00

DWARF MAYO #SR117
90 days. A fascinating new introduction bred by Dr. Sam Moyer, Seed Savers member and broomcorn enthusiast. Dwarf plants seldom reach 5 feet in height. Seedheads are richly colored in shades of red through brown; extra long panicles to make long-brushed brooms. Pkt $3.00

INDIA RED POPPING #SR118
90 days. This red-to-black seeded variety originated in India, which is where foundation seed was collected by Texas organic grower Ken Hargesheimer, who shared them with us. The stalks reach 7-9 feet tall and look gorgeous standing in the field. They seem to resist lodging and send out more tillers (side shoots) than most, and these often yield grain as well. Pretty popped like popcorn! Pkt (25 seeds) $3.00

IOWA SWEET #SR121
125 days. A very sweet syrup type, about 9' tall with thick, juicy stalks. Preserved for years at Sand Hill Preservation Center and propagated by our very good friend and gardening mentor, the late Merlyn Neidens. Pkt $3.00

MENNONITE #SR104
A Mennonite heirloom from Missouri. The tall canes are juiced and boiled to make a very sweet, light, sorghum syrup, excellent on pancakes. This variety gives good yields and also produces lots of grain. Pkt $3.00

ONAVAS RED #SR111
Vigorous, 10 foot plants send out many tillers (side-shoots,) and all produce sweet juicy sap suitable for boiling down into syrup. Beautiful burgundy seed heads. From the Pima Bajo village in Sonora, Mexico. Pkt $3.00

RED'S RED SWEET #SR103
This heirloom has been grown in northern Missouri for many years. More adapted to northern climates than many sorghums. Makes excellent syrup. From our friend Steve Salt. Pkt $3.00

TUNISIAN #SR116
Excellent grain-type sorghum, originally collected in a market in Tunis. Smallish, brown to almost olive-colored grains are ground for use as porridge in their native land. Slender stalks and narrow leaves might be an adaptation to their native land. Compact seed heads occasionally cause lodging, so plant a bit deep. Needs really warm temperatures to thrive; recommended for dry-summer areas. Pkt $3.00

TARAHUMARA POPPING #SR110
120 days. From the Tarahumara people of Northern Mexico's Batopilas Canyon area. This variety isn't grown for syrup, but rather for the plump white seeds, which can be popped and eaten like miniature popcorn. Vigorous plants reached ten feet in our 2008 trials. Pkt $3.00

UMBRELLA #SR122
100 days—This older variety from Kentucky has unusual umbrella-shaped seed heads. Modest size type reaches 7-8 feet in height; stalks seldom lodge. Yields of mild-flavored syrup are moderate, but the quality is very high! Sent to us by Robert Ayer of Hartford, Kentucky. Pkt $3.00

WHITE AFRICAN #SR109
Introduced to the USA in 1857 by Leonard Wray from Natal, South Africa, under the name Enyama, it was later named White Mammoth and then White African. This variety produces 10' tall stalks that make great, sweet syrup that is perfect for hot waffles and pancakes. White seeds can be used to grind for flour. Pkt $3.00

YELLOW BONNET #SR119
120 days. A fairly long season syrup-type sorghum, originally from southern Missouri. Medium stalks reach 9-10 feet, showed no lodging in one trial, and only moderate tillering (suckering). Pkt $3.00

Onavas Red Sorghum

Spinach

(Spinacia oleracea) True spinach is very cold tolerant, one of the first crops planted at winter's end, as well as one of the last in early fall. In zone 6 and above, it's possible to harvest at least a few leaves occasionally all winter long, and farther north, it may be possible with row cover or high tunnels. We list some warm weather spinach substitute here as well, and these are quite the opposite: they yield abundant greens in summer's heat, when growing true spinach would be out of the question. Spinach, whether true or warm-season substitutes, requires lots of nitrogen and water. 250 seeds per packet

AMSTERDAM PRICKLY SEEDED #SP108

Traditional crop in Europe for generations. This type was grown by Thos. Jefferson in the early Nineteenth Century. In 1806, Bernard McMahon of Philadelphia said it was "the hardiest kind," and that may well be true to this day. Leaves are more pointed and arrow-shaped than the common type. The sturdy plants yield over a long season, producing flat, tender, medium-green leaves with red-tinged stalks. Slower to bolt than ordinary spinach. Traditionally sown in late-summer or early fall for harvest through autumn and into winter. Pkt $2.50

BLOOMSDALE LONG STANDING

#SP101   50 days. The old standard since 1925, does better in hot weather than most. Glossy, deep green, delicious leaves. So popular with fine chefs. Pkt $2.50 *or 1 oz $4.00*

GIANT NOBLE #SP103

This is the giant of the spinach clan. Plants spread to 25"! Tender leaves are great for canning, steaming, or salads; for those who want quantity and quality. Introduced in 1926. Pkt $2.00

GIGANTE D'INVERNO #SP106

This European heirloom produces large, broad, deep green leaves well into the fall and winter months in many areas. This flavorful variety comes to us from Italy. The English name is Giant of Winter. Pkt $2.00

MERLO NERO #SP105

A fine-flavored Italian spinach that has dark-green, savoyed leaves. This productive variety is fairly early. Rare in the USA. Pkt $2.50

Bloomsdale Long Standing

Amsterdam Prickly Seeded

MONSTRUEUX DE VIROFLAY #SP104

50 days. Big leaves to 10" long, smooth and deep green in color. Very fast growing plants are popular for fall planting. A gourmet French heirloom that was developed prior to 1866. Pkt $2.25

NEW ZEALAND SPINACH #SP102

(*Tetragonia tetragonioides*) 60 days. Not the same species as common spinach, this variety takes the heat and keeps producing all summer. Tasty. Was listed by Fearing Burr in 1863 in his book *Field and Garden Vegetables of America*. Not frost hardy. Pkt (50 seeds) $2.50

RED MALABAR SPINACH #SP107

70 days. This beautiful plant is not a true spinach but a different species (*Basella rubra*). This heat-loving Asian vine has lovely red stems and delicious, succulent leaves that are great in salads and stir-fries. A delicious green that can be grown as an annual in many areas or as a perennial in sub-tropical areas. Pkt (50 seeds) $2.50

New Zealand

STRAWBERRY SPINACH

#GR107 (*Chenopodium capitatum*)

An old-fashioned plant that dates to 1600 in Europe. This curious plant produces greens that are picked and cooked like spinach, but it also produces attractive, red berries that are bland in flavor. These add a nice touch to fruit salads. Easy-to-grow plants are similar to "Lamb's Quarters", a wild relative. Found in a monastery garden. Pkt $2.50

Merlo Nero

Summer Squash

Many of these are also used for winter too! The species is C. pepo on all squash listed here, unless otherwise noted. Minimum 20 seeds per packet. Summer Squash are grown for immature fruits which can be harvested all summer long.

Lemon

BENNINGS GREEN TINT SCALLOP
#SSQ109 50 days. Colorful, light green, scallop-shaped fruit; tender and good quality; excellent yields, easy to grow. We have grown this variety for many years, an old favorite. Good color for market. Pkt $2.50

CASERTA #SSQ138
60 days. All America Selections winner in 1949. Here's an early bush cocozelle type, popular in Italy where they favor a rich, full-flavored zucchini. Fruits slightly club-shaped with mottled striping in olive-green and darker green. Can reach a fairly large size and still be quite tender and delicious as a summer squash. Pkt $2.25

COCOZELLA DI NAPOLI #SSQ121
55 days. Long, slender fruit, ribbed, pale greenish-yellow, striped with dark green; very firm and flavorful flesh. A unique Italian heirloom; tasty. Pkt $2.50

CROOKNECK-EARLY GOLDEN SUMMER
#SSQ116 50 days. An old favorite heirloom, this is one of the oldest types of squash dating back to pre-Columbus times, and it has been popular ever since. Easy to grow and good tasting. Pkt $2.25 *or 1 oz $4.75*

EARLY PROLIFIC STRAIGHTNECK #SSQ115
50 days. AAS Winner from 1938, uniform lemon-yellow, club-shaped fruit; firm flesh is of excellent quality, tasty. Pkt $2.50 *or 1 oz $4.75*

Odessa

GAGAT PATISSON #SSQ142 *New!*
55 days. Stunning dark green scallop fruits. Flesh is snow-white to cream. In Europe, whole fruits are pickled or canned at 2 inches diameter or less; larger fruits are used in all the usual ways for summer squash. Especially nice braised with garlic in a little olive oil. Vigorous bush-type plants. Pkt $2.75

GELBER ENGLISCHER CUSTARD #SSQ136
Clear lemon-yellow fruits are a patty-pan type, but with a bizarre twist. Fruits are oddly flattened—impossible to describe. Productive bush plants yield over a long season if kept picked. Recommended for cooler climates like the Pacific Northwest. This unique variety originated in Gatersleben, Germany. Described in Amy Goldman's book "The Compleat Squash." Pkt (10 seeds) $2.75

GREEN BUSH VEGETABLE MARROW
#SSQ124 Green, zucchini-type fruit are excellent for frying, stuffing, and baking; tasty flesh; bush plants. Very popular with the English. Pkt $2.00

KAMO KAMO #SSQ129
The ethnic heirloom pumpkin of the Maori people of New Zealand; it is also known as Kumi Kumi pumpkin. New Zealanders say this is the best of all squash, for the young fruit can be boiled, fried or baked, and they have a rich, nutty flavor that is quite delicious. Let the green speckled squash ripen, and they are good as a winter squash. They have become rare even in New Zealand. Very ornamental. Pkt $3.00

Patisson Strie Melange

LEBANESE WHITE BUSH MARROW #SSQ112 50
days. Creamy, oblong fruits; tasty and mild, good fried or baked. Harvest when 7" long. Rare Lebanese variety. Early. Pkt $2.00

LEMON SQUASH #SSQ102
The shape, size and color of a lemon, it grows great here, has huge yields and the best resistance to insects I have seen in a summer squash. Very tasty, great fried! A favorite, this is a superb market variety and is very attractive. Our most popular summer squash. Pkt $2.75 *or 1 oz $10.00*

MONGOGO DU GUATEMALA #SSQ130
A Guatemalan heirloom superb for fall decorations. The 4-lb. fruit are pumpkin-shaped with big ribs, with golden yellow and dark green-striped skin. The young fruit are good fried as summer squash, and mature fruit can be made into pies and preserves. Almost extinct in the USA, but sold commercially in Europe. Pkt. $3.00 *or 1 oz $4.75*

ODESSA #SSQ123
The vining plants produce delicious, white, zucchini-type fruit that have an incredible flavor! This variety comes from the fertile valleys near Odessa in Ukraine, the area my great-grandfather farmed many years ago. Produces for a long season and is among the tastiest. Pkt $2.50

PATISSON GOLDEN MARBRE SCALLOP
#SSQ104 A unique French scallop squash. Fruit is a beautiful bright golden-orange color. Young fruit are very tender and well flavored! Also makes good winter squash. Tall bush plants are very attractive and yields are good. A favorite of mine. Pkt $2.50

PATISSON PANACHE BLANC ET VERT SCALLOP #SSQ106
The stunning, pure white scallop with deep green radial streaks. Small fruit may not show streaking, and it can be variable. Its delicious flesh is great fried or baked. A real treat for both taste and visual appeal; a pre-1885 French heirloom. Pkt (15 seeds) $2.50

PATISSON PANACHE JAUNE ET VERT SCALLOP
#SSQ105 Beautiful scalloped fruit are a lovely creamy-yellow with contrasting deep green radial streaks. Small fruit may not show streaking and it can be variable. Stunning displayed with our other scallops! The flavor is delicious as a summer squash or is great baked in the fall. We are happy to offer this French heirloom again this year. Pkt $2.50

PATISSON STRIE MELANGE #SSQ134
We are so excited to finally list this incredible mix of French scallops. This mix contains fruit in many colors, with many being striped and warted! One of the most ornamental varieties we have seen. Fruit are good picked young and cooked, or used when hard for decorations. Add lots of style to your summer and fall displays. Pkt $3.00

RONDE DE NICE #SSQ111
50 days. This is a delicious French heirloom variety. The flesh of this round, green zucchini is very tender and fine-flavored, making it an ideal squash for stuffing. A popular variety for home gardens and specialty growers. Vigorous, quick-growing plants. Pkt $2.00

RUGOSA FRIULANA #SSQ137
Common in northeastern Italy, and nearly the only variety seen in the Venetian shops and markets. The name means "wrinkled of Friuli," but the light yellow fruits are beyond wrinkled, being fantastically warted even when very young. Rich and full flavored, as Italian varieties usually are. Pkt $3.00

STRIATA D'ITALIA #SSQ110
50 days. Medium-long zucchini fruit, somewhat thicker at the blossom end, light ribbing, 8"-9" long. The skin is striped in light & dark green. Superb flavor and texture. This variety is popular in Italy for its flavor & early yield. Pkt $2.00

Gagat Patisson

Golden Zucchini

Fordhook Zucchini

TATUME #SSQ127

A must in Mexican cuisine, and also popular in certain parts of Texas. This old heirloom is picked small and used like zucchini, but these are so much better than standard supermarket zucchini! Round to slightly elongated, flavorful fruit are green in color; vigorous vining plants are fairly resistant to disease. Pkt $2.00

TONDO SCURO DI PIACENZA #SSQ101

Forget the new "Eight Ball" hybrid. There already was an heirloom version. These are a rich, dark-green color, round-shaped and very flavorful; perfect for home or markets. Vigorous plants produce well. Italian seed. Pkt $2.50

WHITE SCALLOP #SSQ107

50 days. A very ancient Native American heirloom squash, grown by the Northern Indians for hundreds of years. This type was depicted by Europeans back to 1591, and is one of the best-tasting and high-yielding varieties still around today! Great fried or baked. Flat fruit with scalloped edges --beautiful! Pkt $2.50 *or 1 oz $4.75*

YELLOW SCALLOP #SSQ108

(Golden Custard) Beautiful, bright yellow fruit with a rich, mellow flavor. Likely predates Columbian times; a rare native American squash. Bush plants with good yields. Pkt $2.50 *or 1 oz $4.75*

ZUCCHINI, BLACK BEAUTY #SSQ120

50 days. The classic dark-green summer squash that has made modern zucchini of this type popular. Introduced in the US markets in the 1920's, and seed companies started listing it in the 1930's. Delicious fried or baked; best picked young. Pkt $2.25 *or 1 oz $4.75*

ZUCCHINI, FORDHOOK #SSQ139

57 days. Classic, cylindrical, dark-green straight to slightly curved zucchinis. Tender, creamy-white flesh freezes well. Vigorous and productive bush plants. Pkt $2.25

ZUCCHINI, GOLDEN #SSQ118

Slender fruit are bright golden-yellow. They are as delicious as they are attractive; bush plants. Pkt $2.50 *or 1 oz $4.75*

ZUCCHINI, GRAY #SSQ114

49 days. Great-tasting, high-quality, gray zucchini squash. Yields are very good; flesh is firm, mild, and very tasty. We have been getting favorable reports from customers about this squash. A real favorite. Pkt $2.00 *or 1 oz $4.75*

ZUCCHINI GREEN BUSH #SSQ141

(C. pepo) A classic deep-green fruited zucchini that yields abundantly and tastes delicious. Bush plants are great for smaller gardens. Pkt $2.25

ZUCCHINI, LUNGO BIANCO #SSQ119

A popular variety from Italy, the light-green/cream fruit are mild and sweet. Beautiful in a zucchini mix. Productive bush plants. Pure imported Italian seed. Pkt $2.00

ZUCCHINO RAMPICANTE #SSQ103

(C. moschata) 70 days. The famous Italian heirloom vining zucchini and pumpkin; long slender 15-inch fruit have a flat bulb at the bottom. They are one of the best eating summer squash: very tender, mild and sweet tasting. The flavor is superb! This squash is also great as winter squash. The Italians use it for stuffing in gnocchi and ravioli; the flesh is rich and flavorful, great for baking and pies! The vines produce good yields of this great all-purpose squash. The mature fruit grow very long. This one is in very high demand at specialty markets. Pkt $2.75

Gelber Englischer Custard

Zucchino Rampicante

Crookneck, Early Golden Summer

Bennings Green Tint Scallop

Tatume

Kamo Kamo

Yellow Scallop

Tondo Scuro di Piacenza

Squash & Pumpkins

20-35 seeds per packet. Harvest in autumn when skins are too tough to be easily punctured with a thumbnail.

AMAZONKA #SQ296 *New!*

85 days. (*C. maxima*) 2-3 pound fruits ripen deep orange. Fruits are slightly flattened globes, are ribbed with some green striping along the ribs and the blossom end. Flesh is orange, and fine for all typical winter squash uses. Productive plants are compact, running 3-4 feet, making this an excellent choice for smaller gardens or container culture. Great keeper, too! A Russian commercial variety of recent introduction. Pkt $3.00

AMBAR #SQ297 *New!*

90 days. (*C. maxima*) Compact, semi-bush plants yield deep green fruits. These weigh to 8 lbs or so. Skin is dark sea-green, rather rough but not exactly warted. The fruits are liberally splashed with lighter, sage-green spangles. The overall effect is pleasing to the eye. Flesh is an intense orange-yellow and very sweet and nutty-tasting. Excellent storage qualities. Pkt $3.00

AMERICANA TONDA #SQ144

(*C. pepo*) A beautiful, ornamental pumpkin that has orange skin with green stripes between the ribbing. They weigh 4-6 lbs each. Pkt $2.00

ALLIGATOR #SQ280 *New!*

110 days (C. moschata) Fruits are tan, pear- to hourglass shape, and covered with the most warts we have ever seen in any moschata squash. Unparalleled for arrangements and centerpieces! And this variety has great eating quality as well—firm, sweet, fragrant dark orange flesh is superb in pies and desserts, jams, and soups. Running about 10-12 inches in length and weighing to 6 lbs or so, the size is ideal for smaller families. Great keeper, too! Pkt. (10 seeds) $3.00

ATLANTIC GIANT PUMPKIN #SQ179

(*C. maxima*) 110-125 days. Lovely, giant, pink-orange pumpkins can weigh over 800 lbs, and do so every year, with some reaching almost 1500 lbs! This variety was introduced by Howard Dill, of Nova Scotia in 1978, and has since broken all records. Pkt $4.50

AUSTRALIAN BUTTER #SQ162

(*C. maxima*) 90-100 days. A large, gorgeous peach-colored squash from 'down under' that has extra-thick, orange flesh that's of excellent quality; perfect for pies and baking. The 15-pound fruit keep for a long period. Very rare Australian heirloom. So beautiful and attractive. Pkt $2.50

BABY BLUE HUBBARD #SQ183

(*C. maxima*) 90-100 days. A lovely little squash that was developed in 1953 by the U of NH; small, Hubbard-shaped fruit weigh around 6 lbs and have fine-grained, yellow-gold flesh that is sweet and of excellent quality. A great variety for marketing or small households. Semi-bush vines are easy to handle. Pkt $2.50

Boston Marrow

Palav Kadu

Queensland Blue

BABY GREEN HUBBARD #SQ199

(*C. maxima*) The 7" green fruit look like miniature Hubbard squash, yet weigh only 5 lbs. The flesh is sweet and nutty--great for baking or in pies! The smaller size makes these perfect for market growing. Pkt $2.00

BIG MAX #SQ123

(C. maxima) 110 days. Huge pumpkins can grow well over 100 lbs! Nearly round, bright orange fruit are stunning and are good for pies and canning. Very thick, orange flesh. Good for county fairs and displays. Pkt $2.50

BYLINKA #SQ279 *New!*

100 days. (C. maxima) A superb example of open-pollinated breeding in the old Soviet Union! Bred to be dry-farmed by the Ukrainian Academy of Agricultural Sciences, the fruits are very thick-fleshed, and reach a workable 4-10 lbs. Attractive fruits are flattened, sometimes slightly segmented, of gray or light gray color; some having pale pink spots. Bylinka has documented disease resistance (anthracnose and powdery mildew). Our grower reports excellent production! Pkt. (10 seeds) $3.00

BLACK FUTSU #SQ106

(*C. moschata*) Rare, black Japanese squash. The fruit is flattened, round, and has heavy ribbing. Very unique and beautiful. The black fruit will turn a rich chestnut color in storage. Flesh is golden color and has the rich taste of hazelnuts. Fruits are 3-8 lbs each, and vines give huge yields. Japanese, dark skinned, flattened; did excellent here. Popular with European market growers. Good insect resistance makes this a winner! Pkt $3.00 1 oz $7.50

BLUE HUBBARD #SQ180

(*C. maxima*) 110 days. Huge, teardrop-shaped fruit weigh 15-40 lbs and have sweet, fine-grained, golden flesh. Great for baking, pies, and soups. The hard, blue-gray shell helps these keep for long periods in storage. Gregory Seed Company introduced this fine New England variety in 1909, and Mr. Gregory considered this his best introduction. Pkt $2.25

BLUE HOKKAIDO #SQ290 *New!*

(also known as Blue Kuri) A lovely little Kabocha type squash, this one weighs 2 to 3 lbs, and is maxes out at about 8 inches in diameter—perfect for individual servings. The fruits are blue-green to gray, flattened, lightly ribbed globes. Dryish flesh is yellow-orange, thick, dense and very sweet. This Japanese variety is a superior storage type as well, and great for marketing! Pkt (15 seeds) $3.00

BOSTON MARROW #SQ221

(*C. maxima*) Lovely 15 lb fruit are hubbard-shaped and a brilliant red-orange in color. This variety was first documented back to 1831 by Fearing Burr, the author of *Field & Garden Vegetables of America*. This variety was first mentioned being grown by Mr. J.M. Ives of Salem, MA. Mr. Ives had received seeds from a friend in Northampton, MA, who had obtained his seeds from a friend in Buffalo, NY. This variety came to be grown in the Buffalo area after a tribe of Native Americans traveled through the area and distributed seed. From this historic introduction, Boston Marrow soon became one of the most important commercial squashes for 150 years. As the 21st century approached, nearly every seed company had dropped this unique treasure. In 1881 D.M. Ferry's catalog said, *"Very dry, fine-grained, and for sweetness and excellence, unsurpassed; a very popular variety in the Boston market".* It has rich, orange flesh that won it a place in Slow Foods' "Ark of Taste" for having superior flavor and taste! Pkt $2.75

BUEN GUSTO DE HORNO #SQ278 *New!*
115 days. (*C. maxima*) Here's a gorgeous and superbly flavorsome little squash from Spain! The name, translated from Spanish, means "good-taste-of-the-oven," and these elegant little squashes are certainly that! The slightly flattened, ribbed and warted fruit reach to about 12 inches across and weigh in at around 7 to 15 pounds. Colors run from deep green to pale sage, and the rinds are occasionally splashed in orange--outstanding in displays! The dense, firm, medium yellow-orange flesh is sweet and fine-grained, and definitely excellent for baking. Add excellent keeping quality, and you've got a real winner that everyone is sure to love! Pkt (10 seeds) $3.00

BUSH BUTTERCUP #SQ168
(*C. maxima*) 95 days. Like standard Buttercup squash, with sweet, dry, orange flesh of excellent quality, but these are produced on 3'-4' bush plants that stay compact; excellent for small gardens. Green-skinned 3-to 4-lb fruit. Pkt $2.50

BUTTERCUP #SQ110
(*C. maxima*) 95 days. Very sweet, dry flesh of excellent quality. Deep orange flesh with green skin. Fruit are around 3 lbs each. Pkt. $2.25

BUTTERNUT–WALTHAM #SQ112
(*C. moschata*) 100 days. An old favorite. Good yields with excellent-tasting, rich, orange-colored flesh. Great baked! Pkt $2.50 *or 1 oz $4.75*

CANADA CROOKNECK #SQ266
(*C. moschata*) 110 days. Old New England variety, preserved at Old Sturbridge Village, Massachusetts, where our foundation seed came from. Reportedly originated among the Iroquois Indians. Introduced 1834 by Boston seedsman Charles H. Hovey, this ancestor of today's Butternut was described in detail in Fearing Burr's book of 1865. The bottle-shaped fruits reach 2-4 lbs, having a curved neck and fine-grained, sweet flesh. Resistant to pests and diseases; a superlative keeper. Formerly quite common, it has become very difficult to find, and we are pleased to offer it. Pkt $3.00

CANDY ROASTER—NORTH GEORGIA #SQ240
(*C. maxima*) Here is a smaller strain of Candy Roaster from northern Georgia. This type of squash is famous among the people of the Southeast. Pink, banana-shaped fruit have a blue tip and weigh around 10 lbs. Delicious, smooth orange flesh is perfect baked, fried and makes great pies; hard to find and quite beautiful. Pkt $3.00

CHICAGO WARTED HUBBARD #SQ127
(*C. maxima*) 110 days. This heirloom was developed by Budlong Gardens of Chicago

Marina di Chioggia

Rouge Vif d'Etampes

and was introduced by Vaughan's Seed Store, of Chicago, in 1894. The 13-lb fruit are dusky-olive-green, deeply wrinkled, and warted, classic Hubbard shape. Fine-grained, sweet orange flesh. Pkt $2.00

CHIHUAHUA LANDRACE #SQ211

(*C. mixta*) 110 days. We collected this squash from a roadside stand in the Mexican desert a little west of the city of Chihuahua. They vary a lot in color: all shades of green, white, yellow and possibly a few other colors. Fruit are large and attractive; used extensively in northern Mexican cuisine. Pkt. (10 seeds) $3.00

CHINESE MINIATURE WHITE #SQ264

(*C. pepo*) Tiny 3"-4" flat white pumpkins are about the same size and shape as "Baby Boo." Great for fall decorations and are also edible. A great squash for farm markets, easy to grow and gives excellent yields. From China. Pkt $2.50

CHIRIMAN #SQ198

(*C. moschata*) This Japanese heirloom was popular in the Edo period (1603-1867). It was first offered in the US by Aggelar and Musser Co., of Los Angeles, in 1922. Beautiful fruit weigh about 5 lbs. This variety is flattened and ribbed, and deep greenish-black in color. They turn more tan in storage. The flesh is deep orange, sweet and flavorful. A great little squash that has become quite rare. Pkt $3.00

CONNECTICUT FIELD #SQ129

(*C. pepo*) 100 days. The heirloom pumpkin of the New England settlers and Indians, several hundred years old. Golden fruit weigh about 20 lbs each. This is a truly old variety; can be used for pies; the traditional American pumpkin. Pkt $2.50 *or 1oz $4.50*

CREAM OF THE CROP #SQ271

(*C. pepo*) 55 days. White bush-type acorn. The fruits are white and on the large side for an acorn, weighing in at 2-3 pounds. This variety is great picked small and used as summer squash, or let ripen and use for winter storage. This variety is perfect for small spaces and was grown in Jere's childhood gardens. Pkt $2.50

CROWN #SQ189

(*C. maxima*) 95 days. Our friend, Mac Condill, found this great squash in Cape Town South Africa. Originally from Australia, this variety first came to the USA in the early 1930's. Stunning, turban-shaped fruit are light blue in color and weigh about 12 lbs. The flesh is bright orange, sweet and of good quality, great for pies, baking and soups. Blue types can be traced back for more than 150 years in Australia, and are among the best for eating. Pkt $2.75

CUSHAW WHITE (JONATHAN PUMPKIN)

#SQ116 (*C. mixta*) 100 days. A rare Cushaw type; white skin and sweet, pale orange flesh. Easy to grow, huge yields, and good resistance to squash bugs. A popular heirloom from the South. (1891) Pkt (10 seeds) $2.50

DELICATA #SQ111

(*C. pepo*) 100 days. High sugar content. Fruit are 1-3 lbs each, and skin color is rust-white with green stripes. Delicate sweet flavor. This old heirloom was introduced in 1894 by Peter Henderson and Co. Pkt $2.00

Golias

Iran

Americana Tonda

Connecticut Field

Galeux d'Eysines

DICKINSON PUMPKIN #SQ281

(*C. moschata*) 100 days. Nearly round to slightly elongated fruit can weigh up to 40 pounds. Tan-colored skin. Vines grow very long and are productive. The dry flesh is orange, sweet and of high quality. For good eating, this is a superb variety! Pkt. $3.00

FORDHOOK ACORN #SQ181

(*C. pepo*) 110 days. Creamy tan-colored, oblong, acorn-shaped fruits weigh about 2 lbs each. Flesh is similar to other acorns. These are also good harvested young and fried like zucchini. This good producer was introduced by W.A. Burpee in 1890 at their Fordhook trial grounds in Doylestown, Pennsylvania. Pkt $2.50

FUNGO #SQ298 *New!*

110 days. Smallish fruits are more-or-less turban shaped, sometimes described as a mushroom shape. Warting or callusing is variable and on some individuals, is very unique and positively spectacular! Colors very enormously but run generally from light to very deep green through yellow-gold to orange. Marketed as an ornamental "gourd" in its native Italy. Pkt $3.00

GALEUX D'EYSINES #SQ156

(*C. maxima*) 95-100 days. Possibly our most beautiful heirloom squash. This flattened, round, 10-15 lb fruit has gorgeous, salmon/peach-colored skin covered with large warts! The deep orange flesh is flavorful, smooth and sweet, making it good for baking. It's also popular among the French for making soup. This is one of the tastiest squash I have tried, and we are delighted to offer this French heirloom. Pkt $2.50 *or 1 oz $8.00*

GOLDEN HUBBARD #SQ200

(*C. maxima*) Also called 'Genesee Red Hubbard' and was introduced in 1898. The 12-lb red fruit are teardrop-shaped, brilliant red and lightly warted, making this the most beautiful of the Hubbard types. The flesh is very thick, sweet and orange with a fine old-fashioned squash flavor. This is an excellent variety for fall decorations, as well as for eating. Pkt $2.50

GOLIAS #SQ299 *New!*

(*Cucurbita maxima*) 120 days. Very large, brilliant orange fruits are oblong, lightly ribbed. They do get large--60 pounds or larger is possible! Yet flavor and texture are not compromised. Makes great pumpkin pie. Great choice for school- or community gardens, food-banks, etc. Pkt $3.00

GREEK SWEET RED #SQ166

(*C. moschata*) 105 days. Here is one delicious squash: the long-necked, reddish tan fruits are filled with sweet, deep orange flesh that's richly flavored. Attractive, large vines are highly productive. It was very resistant to squash bugs, too! This variety is super rare and I believe we are the only source. Pkt (15 seeds) $2.75

GREEN STRIPED CUSHAW #SQ163

(*C. mixta*) 95 days. Big, white fruit with small, green stripes; oblong with crooked necks and bulbous bottoms. The large vines are vigorous and are good for the South. A Native American squash that has an ancient history. Great for fall pumpkin sales. Pkt $2.25

GUATEMALAN BLUE #SQ151

(C. maxima) An heirloom from Guatemala, this variety produces 10 lb, blue, banana-shaped fruit that have tasty, firm flesh. The vines are very productive. This variety is very hard to find. Pkt $3.00

HONEY BOAT DELICATA #SQ159

(C. pepo) 105 days. One of the sweetest squash varieties in existence. Oblong, Delicata-shaped squash have tan skin with green stripes. Excellent quality and produces early. Developed by Dr. James Baggett, Oregon State University. Pkt $2.25

HOPI CUSHAW #SQ213

(C. mixta) 105-110 days. Stunning pear-shaped fruit are beautifully splashed in various amounts of green and orange. Fruit grow to 15-17 lbs, and were used by Native Americans for their tasty seeds. A lovely ornamental variety that is part of Native Americana. Pkt (15 seeds) $3.50

HOWDEN #SQ216

(C. pepo) A large, more uniform Connecticut Field type pumpkin. A hard, orange rind makes this an excellent carving variety. The 22 lb fruit have thick orange flesh; a great keeper and popular commercial variety. Pkt $2.00

HUBBARD TRUE GREEN IMPROVED #SQ120

(C. maxima) 105 days. The original Green Hubbard was introduced around the 1790's, and it has dark bronze-green skin and delicious golden flesh. The fruit are 10-15 lbs each and are excellent keepers. J.H. Gregory's Company made this squash famous back in the 1840's. Pkt $2.00

IRAN #SQ268

(C. maxima) One of the most unusual and beautiful squashes you will ever see! We have been trying for several years to get this variety into the catalog. Collected in 1940 in the northeastern Iranian city of Torbat-e-Heydariyeh, and preserved at the USDA seed bank ever since. Not known to the public until a few years ago, when our friend Glenn Drowns introduced it. This squash is super ornamental, with its unique, foam-green rind that's mottled in soft peachy orange. Round and slightly ribbed fruit are medium to large in size. It keeps for a year or more, and is perfect for fall decorating. Pkt (10 seeds) $2.75

JACK BE LITTLE #SQ160

(C. pepo) 90 days. This tiny, cute pumpkin weighs just 8 ounces; flat and ribbed. These are highly popular and a top-selling fall crop. The flesh is good to eat and the skin is bright orange. This type of squash may have been developed in the Orient as pumpkins of this type are offered to the 'Spirits' by many in Thailand, where they come in 4 or 5 colors. Pkt $2.00

JAPANESE PIE #SQ103

(C. mixta) An heirloom variety from the Land of the Rising Sun. Beautiful, 12 lb black fruit have creamy white flesh. Samuel Wilson, Mechanicsville, Pennsylvania, introduced this variety in 1884, and it quickly became popular because of its novelty and advertising. The seeds are "curiously marked or sculptured in the manner of Chinese letters." Also known as Chinese Alphabet Squash from the unique-looking seed. A real collector's item! Pkt $3.00

JARRAHDALE #SQ119

Fungo

Yokohama

Hopi Cushaw

Yugoslavian Finger Fruit

Yokohama

(*C. maxima*) 100 days. Slate, blue-grey, 6- to 10-lb pumpkins of superb quality. Their shape is flat, ribbed, and very decorative; also a good keeper. Popular in Australia, an excellent variety. Pkt $2.50

JAUNE GROS DE PARIS #SQ122

(*C. maxima*) 100 days. The beautiful giant pumpkin of historic Paris, the big pinkish-yellow fruit can grow to over 100 lbs. They are round, flattened, and have light ribbing. They are good keepers and are still popular in France. Good in pies, soups, and baked. A winner for farm markets! Pkt $2.50

JUMBO PINK BANANA #SQ138

(*C. maxima*) 105 days. Large, pink, banana-shaped fruit can weigh 10-40 lbs. This variety is over 100 years old. We have grown this squash for many years. Fine-flavored, dry, sweet, orange flesh that is superbly fine tasting, one of my favorites. Popular on the West Coast; large yields. Pkt $2.25 *or 1 oz $4.50*

KAKAI #SQ285 *New!*

100 days. (*C. pepo*) Kakai's completely hull-less seeds are superb for roasting! Slightly oblate, delicately ribbed fruits are an unusual shade of yellow-orange, mottled here and there in dark green to virtually black. Simply scoop the seeds out of the 5- to 8-pound pumpkins, rinse, salt if desired, and roast in the oven until slightly browned. Semi-bush plants are compact and great for smaller gardens. Pkt $3.00

KIKUZA #SQ104

(*C. moschata*) This Japanese heirloom is a good producer of small, tan colored pumpkins that are heavily ribbed. Orange flesh is sweet and dry and has a spicy flavor. Very hard to find. A great variety for specialty markets. First offered in America by the Oriental Seed Company of San Francisco in 1927. Pkt $2.75

LAKOTA #SQ245

(*C. maxima*) This colorful variety was grown by the Lakota Sioux. It is pear-shaped, flame-red with green streaks at the bottom. So attractive for fall decorations. The flesh is fine-grained and sweet with a great nutty taste. A wonderful squash that ranks among the most beautiful. Pkt $3.00

LONG ISLAND CHEESE #SQ128

(*C. moschata*) 105 days. A longtime favorite on Long Island, very popular for pies. Flat, lightly-ribbed fruit look like wheels of cheese, with buff-colored skin. A very good keeper, of excellent quality, 6-10 lbs each; a beautiful heirloom variety. Pkt $2.25 *or 1 oz $6.50*

LONG OF NAPLES #SQ134

(*C. moschata*) Large, oblong, butternut-shaped fruit can weigh 20-35 lbs. The flesh is bright orange. Flavor is superb; rich, and very sweet. The skin is deep green, turning tan in storage. These attractive squash are great for areas with warm, long seasons. A good heirloom for home or market growers. A beautiful, very old Italian heirloom listed in America by Fearing Burr in 1863; very rare. Pkt $2.50

LONG PIE PUMPKIN #SQ258

(*C. pepo*)This variety dates back to at least 1832, when it was grown in Maine. The fruits are picked anytime after they begin to change color to orange; they will ripen successfully in storage. Makes wonderful pies! Pkt (10 seeds) $2.50

MAKARONOWA WARSZAWSKA #SQ300
New! (*Cucurbita pepo*) 100 days. New spaghetti squash sort from Poland. Plants are of a bush habit, and have lots of disease resistance. Pale-yellow fruits are the usual elongated oval shape, reach 2-3 pounds each. Flesh is fine-grained and tasty. Pkt $3.00

MARINA DI CHIOGGIA #SQ133
(*C. maxima*) 95 days. The heirloom sea pumpkin of Chioggia, on the coast of Italy. The large turban-shaped fruit are deep blue-green. It is one of the most beautiful and unique of all squash. A perfect variety for market gardeners. The rich, sweet flesh is a deep yellow-orange and of good quality, delicious baked or in pies. The fruits weigh about 10 lbs each and are produced on vigorous vines. Stunning! Pure Italian seed from one of Italy's best heirloom growers. Pkt $2.50

MELONETTE JASPEE DE VENDEE
#SQ190 (*C. pepo*) 90 days. A favorite of our grower, these golden yellow, netted, round, 3-4 lb fruit have some of the most delicious flesh in the squash family. Very sweet and rich, and the perfect size for two servings. The vines are incredibly productive and do well nearly everywhere. An historic variety from Vendee in western France; a great keeper and a favorite with chefs. Pkt $2.75

MEXICAN X-TOP #SQ212 *New!*
(*C. mixta*) 100 days. A round, bowl-shaped Cushaw type with attractive green and white striped rinds and mild yellowish-white flesh. We like these best when picked before they are mature, and then fried. Huge silver- edged seeds are tasty, too. A rare Mexican heirloom that is quite beautiful. Pkt (10 seeds) $4.00

MINI RED TURBAN #SQ201
(*C. maxima*) I just love this adorable little turban squash that is so lovely with its bright red base and cream-colored cap. This squash weighs 2-3 lbs and produces very large yields. Similar to the 'Small Chinese Turban" described in 1885 by Vilmorin. Beautiful! Pkt $2.50

MIRANDA #SQ301 *New!*
(*Cucurbita pepo*) 105 days—Polish hull-less seeded variety. Plants are of a compact running habit, a bonus in small gardens. Fruits are nearly spherical, orange mottled in green outside, weigh-in at 6 to 10 lbs. Inside are plenty of hull-less seeds, just waiting for extraction, drying, and snacking! Pkt $3.00

MORANGA #SQ505 *New!*
(*Cucurbita maxima*) 95 days. We are so excited to at last have seeds for the wonderful "Pink Pumpkin". Very hard to find traditional squash from Brazil. Fruits are ribbed, light pink to salmon in color and weigh in at a modest 4-8 pounds. Traditionally used to make a dish called 'Camarão na Moranga' which means 'shrimps in a squash'. Pkt $3.00

MUSQUEE DE PROVENCE #SQ152
(*C. moschata*) 120 days. These gorgeous, big, flat pumpkins are shaped like large wheels of cheese and are heavily lobed and ribbed. The skin is a beautiful, rich brown color when ripe. The flesh is deep orange, thick, and very

Shishigatani

Scheherazade

Moranga

Thai Kang Kob

Red Kuri

fine flavored; fruit grow to 20 lbs each. This traditional variety from southern France is great for fall markets. Pure European seeds. Pkt $2.75 *or 1oz $7.00*

NEW ENGLAND SUGAR PIE #SQ131
(*C. pepo*) 100 days. The noted small sugar pumpkin of New England. The orange fruit weigh 4-5 lbs and have fine, sweet flesh that is superb for pies. Described by Fearing Burr in 1863. Pkt $2.25

NOOB TAUB #SQ246
(*C. moschata*) 100-110 days. 6-8 lb spotted fruits start out grey-green, turning yellowish when ripe. Shapes vary from a round, slightly flattened pumpkin to a more unusual bottle shape. Flesh is very thick, grading from intense orange nearest the skin to very pale in the interior. Flesh not particularly sweet; our grower recommends it for savory recipes rather than dessert uses. Originated among the Laotian Hmong people. Fascinating and extremely rare variety. Pkt $3.00

NORTH FAULKLAND ISLAND #SQ147
(*C. moschata*) 100 days. Unique, pear-shaped fruit are mostly white, some with greenish yellow and orange stripes; 2-4 lbs. with pale yellow flesh. From the Abundant Life Archives. Pkt (10 seeds) $3.00

OLIVE VERTE #SQ193   *New!*
(*C. maxima*) 110 days. This attractive old heirloom is almost extinct; the 5-lb fruit are the shape of an olive; the rind is an attractive olive-green color occasionally washed in burnt umber. Their flesh is bright orange, very dry, sweet and flavorful. This French heirloom was mentioned by Vilmorin in 1885, who wrote that it "exactly resembles an unripe olive, magnified one hundred times." The variety was also listed by American seedsmen Burpee and Gregory around the same time. Pkt (10 seeds) $3.50

OMAHA PUMPKIN #SQ255
(*C. pepo*) 80 days. Another Oscar Will Seed Company introduction, dating to 1924 but collected much earlier from the Omaha Indians, by Dr. Melvin Gilmore. Weighing 3 to 5 pounds, Omaha matures early with tall, cylindrical, upright pumpkins which make cute Jack o' Lanterns. The vines are vigorous, yielding even in short-season climates. Very sweet fruits store for a few months and are good baked or in pies. Pkt $2.75

PACHECO PUMPKIN #SQ231
(*C. pepo*) A pumpkin that has a beautiful yellow rind and is filled with delicious, creamy yellow flesh; quite tasty! This heirloom is said to be collected at a rancho west of Chihuahua, Old Mexico. Pkt $2.50

PALAV KADU #SQ270
(*C. moschata*) 125 days. Very old central Asian variety, almost unknown to the rest of the world. The fruits are hourglass-shaped, reaching to about 3-4 lbs. Starts out green with cream-colored spots, which turn a dull buff-orange as the fruits mature. In the Tajik language, the name means "squash for pilav," a well-known dish from Central Asia. Superb flavor, excellent keeper! Pkt (10 seeds) $4.00

PENNSYLVANIA DUTCH CROOKNECK

#SQ218 *(C. moschata)* A popular 19th century Pennsylvania variety that is still grown in many Amish communities. Sometimes called "Neck Pumpkin" because of its long, flesh-filled neck. It somewhat resembles a giant butternut squash with a very long neck. They can reach 20 lbs in size! The flesh is superb, being deep orange and richly flavored, making it so popular with Amish wives for making their delectable pumpkin pies, butters and other deserts. A favorite of ours, and a good keeper. Pkt $2.50

QUEENSLAND BLUE #SQ135

(C. maxima) 110 days. Popular in Australia, this heirloom was introduced to the US in 1932. Beautiful, blue, turban-shaped 12-lb fruit, deeply ribbed. Very fine, deep golden flesh that is sweet and fine flavored. A good keeper. Pkt $2.25

RED KURI (HOKKAIDO) #SQ101

(C. maxima) 92 days. A red-orange Japanese winter squash, fruit are 5-10 lbs each and teardrop-shaped. The golden flesh is smooth, dry, sweet, and rich; a great yielding and keeping variety. Pkt $2.50

ROUGE VIF D' ETAMPES #SQ118

(C. maxima) 95 days. Most beautiful, flattened, and ribbed large fruit are a gorgeous deep red-orange. A very old French Heirloom, this was the most common pumpkin in the Central Market in Paris back in the 1880's. The flesh is tasty in pies or baked. Like summer squash, this one can also be picked small and fried. As a bonus, it's a good yielder, too. Pkt $2.50 *or 1 oz $5.50*

SCHEHERAZADE #SQ303 *New!*

85 days. Beautiful, warted, orange and green striped fruits weighing 5-10 pounds. This is a great choice for fall decorations. This was developed as an oil seed pumpkin so the seeds can be pressed to yield a dark nutty oil perfect for salad dressings or as accents in squash soups. Also, the flesh is good to eat. You can bake it like spaghetti squash because it has a similar texture. Pkt $3.00

SHISHIGATANI or TOONAS MAKINO

#SQ105 *(C. moschata)* This unique Japanese pumpkin was developed in the Bunka era of the Edo period (1804-1818). This is one of our rarest and most historic varieties! The fruit are uniquely shaped, like a bottle gourd, and are ribbed and very warty. They are dark green, turning to tan at full maturity. The fine-grained flesh has a delicious, nutty flavor. Traditionally believed to keep people from getting paralysis if eaten in the hottest part of summer. Shishigatani pumpkin is a famous vegetable in Kyoto cuisine. Very rare and hard to find even in its native Japan. Pkt $4.00

SIBLEY or PIKES PEAK #SQ150

(C. maxima) 110 days. Oblong, teardrop-shaped, slate-blue-colored fruit weigh 9 lbs each. It has thick orange flesh that is sweet and tasty. An excellent keeper, this variety was popular in Missouri and Iowa back to at least the 1840's. Believed to be of Native American origin, possibly from Mexico, it was introduced commercially by Hiram Sibley & Co. in 1887. Pkt $2.50

Jack Be Little

Alligator

Chicago Warted Hubbard

Buen Gusto de Horno

SILVER EDGE #SQ222

(*C. mixta*) Grown for its beautiful, delicious seeds that are very large and white, with silver edges, hence the name. The fruit are round-to-pear-shaped, and are white with green stripes, attractive for decorations. A unique squash that is still popular in some parts of Mexico. Pkt $3.00

SUCRINE DU BERRY #SQ171

(*C. moschata*) A famous, old, traditional variety from the heart of France. It has a sweet, musky fragrance and a delicious, sweet flesh that is used in jams, soups, and many French recipes. Small 3-5 lb. fruit are perfect for roasting and have deep orange flesh. Oblong, bell-shaped fruit are tannish-orange in color when mature. We are happy to introduce this flavorful variety to America. Pkt $3.00

SWEET DUMPLING #SQ137

(*C. pepo*) 90 days. One of the sweetest; 1lb fruit has white skin with green stripes. The sweet, tender, orange flesh makes this variety the favorite of many. Pkt $2.50

SWEET MEAT #SQ113

(*C. maxima*) 95 days. A delicious heirloom from Oregon; excellent-flavored deep orange flesh, very sweet. Fruit are large and flattened in shape. Skin color is a beautiful deep-sea-blue-green. Our family grew this one more than twenty years ago when we lived in Oregon. Pkt $2.00

TABLE GOLD ACORN #SQ136

(*C. pepo*) 90 days. Beautiful glowing gold acorn-shaped fruit are perfect for fall displays. Nutty-flavored yellow flesh; compact bush plants produce 1½ lb. fruit. Or pick this one young and sell as a specialty summer squash, as they are tender and delicious! Pkt $2.00

TABLE QUEEN ACORN #SQ126

(*C. pepo*) 80 days. Dark green Acorn-type fruit. Iowa Seed Co. introduced this variety in 1913 and is possibly of Native American origin. The small fruits have sweet, orange flesh. Pkt $1.75 *or 1 oz $4.50*

TABLE QUEEN BUSH ACORN #SQ173

(*C. pepo*) Here is an exciting true bush version of 'Table Queen Acorn'. 36" plants stay compact and produce heavy yields of these delicious squash with dry orange flesh. A great variety for small gardens, and will produce almost anywhere in the USA. Pkt $2.25 *or 1 oz $6.00*

THAI KANG KOB #SQ204

(*C. moschata*) A lovely sea green-colored squash that turns chestnut color in storage; pumpkin-shaped, very ribbed and warted. Weighs about 6-8 lbs and a favorite here at Baker Creek; vines produced well and had good resistance to squash bugs and other pests. The orange flesh is richly flavored, sweet and fragrant; great for curries, soups, stir-fries and more. Andrew Kaiser brought back this great variety from Thailand in 2006. Good for fall displays and markets. Pkt $3.00

THAI RAI KAW TOK #SQ203

(*C. moschata*) Green 8-lb fruit have tan spots on the rind. Flesh is yellow-orange, sweet and flavorful with a smooth texture; a great eating variety that performs very well in our Missouri summers, and stands up well to pests and disease. Attractive for decoration and superb for the table; a rock-hard rind makes this a great keeper. A Thai market variety that is sure to become popular here. Pkt $3.00

THELMA SANDERS SWEET POTATO #SQ195

(*C. pepo*) Wow! A lovely cream-colored, heirloom acorn-type squash that is super productive, tasty and perfect for small families. This variety was introduced by the members of Seed Savers Exchange. Pkt $2.50

TRIAMBLE or SHAMROCK #SQ172

(*C. maxima*) 100 days. A very rare and unique variety that was imported from Australia in 1932, from seed secured from Arthur Yates and Co., of Sydney. This squash is lobed like a three-leaf clover, making this light sea-green squash unusual looking. They weigh about 10 lbs each and have sweet, orange, fine-grained flesh. A fine variety for decoration or the table. Pkt $4.50

TURK'S CAP OR TURBAN #SQ117

(*C. maxima*) 90 days. A beautiful squash striped in red, orange, green, and white. A very old variety from France (pre-1820); fine thick orange flesh, good-sized fruit. Unique. Pkt $2.25

UCONN #SQ273

(*C. pepo*) 80 days. Very early bush-habit winter squash variety. Green, acorn-type fruits are rather small. But their earliness commends them in short-season climates or wherever a quick harvest is of special concern. Developed by the University of Connecticut. Pkt $2.50

UTE INDIAN #SQ269

(*C. maxima*) 100 days. Here's a different look in a turban squash: a sophisticated grey-green outside, with a very appealing bright-yellow flesh. The flavor is mild and delicately sweet. Our grower says: "Raw, it carries a hint of melon." Originally grown by the Ute Indian people of the US Southwest, and, so far as we know, offered commercially nowhere else. Pkt (10 seeds) $3.00

VEGETABLE SPAGHETTI #SQ102

(*C. pepo*) 88 days. This is the popular squash with stringy flesh that is used like spaghetti. Introduced by Sakata Seed Co. of Japan, in 1934. May have originated in China. Pkt $2.50 *or 1 oz $4.75*

VICTOR or RED WARTY THING S #SQ228

(*C. maxima*) One of the most stunning squashes around! The big glowing, oblong globes are a glowing, brilliant orange-red and covered with fantastic bumps! This old variety was introduced by James J.H. Gregory of Marblehead, MA in 1897 as Victor. It was recently reintroduced as Red Warty Thing. Pkt (15 seeds) $2.50

WINTER LUXURY PIE #SQ167

(*C. pepo*) This beautiful pumpkin was introduced by Johnson & Stokes in 1893. Lovely 6-lb golden fruit have white netting and are perfect for pies. In fact, this is one of the best tasting pie pumpkins you can grow; with very sweet and smooth flesh, it's a favorite of all who grow it. Pkt $2.75

WHITE ACORN #SQ205

(*C. pepo*) 90 days. A lovely, almost snow white Acorn squash. Heavy yields of beautiful fruit are produced on compact bush plants, making this a superb Acorn type for small gardens. This

Blue Hokkaido

Jaune Gros de Paris

Ute Indian

Chiriman

Buttercup

Curried Heirloom Squash and Pippin Apple Bisque

Because these hard squash keep for long periods of time, they are easy to enjoy year round. Recently at our National Heirloom Expo in Santa Rosa Ca, we grew several hundred varieties of squash and pumpkins. I have selected one of our best for your enjoyment.

INGREDIENTS
1 Marina De Chiggoa squash
1 T olive oil
1 T of sea salt
3 each Pippin or heirloom apple
Artisan Pepper Mill
2 C of heavy coconut cream
2 C of water
3 T of brown sugar
½ C of peeled ginger
1/2 yellow onion
2 T of fresh garlic
1 Carrot peeled
1 T of toasted red curry paste
1 T of chopped cilantro
Artisan Bread made into toast

PREPARATION
1. Preheat oven to 350 degrees F (175 degrees C).
2. Place squash onto a baking sheet cut-side down.
3. Bake squash in preheated oven until the skin loosens from the flesh, about 40 minutes.
4. Heat olive oil in a 5-quart stockpot over medium-high heat. Cook and stir garlic in hot oil until the onion is translucent, 5 to 7 minutes. Add water, curry paste, carrots, ginger, brown sugar and apples to the stockpot; bring to a simmer, stirring frequently. Reduce heat

Pumpkin Scones with Green Tomato and Goji Berry Chutney

A retro spin on a classical chutney. A great way to use the green tomatoes that wont have time to develop or drop early.

- **SCONES**
- 4 C of Flour
- 11/2 C of sugar
- 3 C of mashed pumpkin
- ½ C of apple sauce
- 2 T of baking powder
- 1 t of baking soda
- ½ t of salt
- ½ C of organic canola oil
- ½ t of mace
- ½ t of allspice
- ½ t of cinnamon
- ½ t of almond extract
- ½ t of vanilla
- ½ t of lemon zest

- **CHUTNEY**
- 2 whole green tomatoes diced
- 1 jar of mango chutney
- 2 T of Goji berries
- 1 cardomom pod
- Salt and Pepper to taste
- 1 T of fresh cilantro
- ½ C of small diced hot peppers
- 1 t of sugar
- ½ t of tamarind powder

PREPARATION
1. Mix all ingredient for scones. Bake on greased baking pan for 8 min at 350 degrees
2. Small diced tomatoes and peppers. Add to pot with jar of mango chutney. Cook on Med heat for15 min or until tomatoes are soft
3. Add the rest of the ingredients to the pot.
4. Pour in shallow pan to cool off
5. Place the chutney in jar and store in cooler or can if you want to put this up

Swiss Chard

(Beta vulgaris) Chard is actually the same species as beets, but these varieties are grown for leaves rather than roots. The plants put all their energy into making large, tender leaves, with succulent mid-ribs massive enough to be a vegetable in their own right. The range of colors comes as a spectacular bonus! Chard is usually direct-seeded into the garden as early as a couple of weeks before the last frost, and it can be sown anytime until midsummer, since the plants tolerate both heat and moderate cold of late fall, and even grow into the winter in milder climates. Prefers rich soil, full sun and ample moisture. 100 seeds per pkt

BIONDA DI LYON #SC110

50 days. Pale green leaves almost golden in color, and thick white midribs, give this chard a different look. Makes exquisite baby greens at 25 days. A great new addition to the ever-expanding color range of this old-fashioned veggie. Lovely! Pkt $3.00

FIVE COLOR SILVERBEET #SC101

(Rainbow Chard) 60 days. A beautiful chard, its colors are brilliant (pink, yellow, orange, red and white). This chard originated in Australia. Very mild, ornamental, and tasty. Great for market growers and specialty markets. Pretty enough to plant in the flower garden; so delicious; one of our favorite greens! (Sold in stores as "Bright Lights") Pkt $2.50 *or 1 oz $5.00*

FLAMINGO PINK CHARD #SC104

60 days. Neon hot-pink chard is so pretty and is perfect picked small for salads or larger for braising. Pkt $2.50

FORDHOOK GIANT CHARD #SC102

60 days. Introduced in 1924 by W. Atlee Burpee, large green leaves and white stems. Tasty. Pkt $2.00 *or 1 oz $4.50*

ORIOLE ORANGE CHARD #SC103

60 days. A stunning all-orange selection, perfect for home and markets. Orange chard is just delicious. Pkt $2.50

PERPETUAL SPINACH #SC107

(Beta vulgaris var cicla) 50 days. Belongs to the same species as chard and beets, but it has distinctive differences. The taste is more like a true spinach than ordinary chard, and the leaves look like spinach too—flatter and more pointed than chard, with slimmer stems. Very longstanding in the garden, yielding from late spring through autumn if planted early. Seldom bolts during its first year. Pkt $2.00

VERDE DE TAGLIO #SC109

(Green Cutting Chard) Very thin stems support large leaves of unusual substance. Outstandingly sweet and tender variety. Excellent for "cut and come again" style harvesting. One of the best-tasting chards. A delightful, traditional Italian variety. Pkt $3.00

VULCAN CHARD #SC106

60 days. An improved rhubarb chard developed in Switzerland. Very attractive and uniform red chard, this variety has great flavor and is perfect for marketing. Pkt $2.00 *or 1 oz $6.50*

Five Color Silverbeet

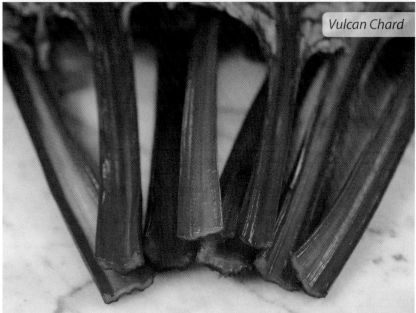

Vulcan Chard

Bionda di Lyon

Tomatillo

(Physalis ixocarpa) Also called "husk tomato," for the paper-like calyx or husk that encloses each fruit. They are grown about like tomatoes, except that they are seldom staked; they do tend to be a bit faster from seed than most tomatoes, and a little more tolerant to cold weather. Tomatillos are used in fresh salsas, and cooked in any number of sauces, including Mexican-style chili verde. 30 seeds per packet.

Rio Grande

Tomatillo Purple

San Juanito

Purple From Coban

AMARYLLA #TL109 *New!*
60 days. A Polish twist on an old Mexican staple vegetable! Immature fruits are green, morphing to pretty yellow as they ripen and begin to split their protective husks. The fruit is firm, juicy and very sweet, perfect for jams, jellies and don't forget the salsa! We also love these in the garden for fresh snacking and salads. Bred to thrive in the cooler summer conditions of inland eastern Europe. Pkt $3.00

TOMATILLO PURPLE #TL101
(*Physalis ixocarpa*) 68 days. Beautiful purple fruit, large size. Many are a bright violet color throughout their flesh. Much sweeter than the green types, it can be eaten right off the plant. Turns purple when ripe; rare! Pkt $2.50 *or 1/8 oz $8.50*

TOMATILLO VERDE #TL102
Deep green fruit; a standard, richly-flavored type. Huge yields as with most tomatillos. Pkt $2.50 *or 1/8 oz $8.50*

RIO GRANDE VERDE #TL104
83 days. This special selection of Tomatillo yields large, apple-green fruits. The medium-sized, determinate plants need no staking. The globe shaped fruits reach 3-4 ounces, very large for a tomatillo, and the yields are very high. Recommended for fresh market. Pkt $2.25

SAN JUANITO #TL105
80 days. Large green fruits ripen eventually to cream. At 3 ounces, the fruits are very large. Great in green salsas or in cooked chili verde stew. Its reliability makes it a great choice for market! Pkt $2.50

TINY FROM COBAN # TL108
Here's another variety collected by Jere Gettle on his 2005 trip to Central America, and preserved in our seed bank until grown out in 2013! This is a true tomatillo, having the typical husk, but the fruit is smaller, about the diameter of a dime. Fruits ripen to green or purple and are posessed of an unusual savory taste—some what different from other tomatillos we sell. Pkt $2.50

PURPLE COBAN TL103
70 days. A flavorful tomatillo that is 1 inch in diameter, being green with varying degrees of purple on many fruit. Very popular in Guatemalan cuisine; we collected this heirloom at Coban, Guatemala, a beautiful mountain town. Pkt $2.50

Amarylla

Green Tomatoes

Green Moldovan

AUNT RUBY'S GERMAN GREEN #TG101

85 days. One of the largest green beefsteaks. Can grow to over 1 pound and are just delicious. They have brilliant, neon-green flesh with a strong, sweet, and fruity flavor, much tastier than most red tomatoes. This family heirloom from Germany is beautiful. The winner of the 2003 Heirloom Garden Show's taste test. Pkt $2.50 *or 1/8 oz $8.50*

EMERALD APPLE #TG116

85 days. A rare variety from Russia where it is used for fresh eating, cooking and canning. Very large green fruit often exceed a pound and a half. This tomato is deliciously tart yet with a suprising sweetness. A wonderful eating tomato that has become a favorite here at the farm. It is one of the best and biggest green tomatoes we've tried. Pkt $2.50

EMERALD EVERGREEN #TG102

80 days. Medium-large fruit that stay "evergreen." This heirloom variety was introduced by Glecklers Seedsmen around 1950. The large plants set heavy yields of these beauties, which have a lovely lime-green color. The flavor is rich and superbly sweet. It's one of the best. A popular market variety, now being sold in many upscale stores. This should be the official tomato for the Green Party. Pkt $2.50 *or 1/8 oz $8.50*

GREEN BELL PEPPER #TG120

75-80 days. Very well flavored, unusual stuffing-type tomato, having stunning stripes of light and dark green, maturing to yellow and green. Four-ounce, three- to four-lobed fruits are apple-shaped, and look like small blocky bell peppers. The seeds and pulp are contained in a mass near the stem, just like a pepper, and so are easily removed to prepare the fruits for stuffing. Pkt (15 seeds) $2.50

GREEN DOCTORS #TG118

A favorite green cherry variety, having a good sweetness and put yet still has lots of tart flavor. Named after Dr. Amy Goldman and Dr. Carolyn Male who have both written great tomato books. Fruit is yellowish-lime green with kiwi-green colored flesh. Large vines produced huge yields of these little cherries. Some plants produce bright green fruit others produce "frosted" fruit with are lighter in color and even sweeter. Pkt $2.50

Green Doctors

GREEN GIANT #TG126

85 days, potato leaf plants. The most productive and best tasting tomato in our trials for the last two seasons! Large emerald-green fruit are over one pound in weight, they are uniform, very smooth and blemish-free. Color stays pure green even when dead ripe! Plants are very robust and require staking. Very few seeds; outstanding, complex flavor—very sweet and juicy. Pkt (15 seeds) $2.25

GREEN MOLDOVAN #TG109

80 days. Bright lime-green fruit have a tropical taste. This variety has round, flattened, 10-oz beefsteak-type fruit which reveal lovely, neon-colored flesh when sliced. A very rare heirloom from Moldova that has been a favorite of mine for years and one of the first green varieties I grew. Pkt $2.50

GREEN PEAR #TG127

70 days. An outstanding producer of uniform, little, green pear-shaped tomatoes over an extended season. Rich, complex "old-fashioned" tomato taste! Great for salads, canning whole or for market. Tolerates almost any growing conditions. Pkt $2.50

GREEN SAUSAGE #TG105

86 days. Determinate. A stunningly beautiful, banana-shaped paste tomato that is lime green and yellow striped when ripe! The flavor is rich and tangy. This will be a hot item for high-priced, groovy markets. So cool when mixed with orange, white, yellow, and red-striped paste types. Short, bushy plants produce 4"-long fruit in abundance. Pkt $2.50

Emerald Evergreen

Emerald Apple

Jolly Jack with Green Giant Tomatoes

GREEN SKIN LONG KEEPER #TG114
85 days. An unusual winter storage tomato; the fruit have thick green skin and pink flesh! Good-sized fruit can keep for a long period if picked a little prematurely and kept cool and dry. Nice-flavored winter tomatoes are such a treat compared to grocery store tomatoes. A hard-to-find tomato that has been preserved by members of Seed Savers Exchange. Pkt $2.50

GREEN ZEBRA #TG103
75 days. One of my favorite tomatoes. Beautiful chartreuse with deep lime-green stripes, very attractive. Flesh is bright green and very rich tasting, sweet with a sharp bite to it (just too good to describe!). A favorite tomato of many high class chefs, specialty markets, and home gardeners. Yield is excellent. The most striking tomato in our catalog, a real beauty. Around 3 ounces. This is the tomato colored for the Green Bay Packers. Pkt $2.50 *or 1/8 oz $8.50*

MALAKHITOVAYA SHKATULKA #TG113
70 days. The name, translated, means Malachite Box, named after the lovely green jewelry boxes named after the malachite mineral that comes from the Ural mountains and other areas. This early, light-to-olive green, medium-sized tomato has succulent, bright-green flesh that is very flavorful and tasty. Plants are productive even in the North, as this variety was developed at Svetlana Farm in Russia, and it has been tested in Siberia! Our grower likes to make a unique green ketchup from this variety. Pkt (15 seeds) $2.50

SPEAR'S TENNESSEE GREEN #TG108
A wonderful heirloom grown by the Spear family of Tennessee since the 1950's and brought to us by a local customer who has been preserving it in his garden. The round fruit weigh 8-10 oz and have the taste of tomatoes from Grandma's garden. They make your mouth water just thinking about them. This rare and historic variety deserves a place in every garden and certainly a place on our table in the future. Pkt $2.50

"As long as there is a few farmers out there, we will keep fighting for them."

—WILLIE NELSON

Tomato Seed:
All varieties are believed to be 'indeterminate' (long vines), *unless specified* 'determinate' (short vines). The best tasting varieties tend to be indeterminate, as most of ours are unless otherwise noted.
Packets contain a min. of 25 seeds (unless stated otherwise).

Orange Tomatoes

AMANA ORANGE #TO106
80 days. Big, 1 lb glowing orange beefsteaks have an intense, full flavor that most tomatoes don't match! This very attractive heirloom tomato is a favorite among our customers. Pkt $2.25 *or 1/8oz $8.50*

DJEENA LEE'S GOLDEN GIRL #TO125
78 days. Indeterminate. Family heirloom that dates back to the Roaring Twenties. Medium-sized fruits have a beautiful golden-orange color. Flavor is a balance of sweet and tart, fruity and very tasty. This variety won first prize at the Chicago Fair 10 years in a row! Djena was the granddaughter of Minnesota financier Jim Lee. She grew this tomato in Minnesota, and in 1929 gave plants to Reverend Morrow, then 15 years old, who maintained it. Listed in the Slow Foods Ark of Taste. Pkt $2.50

DR. WYCHE'S YELLOW #TO108
80 days. This heirloom was introduced to Seed Savers Exchange by the late Dr. John Wyche, who at one time owned the Cole Brothers Circus and used the manure of elephants to fertilize his heritage gardens. The 1 lb fruit is solid and smooth; their color is a glowing tangerine-orange that always stands out in the kitchen or off the vine. One of the best heirloom orange types for market, with its smooth texture and tropical, sweet taste. Heavy yields. Pkt $2.50

GIRAFFE #TO123
75 days. Semi-determinate. Intriguing long-keeping variety from Russia. 2- to 4- ounce round fruits are meaty with a red interior and skin that changes from green to yellow as the fruit ripens in storage. Vine-ripened fruits eventually reach a unique orange color. Reportedly keeps up to 5 months! Originally bred at the Timirjazev Agricultural Academy, Russia. Pkt $2.50

GOLDEN JUBILEE #TO105
70-80 days. A very popular orange variety; fine, sweet, mild flavor; good size and yield. An old standard. Pkt $2.50 *or 1/8 oz $8.50*

GOLDEN SUNRAY #TO109
80 days. Uniform, golden-orange globes are so smooth and uniform they look like a commercial variety, but these have a rich, full, tomato flavor that is missing in modern varieties, being both sweet and tangy. Productive vines yield lots of 8 to 10-oz. fruit that excel at markets; great for fresh use and sauce. This tomato was preserved by the late Ben Quisenberry. Pkt $2.50

KELLOGG'S BREAKFAST #TO101
A beautiful orange beefsteak preserved by our friend Darrell Kellogg, a railroad supervisor from Redford, Michigan. Its fruits are very flavorful and superbly sweet! This delicious heirloom originated in West Virginia. A favorite of Dr. Carolyn Male, author of "101 Heirloom Tomatoes." Pkt $2.50

ORANGE BANANA #TO104
80 days. Unique, orange, banana-shaped paste tomatoes that are bursting with fruity sweetness.

Perfect for drying, canning, and paste. Also delicious fresh and great for specialty markets. Orange color is rare in paste tomatoes.
Pkt $2.00

ORANGE ICICLE #TO124

Sweet, rich and flavorful with strong citrus overtones made this Jere's favorite eating variety last season. We just couldn't get enough of the sweet, luscious, glowing orange icicle-like fruit that are like an extra long paste tomato. This variety also makes a lovely orange ketchup and a superb salsa. It was a definite winner, and plants were quite productive. In our opinion, this is some of the Ukraine's finest tomato breeding. Fruit have relatively few seeds. Pkt (15 seeds) $2.50

ORANGE PEACH #TO131

75 days. Indeterminate. A chance cross in the fields of our good friend James Weaver led to this exciting new variety. The fruits are orange, range from golf-ball to tennis-ball size, and are very sweet and flavorful. The fuzzy skin, reminiscent of a real peach, comes as an interesting bonus. Believed to be a cross of Mini Orange and Yellow Peach, which is an old French variety that was once used to make a very passable "marmalade." Pkt $2.50

ORANGE STRAWBERRY #TO130

75 days. Brilliant orange, oxheart fruits have a pronounced point at the blossom end, giving them one of the most perfect heart shapes of any tomato variety known. The fruits sometimes reach a pound in weight. The flavor of the meaty fruits is robust, complex and surprisingly tart for an orange variety. Few seeds and solid flesh make this variety good for canning or sauce. Introduced by Dr. Carolyn Male via Seed Savers in 1995. Pkt $2.50

OXHEART ORANGE #TO135 *New!*

80 days. Gorgeous golden oxheart-shaped fruits. Sweet, flavorful oxhearts are meaty and great for slicing as well as processing. Fruits reach 3 inches in diameter, look so lovely developing on the luxuriant vines. Pkt $2.50

WOODLE ORANGE #TO112

75 days. Large, round, smooth fruit are nearly perfect in shape, being a brilliant tangerine color. A super fancy-looking variety that makes a good market tomato; it has an incredible rich and sweet complex flavor that is among the best. This fine heirloom was sent to us from Iowa, and has proven to be a favorite for flavor and yield. A good main-season producer. Pkt $2.50

YELLOW BRANDYWINE #TO102

90 days. Superbly rich and delicious-tasting large fruit, the golden variety gives good yields and, in our opinion, the fruit are better tasting than Pink Brandywine. Large potato-leaf plants are very sturdy and deep green. This heirloom is delicious any way you eat it! Pkt $2.50

HARLESS CREEK GOLD #TO133- *New!*

75 days—Enormously heavy yielder of softball-sized, glowing golden fruits. Fruits are as flavorsome as they are beautiful, too—rich, sweet and fruity. Pkt $2.50

Amana Orange

Orange Strawberry

Harless Creek Gold

Pink Tomatoes

ARKANSAS TRAVELER #TK108

80 days. A medium-sized pink tomato that is smooth and a beautiful rose color. An excellent variety from Arkansas, tolerant to heat and humidity; crack and disease resistant. Good flavor, an excellent hillbilly favorite. Pkt. $2.50

BALI #TK147

A new Oriental favorite here. Flat, ribbed, 2"-3" delicious fruit are a fantastic raspberry-pink in color. In flavor they are sweet and spicy, with a pronounced fragrance that makes them a delight to eat. Large plants produce loads of fruit. Good for home and market gardeners. This heirloom comes from the Island of Bali, Indonesia. Pkt $2.25

BELIZE PINK HEART #TK136

We had just entered the quaint mountain town of San Ignacio, Belize, on a balmy December evening, when we spotted a large farmer's market on the edge of town; we stopped, and I was in vegetable heaven! This is one of the jewels we collected that night; the fruit are medium large, burgundy pink and heart shaped. The flesh is a real treat, being very tender, juicy and perfect in flavor. Fruit sets on rather early. I will always remember that delicious winter tomato in tiny Belize. Pkt $3.00

BRANDYWINE (SUDDUTH'S STRAIN) #TK115 80 days. The most popular heirloom vegetable! A favorite of many gardeners, large fruit with superb flavor. A great potato-leafed variety from 1885! Beautiful pink fruit up to 1½ lbs each! Pkt $2.25 *or 1/8 oz $8.50*

BRAVE GENERAL #TK148

We are proud to introduce this big, beautiful tomato to gardeners everywhere. This Russian variety was sent to us by a gardener from Kazakhstan. Rich, sweet taste and raspberry-pink color make these 1 lb, flattened globes perfect for slicing. Very productive and a favorite here. This fine variety was sent to us by Mr. Valerii Popenko of Kazakhstan. Pkt (20 seeds) $2.50

BREAD AND SALT #TK149

Named for the long-held tradition in Russia to give special guests a loaf of bread and salt as they arrive. In Russian culture bread is associated with hospitality, and salt has an association with long friendship. Forget bread, and just give your guests this tomato; they will love it! Big, sweet fruit are round to slightly wedge-shaped and pink in color. Pkt (15 seeds) $2.50

GERMAN JOHNSON #TK117

80-90 days. Very large, 1 to 2-lb fruits are deep pink, very flavorful, and crack-resistant. The plants are very productive; the superb quality fruits are great for farmers' markets or home gardens. Delicious. Pkt $2.00

GERMAN LUNCHBOX #TK129

70-80 days. This heirloom was brought into the seed store a few years ago by a local gentleman who had been saving this tomato for many years. His family brought this variety to the USA when they immigrated here. The fruit are the size of a small egg, vibrant pink, sugar sweet, and begging to be eaten. Perfectly sized for salads or putting in

Pink Elephant

Pearly Pink

Rebekah Allen

Henderson's Pink Ponderosa

Raspberry Lyanna

Bread and Salt

the lunchbox! A favorite of mine. Pkt $2.50 *or 1/8 oz $8.50*

GERMAN PINK #TK173

85-90 days. One of the tomatoes that originally ignited the heirloom movement in America, this variety originated in Bavaria. It made its US debut in 1883, brought here by Michael Ott, a great-grandfather of Seed Savers Exchange co-founder Diane Ott Whealy. The luxuriant potato-leaf plants give high yields of 1- to 2-lb, nearly seedless meaty fruit. The prestigious Slow Foods USA Ark of Taste enthused: "a full sweet flavor, even floral, and...tender skinned." These gorgeous pink fruits are extremely versatile, excellent for canning and freezing but also for slicing and juicing. This one is sure to become a favorite in your garden! Pkt $2.50

HENDERSON'S "PINK PONDEROSA" #TK107

85 days. Huge size, some over 2 lbs; a meaty pink-red beefsteak introduced by Peter Henderson & Co. in 1891, and the most famous of their varieties. In 1903 their catalog said "Quality Beyond Praise, Rich and meaty-sliced. Thick and delicious canned." Still popular with gardeners. Pkt $2.00

HUNGARIAN HEART #TK171

80 days. Brilliant reddish-pink oxheart type fruits are enormous—frequently exceeding one pound! The fruits of this heirloom are firm and meaty like all oxheart types—great for paste, canning or fresh use. The crack-resistant fruits contain very few seeds and show very little tendency to develop cores—just rich tasting, solid flesh across each hefty slice! Heavy production all season long. Originated outside of Budapest, Hungary around 1900. Pkt $2.50

MORTGAGE LIFTER #TK120

85 days. Large, smooth, 1-lb pink fruit have a delicious, rich, sweet taste. This variety has become very popular in recent years, and was developed by M.C. Byles of Logan, West Virginia. After crossing varieties for 6 years and selecting the best, he introduced this beauty that he named Mortgage Lifter in the 1940s, after he sold plants for $1 each and paid off the $6000 mortgage on his house. See the article in the Spring 2003 issue of *Heirloom Gardener* magazine! Pkt $2.25 *or 1/8 oz $8.50*

MISSOURI PINK LOVE APPLE #TK128

Big, pink fruit are very rich-tasting, certainly a favorite pink tomato. This potato-leaved variety has a long history in the "Show Me" state. It was grown since the Civil war by the Barnes family, who grew it as an ornamental, believing (as many people did at the time) that tomatoes or "love apples" were poisonous. We are grateful the Barnes family kept this variety going so we can enjoy the wonderful fruit today. Pkt $3.00

OMAR'S LEBANESE #TK118

80 days. Huge, pink fruit can grow as large as 3-4 lbs! One of the largest tomatoes you can grow. The mammoth fruit have a superb flavor: sweet, perfect tomato taste. Good yields on vigorous plants, good tolerance to disease; a rare family heirloom from Lebanon. Perfect for anyone who wants to grow huge, tasty tomatoes. Pkt $2.50

OZARK PINK #TK151

A wonderfully smooth tomato with attractive

pink color, good flavor and the ability to make the perfect tomato for the kitchen or the market. Fruit are medium to large in size and are produced in abundance on very productive, disease resistant plants. The perfect tomato for Ozark Mountains and all hot, humid areas. Developed by the University of Arkansas. A favorite of area farmers market growers. Pkt $2.00

PINK ELEPHANT #TK168
80 days. Large, beautiful fruit are one of the most attractive varieties we grow. Big, glowing pink fruit are tender and delicious, and produced in abundance over a long season. A variety from the former USSR. Pkt $2.50

PEARLY PINK #TK127
75 days. Crisp, incredibly flavorful cherry tomatoes that are bright pink, perfect for snacking. The vines produce very well, making them great for marketing. One of the prettiest tomatoes we carry. Mmmm, so good! Pkt $2.00

PECHE #TK174
75 days. Here is something a little different: small to medium sized fruits are very slightly fuzzy, reminiscent of peaches. Sizable plants yield large amounts of the pink-to-red fruits over the entire season. Fruits are very well flavored, and the vines are productive! This variety was listed in the catalog of the prestigious French seed firm, Vilmorin Andrieux, in the 1890s. Pkt $2.50

PINK ACCORDION #TK152
Truly unique, large pink fruit is ruffled like an accordion. Very attractive—one of the most beautiful I have seen. Perfect for specialty markets, the cut slices are stunning. This tomato is semi-hollow, so it is excellent for stuffing; the flavor is sweet and mild. Pkt (10 seeds) $2.00

PINK ICICLE #TK165
Very delicious, bright pink fruit are shaped like a dazzling pink icicle. The flavor is very sweet and rich, being one of the best tasting pink paste types we've tried. Perfect for salsas and preserving, but also one of our favorites last season to eat fresh out of hand right in the garden. This variety was an incredible producer, and even though it has a small amount of seeds per fruit, we were still able to get a large crop of seeds due to its productiveness. Developed in the former Soviet Union, this is truly a masterpiece of tomato breeding. Introduced by us from the Ukraine along with its yellow, orange and black sisters. Pkt $2.50 or 1/8 oz for $8.50

PINK OXHEART #TK113
85 days. Beautiful, big, oval, pointed fruit with a fine, sweet, old-fashioned flavor! Popular with old-timers, a good all-purpose variety. Pkt $2.00 *or 1/8 oz $8.50*

RASPBERRY LYANNA #TK166
Simply stunning, raspberry-pink fruits are of medium size. Firm flesh is very sweet and richly flavored. This variety from Russia is perfect looking, one of the prettiest tomatoes we have grown. It is almost free of imperfections, making it perfect for marketing. Pkt $2.25

Belize Pink Heart

German Lunch Box

Tlacolula Pink

Pink Brandywine

Pink Accordion

REBEKAH ALLEN #TK175 *New!*
70 days—The first tomato we harvested in our 2014 Missouri garden. This pink slicer boasts positively superb flavor—everyone who tried it was impressed! The flavor is perfect—an ideal balance of sweet to tart, with complex "old fashioned" undertones. Heavy yielder of large pink fruits, on vines that appeared to have some disease resistance. Pkt $2.50

UMBERTO PEAR #TK172
80 days. (also known as King Humbert) Very old Italian heirloom, listed by the renowned French seedhouse Vilmorin-Andrieux in 1885. Named after King Umberto I, King of Italy in the late 19th century. The plants produce unbelievable harvests of small, pear-shaped fruits. These meaty morsels have a nice balance of sweet and tart, with full Old World tomato flavor. Great for paste, sauce or for drying under the late-summer sun! Pkt $2.50

ROSE DE BERNE #TK135
70-80 days. Beautiful, nicely-shaped 4-to 8-oz fruit are a rose-pink color, and have an excellent sweet flavor that has made it a hit with many growers. The vines set good yields of this lovely variety from historic Switzerland. Pkt $2.25

THE DUTCHMAN #TK104
90 days. Introduced by the legendary Merlin W. Gleckler of Glecklers Seedsmen (who was one of the first rare seed dealers). Their 1958 catalog states, *"Here is an extremely old, large-fruited pink-skinned tomato. It is practically extinct as far as securing seed. In fact, it is doubtful if seed has ever been sold by any seedsmen. Only by handing down by generations of one family has this tomato existed."* The pink-red fruit are very large, up to 3 lbs or more. Very sweet. Pkt $2.00

THAI PINK EGG #TK102
75 days. Delicious grape tomatoes from Thailand, "The Land of Smiles!" This tomato is popular all over the Kingdom. The brilliant pink, grape-shaped, 2-ounce fruit are perfect for fresh markets, restaurants and more. Good yields and the fruit is nicely uniform. Pkt $2.50

TLACOLULA PINK #TK130
75-85 days. A unique tomato collected by a friend in Tlacolula, Mexico; these pear-shaped fruit have deep ribs and ruffles that give them a distinctive look. They have a mild, sweet pink flesh and pink skin with gold-splotched shoulders. A rare tomato grown in Mexico for several generations. Pkt (10 seeds) $2.50

"And God said, Behold, I have given you every herb bearing seed, which is upon the face of all the earth, and every tree, in the which is the fruit of a tree yielding seed; to you it shall be for meat."

—GENESIS 1:29

Purple, Black & Brown Tomatoes

BEDUIN #TP123

A very flavorful and delicious fruit is a deep, dark brick color, pear shaped and weigh 3-6 ounces. Meaty and rich, perfect for canning or fresh eating. Named for the Nomadic tribe from the Near-East and North Africa. Distinctive and well worth growing. Pkt (20 seeds) $2.50

BLACK CHERRY #TP106

75 days. Beautiful black cherries look like large, dusky purple-brown grapes; they have that rich flavor that makes black tomatoes famous. Large vines yield very well; very unique and delicious. Pkt $2.50

BLACK ICICLE #TP132

Stunning, perfectly shaped, deep purplish-brown fruit that are almost black. A great variety for both home gardeners and chefs. This tomato has the incredible rich taste that is in many of the large, dark beefsteak types, sweet, rich with earthy overtones. This variety has so much potential for introduction commercially and was among our best tasting varieties last season. Another variety we are introducing from the Ukraine along with its other jewel-toned icicle sisters. Pkt (15 seeds) $3.00

BLACK KRIM #TP102

80 days Dark red-purple fruit, rich sweet flavor. One of the best. It always places high in tomato taste trials. It's very juicy. An heirloom from Russia with very unique looking, large fruit. I really like the wonderful flavor. It's popular at many markets on the West Coast; also a favorite of many fine chefs. The most nutritious tomato in our recent study. Pkt $2.50

BLACK MAURI (BLACK MOOR) #TP134

A beautiful, deep chocolate-brown, grape tomato that is sweet, flavorful and has a crisp, crunchy texture. This fine variety comes from Russia and produces high yields, even in hot conditions. This will be a great addition to fresh markets as well as for chefs and home gardeners. A perfect salad tomato that has that real dark tomato taste, delicious! Pkt $2.50

BLACK PLUM #TP129

70 days. Indeterminate plants covered in dainty little plum-shaped fruits, 2" long by 1" wide. Mahogany-skinned berries show some green-shoulders, and have the complex flavor gardeners expect in a black/purple type. Makes a wonderful salsa or spaghetti sauce, yet juicy enough for fresh use. Pkt $2.50

BLACK PRINCE #TP104

70 days. An heirloom from Irkutsk, Siberia. The 5 oz tomatoes are round and very uniform; the color is a wonderful deep blackish-chocolate brown. The flavor is as deep, sweet and rich as the color. A unique salad tomato, the plants produce a large and early crop. A good tomato for fine markets. Pkt $2.50

BLACK FROM TULA #TP103

70-80 days. A unique, large, 8 to 12-oz, dark tomato exhibiting a rich, deep purplish-brown color. Some seed savers say it is the best tasting of all the dark tomatoes. Very rich, old-fashioned flavor, sweet and spicy. A rare Russian heirloom. Pkt $2.50

Black Plum

True Black Brandywine

Chocolate

Black Cherry

Black Icicle

CARBON #TP112

90 days. Winner of the 2005 "Heirloom Garden Show" best-tasting tomato award. These have won taste awards coast to coast in the last few years, so we were proud to locate a small supply of seed. The fruit are smooth, large, and beautiful, being one of the darkest and prettiest of the purple types we have seen. They seem to have an extra dose of the complex flavor that makes dark tomatoes famous. Pkt (20 seeds) $2.50

CHEROKEE PURPLE #TP101

80 days. An old Cherokee Indian heirloom, pre-1890 variety; beautiful, deep, dusky purple-pink color, superb sweet flavor, and very-large-sized fruit. Try this one for real old-time tomato flavor. My favorite dark tomato and one of our best selling varieties. Pkt $2.50 *or 1/8 oz $8.50*

CHOCOLATE #TP141

Medium-sized slicing type fruits, about 6 oz, round and slightly flattened, rich bronze-red in color, with slight green shouldering. The flesh is deep red and fragrant, being sweet and minerally tasting. They vary somewhat in shape. From Russian seed. Pkt $2.25

CHOCOLATE CHERRY #TP153

75 days. Deep rosy-purple little cherries are very uniform at 1-inch in diameter, sweet and juicy, but with rich "old-fashioned" tomato flavor. Crack-resistant fruits are produced non-stop on trusses of 6-8 fruits; plants are vigorous and will get as large as 5 feet in height, so staking is a must. "Chocolate Cherry" is great for markets—an elegant little addition to this color class! Pkt $2.50

CHOCOLATE PEAR #TP155

70 days. Expect huge crops of "black," pear-shaped tomatoes over a very long season. Chocolate Pear has the rich tomato flavor that have made heirlooms so popular! A great variety for CSAs and market growers. Light red in color, overlaid with swirls of varying hues of green or brown. Very unusual and decidedly one of the best! Pkt $2.50

CRÈME BRULEE #TP136

A lovely tomato from the former Soviet Union. This variety produces pretty, globe shaped fruit of medium size. They are a stunning deep caramel color with hints of red and chocolate. The flavor is rich, sweet and full-bodied, and the texture is tender and smooth. An attractive tomato that is great for both home and market. Pkt $2.50

EVAN'S PURPLE PEAR #TP161 *New!*

(Also known as Evan's Purple Plum) 75 days. Selected from a chance cross from Pruden's Purple by Brad Gates, released in 2008. Fruits are plum to pear shaped, with an occasional round one. The 2 ounce fruits hang in clusters—very pretty! Flavor is very exceptional, one of the best tasting in last years trials! Great for sauces, pastes and canning, as well as for fresh use. Potato-leafed plants are vigorous and productive. Pkt $2.50

GOLOVA NEGRA #TP137

80 days. Full-sized slicer in warm tones of deep red to mahogany. The oblate fruits reach 12 ounces, and are richly pleated and folded. Fruits are extravagantly juicy, and it is for juicing that we mainly recommend this variety. It is also unusually mild for a "purple" tomato, having just a hint of the earthiness and complexity that this category is known for. Originally from Russia. Pkt $2.75

Japanese Black Trifele

Cherokee Purple

Chocolate Pear

Gypsy

GYPSY #TP121

Named for the Gypsies who live in Russia, this is one of the deepest, purplest, maroon tomatoes we have ever grown. It has a gorgeous color and good taste. Perfect, medium-sized globe fruit make this one of the nicest dark varieties. A lovely and colorful introduction from the great Soviet plant breeders. Pkt (15 seeds) $2.50

JAPANESE BLACK TRIFELE #TP107

80-90 days. Attractive tomatoes are the shape and size of a Bartlett pear, with a beautiful purplish-brick color. The fruit are perfect and smooth with no cracks. The flavor is absolutely sublime, having all the richness of fine chocolate. This was our heaviest producer for 2004. The plants produced loads of fruit all summer long. It has become a favorite with many seed savers, and we are glad to be able to offer such a colorful variety that is believed to have come from Russia... Don't ask me about the name! Pkt $2.50

MORADO #TP113

85 days. This very rare tomato produces delicious 1 lb fruit that are dark purplish-pink in color, with green shoulders. The plants have excellent production, and fruit is uniform and crack resistant. Another great-tasting "black" tomato that should be a good variety for the market grower. Pkt $2.25

NYAGOUS #TP109

90 days. A wonderful, dark-colored 'cluster tomato' that produces perfect globe-shaped fruit that have smooth shoulders and are borne in clusters of 3-6 tomatoes! They are aromatic and have sweet, meaty flesh that has a rich taste. Another tomato that is superb for marketing and a must for every garden; simply lovely. This variety came to the USA from our friend, Reinhard Kraft, of Germany. Pkt $2.25

PAUL ROBESON #TP110

90 days. This famous tomato has almost a cult following among seed collectors and tomato connoisseurs, who simply cannot get enough of this variety's amazing flavor that is so distinctive, sweet, and smoky. 7 to 10-oz fruit are a black-brick color. Named in honor of the famous black opera singer, star of King Solomon's Mines, 1937. Paul Robeson, an American, was also a Russian Equal Rights Advocate for Blacks. This Russian variety was lovingly named in his honor. We are proud to offer such a wonderful variety. Pkt (10 seeds) $2.50

PIERCE'S PRIDE #TP111

90 days. A stabilized cross that was selected by our seed grower, Larry Pierce. Medium-sized fruit are very flavorful and rich. They are nicely shaped, deep, dark black-red in color. This is certainly one of our tastiest tomatoes. Pkt $2.50

PURPLE CALABASH #TP125

85 days. May be the most purple of all "purple" tomatoes; a deep purple/burgundy and very colorful! The shape is also exciting, with the 3" fruit being very flat, ribbed and ruffled. Flavor is intense, sweet and tart, with a lime or citrus taste. A most uniquely flavored tomato! The plants give huge yields. This tomato resembles tomatoes pictured in 16th-century herbal diaries. Pkt $2.50

PURPLE RUSSIAN #TP108

75 days. Delicious purplish, egg-shaped fruit are smooth and perfect. They have no blemishes and have flavor that tops the charts. One of

the best varieties we carry for salsa, fresh eating, and preserving. This variety will make market gardeners and chefs happy, as this Ukrainian heirloom is at the top of its class and a favorite of our grower. The plants are very productive; fruit weigh about 6 ounces. Introduced to the USA in 1980. Pkt $2.50 *or 1/8 oz $8.50*

Paul Robeson

TRUE BLACK BRANDYWINE #TP114

80-90 days. Potato leaf . This fine variety was sent to us by our friend, famed seed collector and food writer, William Woys Weaver, of Pennsylvania. It was passed down to him from his Quaker grandfather's collection dating back to the 1920s. As to its history, Will states "The 'true' Black Brandywine was bred sometime in the late 1920s by Dr. Harold E. Martin (1888-1959), a dentist turned plant breeder who is best remembered today for his famous pole lima with huge seeds. Dr. Martin lived in Westtown, PA, only a few miles from my grandfather's place in West Chester, and the two were gardening buddies. It was through that connection that his grandfather managed to wheedle seed out of the good doctor, as well as the details on how he created it. Dr. Martin always had a high opinion of his plant creations and did not like to share them. He charged 25 cents a seed for his lima, unheard of in those days. And he never released his Black Brandywine to a seed company, nor did he share it with many people, so I am fairly certain it never circulated among growers like his popular lima bean. According to my grandfather, Black Brandywine was a controlled cross between Brandywine and the original brown Beefsteak tomato otherwise known as Fejee Improved. Fejee Improved is probably extinct." We thank Will for entrusting us with this great-tasting tomato that is extra large in size and full of the deep, earthy and sweet flavor that has made blackish-purple tomatoes so popular. Some fruits tended to crack, but the yield was heavy, and the plants were vigorous and did well in our hot Missouri summer. Superior for salsa and cooking. We enjoyed these all summer, both fresh and in countless recipes. A great home garden variety that will surely become a favorite. Pkt $2.75

Tsungshigo Chinese

TSUNGSHIGO CHINESE #TP147

Unbelievable production of small, reddish-chocolate colored, grape-shaped tomatoes. These have the sweet, earthy flavor of the classic 'black' types, but packed into a small package. Seed originally from a Chinese commercial vendor. Pkt $2.50

VIOLET JASPER or TZI BI U #TP127

When these little Oriental jewels ripen, your eyes will be stunned with color. They have pretty violet-purple fruit with iridescent green streaks! Fruit weigh 1-3 ounces, are smooth and have good tasting, dark purplish-red flesh. This variety will also amaze you with its yield: it's not only high, but incredibly high, being one of the most productive tomatoes we have grown. A great variety for marketing. Introduced to you from China along with its twin sister "Topaz"; see our yellow tomato section. Pkt $2.50 or 1/8 oz $8.50

VORLON #TP128

We are introducing this large variety received from Bulgaria. A stunning purple-black tomato that was the best-tasting tomato we grew last season and is sure to become a new favorite. Rich dark flesh is full of the rich, smoky, organic taste that makes dark varieties among our favorite. Though named for the Vorlons, a fictional alien race, this tomato won't stay an alien long. Pkt (15 seeds) $2.50

Black from Tula

God Almighty first planted a garden. And indeed, it is the purest of human pleasures.
-Francis Bacon

Red Tomatoes

A GRAPPOLI D'INVERNO #TM205
This is the "Winter Grape" tomato of old Italy, where farmers would hang the fruit-covered vines and the fruit would stay fresh well into the winter. They also dry perfectly and resemble little "Roma" tomatoes. The flavorful fruit are delicious and great for snacking, fresh or dried. Pkt $2.50

ABU RAWAN #TM232
Determinate. Another variety contributed to the tomato world by our friend, expatriate Iraqi seed collector Nael Aziz. He stated that it is a bit unusual for an Iraqi type, because in Iraq the people tend to favor tart tomatoes, while this one is sweeter. Having solid, all-purpose flesh, it will take the heat, like Iraqi types generally. Named for the onetime caretaker of the greenhouses at the Agricultural College at Al Ghraib. Maintained in cultivation in private gardens there since the 1970's. Pkt (10 seeds) $2.50

AMISH PASTE #TM126
80 days. Many seed savers believe this is the ultimate paste tomato. Giant, blocky, Roma type tomatoes have delicious red flesh that is perfect for paste and canning. It has world-class flavor and comes from an Amish community in Wisconsin. Pkt $2.50

ATKINSON #TM172
Bred for Southern conditions, this medium-height variety produces 8-oz red globes even through hot, dry summers. A tomato with considerable merit, which was no longer being offered commercially. Pkt $1.75

BASRAWYA #TM207
80 days. Beautiful, round-globe fruit that have a delicious tomato flavor and are quite smooth and perfect looking. We received this great tomato from Aziz Nael whose brother collects seeds in occupied Iraq. These come from the southern town of Basra and seem to be adapted well to hot weather as Basra is in the hot, southern part of Iraq. Nael Aziz continues to send us seeds from Iraq and continues to write about the vast genetic depletion in vegetable crops since the war. Pkt $3.00

BETALUX #TM134 *New!*
Determinate, 60 days. Early Polish variety whose "rigid stem" habit doesn't require staking or pruning. Handsome potato-leaf vines are very productive, yielding 3- to 6-oz round to oblate fruits. These were very smooth and blemish-free in our trials. The fruits are well flavored and excellent for canning, sauces or paste. Pkt $2.25

BONNY BEST #TM181
The famous old canning tomato that was selected out of Chalk's Early Jewel by one George W. Middleton and introduced in 1908 by Walter P. Stokes seed house. It became one of the most respected canning varieties in America in the first half of the twentieth century. Medium-sized fruit are round, red, meaty and loaded with flavor. A good producer that makes a fine slicer too. Becoming hard to find due to modern, flavorless hybrids. Pkt $2.25

Marmande

Minibel

BUCKBEES NEW FIFTY DAY #TM141

75 days. A pre-1930 variety introduced by H.W. Buckbee of Rockford, Illinois. Their 1930 catalog states, "The largest fruited, the smoothest, the finest in quality of all early scarlet tomatoes." Not as early as 50 days, but this is indeed a good producer that has an old-fashioned tomato taste; red and medium-sized.
Pkt $2.25

CHADWICK CHERRY OR CAMP JOY
#TM179 80 days. Delicious, sweet flavor makes this 1-ounce cherry popular with home gardeners. Large vines set huge yields and are disease resistant. Developed by the late horticultural expert Alan Chadwick. He sure had a winner with this one! Pkt $2.50

COMSTOCK SAUCE AND SLICE #TM240

85 days. Indeterminate. Gorgeous deep-red fruits reach to one-pound-plus, containing very few seeds. Originally introduced by Comstock, Ferre and Co in the 1980's, having been received as a gift from a customer who reportedly brought the seeds from his native Italy. Preserved and beloved by local gardeners in and around Comstock's hometown of Wethersfield, Connecticut. A dual-purpose type equally at home canned or in paste, or atop your favorite garden-fresh sandwich! Pkt $2.50

COSTOLUTO GENOVESE #TM210

The fluted, old Italian favorite that has been around since the early 19th century. Fruit are rather flattened and quite attractive with their deep ribbing. This variety is a standard in Italy for both fresh eating and preserving, known for its intensely flavorful, deep red flesh. This variety has also became very popular with chefs in this country. Pkt $2.25

COUR DI BUE #TM121

70 days. A wonderful, Oxheart-type heirloom has been a favorite in Italy for many years. Beautiful, 12-oz, heart-shaped fruit have a delicious sweet taste; similar to the shape of a heart, great for fresh eating or cooking. Large vigorous vines. One of the best tasting tomatoes I have ever tasted, these have perfect flavor! Hard to find and so beautiful looking.
Pkt $2.50 *or 1/8 oz $8.50*

FOX CHERRY #TM160

75 days. Delicious large, red heirloom cherry tomatoes that seem to be one of the best-tasting large cherries around. The vining plants are very reliable; even in years when the wilt kills just about everything else, these seem to thrive! The fruit weigh about 1 oz each and are perfect for salads. Pkt $2.50

GERMAN RED STRAWBERRY #TM128

85 days. Big, flavorful 1-pound fruit are shaped like giant strawberries. These beautiful tomatoes are loaded with a rich, sweet flavor and have few seeds. With only a small amount of seeds or juice, they are great for canning and sandwiches. This superior-tasting tomato is a family heirloom from Germany. Pkt $2.50

GLACIER #TM244

55 days. Semi-determinate. Loads of round, 2-3-inch, red to slightly orange fruit are produced on compact, potato-leafed plants to 3 feet tall. Use in salads or in colorful tomato

Betalux

Tappy's Heritage

San Marzano

salads! Excellent flavor for an early-season type. Reliable in cooler-season climates, setting fruit all summer long. Pkt $2.50

GRANNY CANTRELL TM202

80 days. This meaty beefsteak-type tomato is named after Lettie Cantrell, who received seeds from a soldier returning from Germany during World War II. She grew this tomato in the hills of eastern Kentucky for many years. This was her favorite tomato and the only one she grew. Each year she saved seeds from the largest tomatoes, some of which reached 2 1/2 lbs. Our growers find it to be quite productive. Ahh! What a flavor! This variety was named best tasting tomato of the year at the 2006 Heirloom Garden Show in our taste testing contest. Pkt $2.50

ILLINOIS BEAUTY #TM168

An excellent home and market garden variety with great flavor. A heavy producer of 4 to 6 ounce fruits which are usually free of any blemishes or cracks. This disease-resistant type sets fruit in hot, dry summers and produces prolifically all season—six plants yielded nine gallons of tomatoes the first picking and six gallons the second picking! A lucky, accidental cross with some of the best qualities you can ask for in a tomato. Pkt $2.25

JERSEY DEVIL #TM235

90 days. Pendulant, pointed, pepper-like fruits are slow to set on but yield very heavily. 5-6-inch, ruby-red, paste-type fruits are very meaty and have but few seeds. Incredible flavor. This variety was another pillar of the New Jersey tomato industry, and is an ancestor to "Jersey Giant." Jere has been growing these for 20 years and they are a favorite! Pkt (10 seeds) $2.50

JERSEY GIANT #TM192

This New Jersey canning variety is on the verge of extinction! Large, 6-inch long, pepper-shaped fruit are packed with great tomato flavor. Delicious fresh from the garden. Their large size makes them a snap to can. Their thick, rich flesh is much tastier than modern paste types, and the fruit have very few seeds. One of my personal favorites. Pkt $2.50

JUJUBE CHERRY #TM193

75 days. Here is a wonderful red grape tomato from our friend, Reinard Kraft, of Germany. Fruits are produced in long clusters, each one being about the size and shape of a jumbo olive. The crisp fruit are delightfully refreshing and are perfect for snacking. Pkt $2.00

LARGE RED #TM139

80 days. This pre-1830 variety was documented as being grown in Hancock, Mass., by the Shakers in the 1830's. In 1865 Fearing Burr stated, "from the time of introduction...the large red was almost the only kind cultivated, or even commonly known." Unique, 12-oz. fruit are deeply fluted and have a sweet, rich tomato flavor. A rare treasure for historic gardeners. Pkt $2.50

MARGLOBE SUPREME #TM104

Determinate. 73-77 days. Medium-sized, red fruit make excellent canning tomatoes. Good size and uniform deep scarlet color. Great for humid climates. Pkt $1.50

MARMANDE #TM119

Semi-determinate. 70 days. Popular, old French variety developed by the Vilmorin Seed Co. Scarlet, lightly ribbed fruit, have the full rich flavor that is so enjoyed in Europe. Medium-large sized fruit are produced even in cool weather. Productive market variety. Imported European seed. Pkt $2.00

MARTINO'S ROMA #TM247

70-80 days. Determinate. Fantastic yields of richly flavorful plum-shaped tomatoes, on compact plants that require very little staking! Resistant to early blight, reliable for home or market gardens! The paste-type fruits weigh in at 2-3 ounces, dry-fleshed and very meaty with few seeds. Great for sauces, salsas and pastes. Pkt $2.50

MINIBEL #TM248

65 days. Determinate. Bite-sized fruits are sweet and flavorsome. Tiny ornamental plants reach only to about a foot in height, require no support. Covered in tasty little tomatoes. Excellent choice for containers, pots or hanging baskets; pretty enough for the patio or deck. So cute! Pkt $2.50

MONEYMAKER #TM116

75-80 days. An old English heirloom; greenhouse variety; produces 4 to 6-oz globes that are intensely red, smooth, and of very high quality. This variety grows well in hot, humid climates and greenhouses; sets in most any weather. Flavorful and becoming rare. Pkt $2.00

MOSKVICH #TM237

60 days. Semi-determinate. Smallish, 4-6 ounce fruits; very uniform, globular and deep red. Produced early and abundantly, the crack-resistant fruits are of outstandingly good flavor; used fresh or for canning and cooking. Performs well in cool to cold conditions, like so many of the Russian types. Pkt $2.25

NINEVEH TOMATO #TM191

A very acid, almost sour-tasting tomato that is best for cooking uses. This tomato comes from Mosul (formerly Nineveh) Iraq, but is now said to be lost to cultivation due to the long on-going war and promotion of hybrid and gene-altered seeds. Bush plants set bright red, small to medium sized fruit. From Aziz Nael, an Iraqi friend that supplied us with a few seeds. Pkt $2.50

PANTANO ROMANESCO #TM127

70-80 days. A Roman heirloom that was sent to us by Mr. Barbetti, from Italy. The fruit are large and are deep red, with almost a purple tint. The flesh is very rich, flavorful, and juicy. An excellent tomato for home and market gardeners; very rare and delicious. Pkt $2.50

PERON #TM155 *New!*

68 days. (Also known as Peron Sprayless) Compact, semi-determinate vines are fairly disease resistant. Deep-red, dual-purpose canning and slicing sort. Smooth, slightly oblate fruits are very dense-fleshed and meaty, and

"The federal government has sponsored research that has produced a tomato that is perfect in every respect, except that you can't eat it. We should make every effort to make sure this disease, often referred to as 'progress', doesn't spread." -Andy Rooney

A Grappoli d'Inverno

Amish Paste

Cour di Bue

show very little core. Skins are very thick and tough, simplifying peeling when processing, and making the crack-resistant fresh fruits keep extremely well. Fruits run 3-6 ounces; flavor is very good, and sweet enough for fresh use as well. Developed prior to 1954 by Prof. Abelardo Piovano of Argentina. Pkt $2.50

PLACERO #TM196
A flavorful, small tomato from our friend Herb Culver. He collected this tomato in Cuba from a man named Orlando at Mission Mundial. This tomato also is said to have a very high beta-carotene content. Tasty, red fruit grow on very productive plants. Pkt $2.00

PRINCIPE BORGHESE #TM122
70-75 days. Determinate. The Italian heirloom that is famous for sun drying. Small 1-to 2-oz, grape-shaped fruit are very dry and have few seeds. They have a rich tomato taste that is wonderful for sauces. Determinate vines yield clusters of fruit in abundance, perfect for selling in fresh markets and making specialty products. We offer pure Italian seed. Pkt $2.25

RED FIG or PEAR-SHAPED #TM106
75 days. Small, 1½" red fruit are pear shaped. This heirloom dates back to the 1700's. It was offered by many seedsmen and was very popular for making "Tomato Figs." The fruit is sweet and tasty. Pkt $2.00

RIESENTRAUBE #TM132
76-85 days. This old German heirloom was offered in Philadelphia by the mid-1800's. The sweet, red 1-oz fruit grow in large clusters; the name means "Giant Bunch of Grapes" in German. This is likely the most popular small tomato with seed collectors, as many favor the rich, full tomato flavor that is missing in today's cherry types. Large plants produce massive yields. Pkt $2.50 *or 1/8 oz $8.50*

REISETOMATE #TM198
The most novel tomato we have seen, this tomato is like a big bunch of cherry tomatoes all fused together: an amazing trait that had everyone here asking questions about the alien-looking, bumpy tomatoes. Also called "Traveler Tomato" (*"reise"* is German for "travel" or "journey") for the ability to tear it apart a piece at a time, with no need for a knife. This type of tomato traces its roots to Central America where the native people would carry traveler tomatoes on trips, to eat as they walked. Bright red tomatoes taste—well, rather sour, strong and acid. The perfect tomato for those who love raw lemons, but who cares? They are still far-out and groovy. Pkt (10 seeds) $2.50

ROMA #TM110
76 days Determinate.. A quality paste variety, very thick flesh. A popular old favorite; good yields. Pkt $2.00

RED ROSSO SICILIAN #TM245
80 days. Indeterminate. Deeply ribbed, intensely red fruits reach up to 5 ounces. Firm, solid flesh and somewhat hollow seed cavity make this a star for stuffing or paste, but the ribbing also gives slices a scalloped appearance which is lovely on a plate. First grown in this country by Ann Fuller of Mitchell, Indiana, who received seed from a Sicilian man in 1987. Richly flavored, just

as the Italians like their tomatoes, and stunningly beautiful! Pkt $2.50

ROYAL CHICO #TM103
80 days. Determinate. Very productive Roma type, vigorous; yields bright-red, pear-shaped fruit that are uniform and perfect for paste or canning. Very resistant to disease, perfect for the home garden or market. This variety is becoming rare. Pkt $1.50

RUTGERS #TM102
60-100 days. Determinate. Good for canning, also excellent fresh; large red 8-oz globes. Good yields and flavor, large vines. A fine N.J. heirloom. Pkt $2.25

SAN MARZANO LUNGO NO. 2 #TM213
This is a newer selection of this famous Italian cooking tomato. Long, cylindrical fruit are filled with thick, dry flesh and few seeds. This heavy producing variety is a standard for many Italian farmers and chefs. Pkt $2.00

SIOUX #TM143
70 days. One of the best-known historic tomatoes; the medium-sized fruit are produced from early until late in the season. Productive plants and great flavor made this one of the most popular Midwestern tomatoes in the late 1940's. In 1947, Oscar H. Will & Co. stated, "It out-yielded all other varieties in South Dakota trials." Per Henderson & Co., in 1951, "Two weeks earlier than Marglobe or Rutgers." This tomato was one of our most requested, as people love the smooth, beautiful fruit and heavy yields. Introduced in 1944 by the University of Nebraska. Pkt $2.50

STUPICE #TM199
A great, potato leaf variety that comes from Czechoslovakia. One of the best early tomatoes, this is among the earliest. Perfect for gardeners in northern climes. Excellent flavor for an early type, these produce lots of red, small to medium sized fruit over a very long season. Highly popular in areas with short summers. Pkt $2.00

SUB-ARCTIC PLENTY OR "WORLD'S EARLIEST" #TM130
50 days. Determinate. One of the very earliest tomatoes, the compact plants produce lots of 2-oz red fruit. One of the best for cool conditions and will set fruit in lower temperatures than most. It has even been grown in the Southern Yukon. Developed by Dr. Harris, Beaverlodge Research Station, Alberta, Canada. Pkt $2.00

TATAR OF MONGOLISTAN #TM137
70-85 days. We were sent this rare tomato in the late 1990's by Iraqi seed collector Aziz Nael, who was living in France. Medium-sized fruit are very flavorful, red, and flattened in shape. These have become popular with seed savers since we introduced it about 5 years ago. We are glad to have this tasty type back. Great fresh or dried. Pkt $2.50

TAPPY'S HERITAGE #TM112
85 days. Beautiful, smooth, large red fruit are globe-shaped. With good disease resistance, great yields, perfect shape, and wonderful flavor, it's superb for market growers. This variety was developed by Merlyn and Mary Ann

Glacier

Granny Cantrell

Nineveh

Niedens, longtime seed growers in Illinois. Bred from heirloom varieties, it has fantastic taste and is one of our all-time best-selling varieties. Try it and you will see why! Pkt $2.50

TEN FINGERS OF NAPLES #TM249

(Dix Doights de Naples) 75 days, determinate. A paste or canning type that produces huge yields of elongated, pointed fruit reaching 5-6 inches in length, weighing to 3 ounces. Fruits are produced in bunches, giving rise to fanciful comparison to hands! The flavor is much superior to many modern types, being sweet and rich. This fine variety is from Naples, Italy. Pkt $2.50

TESS'S LAND RACE CURRANT #TM156

55-68 days. Deliciously flavored currant tomato that originated from Maryland's southern shore. The tiny fruit of this variety vary in color; most are deep red but some are also rose, gold and yellow. The flavorful fruit are popular with chefs and home gardeners. The sprawling vines produce clusters of these intense tasting miniatures. Pkt $2.25

THESSALONIKI #TM101

60-80 days. A Greek tomato that was introduced to the USA in the 1950's by Glecklers Seedsmen, of Ohio. It is a popular, large, red, uniform fruit with excellent flavor, high yields, and disease resistance. An early variety, perfect for home or market; keeps well. Pkt $2.50 *or 1/8 oz $8.50*

TOMMY TOE #TM246

75 days.Indeterminate. (Also known as Steakhouse) Vigorous plants produce hundreds of small, 1-inch cherries, unfazed by heat and humidity. The flavor is very good, not exactly sweet but with an old-fashioned, full, complex flavor. Originated in the Ozarks around 1900, but also exceedingly popular in Australia—two ostensibly English-speaking regions where puns, apparently, are popular as well. Pkt $2.50

"He that tilleth his land shall be satisfied with bread." —PROVERBS 12:11

·There seem to be but three ways for a nation to acquire wealth. The first is by war, as the Romans did, in plundering their conquered neighbors. This is robbery. The second by commerce, which is generally cheating. The third by agriculture, the only honest way, wherein man receives a real increase of the seed thrown into the ground, in a kind of continual miracle, wrought by the hand of God in his favor, as a reward for his innocent life and his virtuous industry."

—BEN FRANKLIN

Stupice

Ten Fingers of Naples

Jersey Giant

Easy Marinara!

We thank Brande Plotnick, owner of Tomato Envy (**http://tomatoenvy.com**) for this recipe. It is a life-saver when your tomato plants are pumping out tomatoes faster than you can keep up. Most marinara sauce recipes call for canned tomatoes, but this one uses lots of fresh ones at once. The sauce is so versatile – use some now and freeze batches of it for a fresh taste of summer even in the dead of winter.

INGREDIENTS
(Makes about 1 1/2 quarts of sauce)
12 pounds of fresh tomatoes, preferably Amish Paste or a Roma type
1/2 cup extra virgin olive oil
4 cloves of garlic, peeled and chopped
1 cup packed fresh basil leaves
1/4 tsp. crushed red pepper flakes
Kosher salt

Peel the tomatoes. Get a big pot of water boiling and set up a bowl filled with ice water next to your stove. Working in batches, drop the tomatoes into the boiling water and cook for about 45 seconds. Fish them out with tongs and drop them into the ice water for about one minute. You should then be able to easily slip the tomato peels off like a jacket. Cut or dig the cores out with your fingers and tear the tomatoes into pieces and place them into a very large bowl.

Heat the olive oil in large pot over medium-high heat. Add all of the tomatoes, the garlic, the basil, and the red pepper flakes. Stir to combine and bring to a boil. Reduce the heat to a simmer and cook uncovered for anywhere from 2-4 hours, depending on how juicy your tomatoes are.

At first, your sauce won't look like much. It will be watery and light in color. Don't worry, just keep simmering. The sauce will cook way down, concentrating the flavor of the tomatoes. You'll know it's done when the sauce is vibrant in color and considerably thicker. Once you're there, season the sauce with salt.

Freeze this homemade marinara sauce in portions and use it on demand all winter tossed with pasta, drizzled over meatball subs, & baked into cheesy eggplant gratins.

Jujube Cherry

Jersey Devil

Roma

SUN DRIED TOMATOES
Old World Flavor

Solar drying has been at the forefront of culture for thousands of years. Energy from the sun concentrates the flavor of fruit and preserves all the precious nutrients. During your growing season, you will have spurts of rapid growth and harvest. During these times, canning may not be in the cards. Sundried tomatoes, a culinary delight to chefs around the world, are easy to produce and enjoy.

Sun drying, though simplistic to Americans, is pivotal in countries with no infrastructure. The main goal for numerous producers is to dry the product as swiftly as possible. The addition of air flow or wind to the fruit is crucial.

I like to cut the tomatoes in half and sprinkle with coarse sea salt. Take your tomato or fruit harvest and place on a perforated pan. Remember that air flow is key to this drying process. The addition of the salt aids in the drying process as it helps pull out moisture from the fruit. The salt also helps keep bacteria as it lowers the PH of the fruit. I also love the flavor or oregano and fresh thyme sprinkled on the tomatoes. Place these skin side down on the pan and cover with cheesecloth. Place the tomatoes in full sun for 2-4 days. Bring inside when times of high humidity or dew would cause unneeded moisture on the fruit.

Tomatoes will begin to shrivel up, concentrating the color and flavor of the fruit. The moisture content should be around 8%, rendering fruit that should be leathery and tough. Reconstitute in warm water for desired use. The tomatoes will keep for a month if preserved in olive oil.

Reisetomate

Abu Rawan

Striped Roman

Pink Tiger

Green Tiger

Blush

Striped & Bicolor Tomatoes

ANANAS NOIRE #TS117
(Black Pineapple) A most exciting new tomato, it is wonderful in every way. This unusual variety was developed by Pascal Moreau, a horticulturist from Belgium. The multi-colored, smooth fruit (green, yellow and purple mix) weigh about 1½ lbs. The flesh is bright green with deep red streaks. Everyone loves their superb flavor that is outstanding, being both sweet and smoky with a hint of citrus. The yield is one of the heaviest we have ever seen! Be the first at your farmer's market to have this new classic. Pkt $2.75

BEAUTY QUEEN #TS127
80 days. A good producer of very striped red and yellow fruit that have clearly defined markings much like Green Zebra. Small to medium size fruit have excellent flavor. These have proven to be very popular at farmer's markets. Pkt $2.50

BERKELEY TIE-DIE GREEN #TS155
75-80 days—Incredibly colorful and delicious large-fruited slicing variety! Fruits run 8 to 16 ounces. Exterior color is green with stripes in red and yellow. But the flesh is truly tri-color! Creamy green flesh infused with various shades of red and yellow. Each of these colors has a different flavor resulting in a spicy, sweet, tart tomato with good acid all in one fruit. Discovered in a planting of Beauty King. Fair to good production. A truly incredible new open-pollinated variety, and a new favorite of many chefs. Pkt (15 seeds) $2.75

BERKELEY TIE DYE- PINK #TX105
65-75 days. Indeterminate. Compact plants produce beautiful 8-12 ounce fruit with a very sweet, rich, dark tomato flavor. 10 out of 10 people liked the port wine colored beefsteak with metallic green stripes better than Cherokee Purple in a farmers market taste off. Pkt (15 seeds) $3.00

BIG RAINBOW #TS101
Huge fruit up to 2 lbs.; delicious and sweet tasting. These tomatoes are very striking sliced, as the yellow fruit have neon red streaking though the flesh. An heirloom preserved by members of Seed Savers Exchange. Pkt $2.50

BLUSH TOMATO #TS145
60-70 days. Indeterminate. Stunning "Blushed" in red and gold combine with a translucent quality to give these elongated cherries serious visual appeal! The fruits, similar in size and shape to large olives, score high in taste tests. Blush was selected by eight-year-old Alex Hempel from two of his favorite tomatoes, and is an ancestor of the Bumble Bee series! Outstanding! Pkt $2.75

COPIA #TS115
80-90 days. One of our most unique and beautiful large, striped tomatoes, these have lovely fine stripes of glowing gold and neon red. Inside the flavorful flesh is a mix of red and yellow that is swirled together in various combinations. This new variety was developed by Jeff Dawson and named in honor of Copia, the American Center for Food, Wine and the Arts, of Napa, CA. Pkt (20 seeds) $2.25

GOLD MEDAL #TS112

75-90 days. The 1-lb fruit are among the smoothest, bi-colored tomatoes we carry and are one of the most beautiful we have seen. Yellow fruit are blushing with rosy red that radiates from the blossom end. Lovely! The firm flesh is of superior quality, being sweet and mild. They have very little acid; great for fresh eating. From the late, legendary seed collector, Ben Quisenberry. Pkt $2.50

GREEN BELL PEPPER #TG120

75-80 days. Very well flavored, unusual stuffing-type tomato, having stunning stripes of light and dark green, maturing to yellow and green. Four-ounce, three- to four-lobed fruits are apple-shaped, and look like small blocky bell peppers. The seeds and pulp are contained in a mass near the stem, just like a pepper, and so are easily removed to prepare the fruits for stuffing. Pkt (15 seeds) $2.50

GREEN COPIA #TS143

76-80 days. Oblate, beefsteak fruits run in the medium size range. When ripe, the luscious fruits are striped in alternate bands of apple-green and pale pink. The fruits show varying degrees of pleating and make gorgeous and delicious bicolor slices. Superb when showcased on platters or on open-faced sandwiches! Discovered as a sport or perhaps a chance cross of the renowned Copia. Pkt $2.25

GREEN SAUSAGE #TG105

86 days. Determinate. A stunningly beautiful, banana-shaped paste tomato that is lime green and yellow striped when ripe! The flavor is rich and tangy. This will be a hot item for high-priced, groovy markets. So cool when mixed with orange, white, yellow, and red-striped paste types. Short, bushy plants produce 4"-long fruit in abundance. Pkt $2.50

GREEN TIGER #TS147

70 days. Exciting new class of elongated cherry tomatoes! Crack-resistant fruits reach two inches in length, tapering to a pronounced point; color is an amazing green striped with yellow, with a lime-green interior. Chefs rave about their extraordinary beauty and superb flavor. Equally well suited for greenhouse or outdoor culture. Pkt $2.75

GREEN ZEBRA #TG103

75 days. One of my favorite tomatoes. Beautiful chartreuse with deep lime-green stripes, very attractive. Flesh is bright green and very rich tasting, sweet with a sharp bite to it (just too good to describe!). A favorite tomato of many high class chefs, specialty markets, and home gardeners. Yield is excellent. The most striking tomato in our catalog, a real beauty. Around 3 ounces. This is the tomato colored for the Green Bay Packers. Pkt $2.50 *or 1/8 oz $8.50*

HILLBILLY OR FLAME #TS102

80-85 days. A huge, bi-color heirloom; brilliant yellow color with red marbling. Very large with a rich, sweet flavor. Beautiful when sliced. An heirloom believed to be from West Virginia. Pkt $2.00 *or 1/8 oz $8.50*

ISIS CANDY CHERRY #TS128

67 days. Delightful, round one-inch fruits may vary in shades and blush patterns of reds to yellows, usually with golden flesh. Typically carry an intriguing "cat's eye" or star in yellow on the blossom end. The flavor is outstanding, sweet and fruity. Kids adore them. Pkt $2.50

Green Sausage

Purple Bumble Bee

Sunrise Bumble Bee

Pink Bumble Bee

Berkeley Tie Dye Green

Vernissage series, Black, Pink, Yellow and Green

JANET'S JACINTHE JEWEL #TS156 *New!*

85 days Gorgeous striped orange beefsteak from Brad Gates, just released in 2014. Fruits commonly exceed 1 pound and are very meaty. Heavy yields, nice sweet taste. Pkt (15 seeds) $3.00

LARGE BARRED BOAR #TX102

65-70 days. Indeterminate. This regular leaf tomato grows fairly stocky and not as tall as most indeterminate varieties. Flattened beefsteak fruit are pink-brown with metallic green stripes and weigh 8-12 ounces. Very meaty pink flesh is very flavorful. Pkt (15 seeds) $3.00

MARY ROBINSON'S GERMAN BICOLOR

#TS119 80-90 days. Large fruit are yellow with lots of red shading and streaks, much more red than many bicolor types. Fruit is very sweet and mild, great for a slicing tomato. Large, vigorous vines produce heavy yields. Given to a collector in 1994 by G. Fitzgerald. Pretty and delicious. Pkt $2.50

MICHAEL POLLAN #TX112

75 days. Bred at Wild Boar Farms, and named for the famous author and activist who has contributed so much to the sustainability movement! Small green fruits are uniquely top-shaped, with the most pronounced blossom end "beak" that we have ever seen! Color is green/yellow stripes. Flavor is mild and sweet. 2- to 4-ounce fruits usually grow in clusters. Amazing! Pkt (15 seeds) $3.00

NATURE'S RIDDLE #TS130

A big, bi-color tomato that we are introducing from Russia. It is such an attractive one too, having fairly smooth fruit, golden-yellow with fanciful streaks of blushing salmon-pink! Great taste, being very sweet and meaty. This fine variety was sent to us by Valerrii Popenko of Kazakhstan. Pkt (15 seeds) $2.00

PEPPERMINT #TS134

A lovely heirloom from the mountains around Crab Orchard, Tennessee, this variety produces large 1lb tomatoes that are beautifully striped with red and orange. The flavor is sweet and mild, perfect for eating like fruit. This hard-to-find variety is both attractive and delicious. We had some plants produce solid red fruit, but selected only for bi-colored fruit, so you may occasionally still get a plant with red fruit. Pkt $2.50

PINK BUMBLE BEE # TS148   60-70 days.

Indeterminate.A stunning cherry tomato, of recent breeding from Artisan Seeds. The fruits have a bright, sweet flavor, and the color is vibrant fire-engine red with golden orange striping. Vigorous vines yield crack resistant fruits over a very long season. Tolerates cool nighttime temps and hot days. Salad will never be the same! Pkt $2.75

PURPLE BUMBLE BEE #TS149   60-70 days.

Indeterminate. Slightly elongated little cherries with the most outrageous striping in lime green and bronzy-purple! Crack-resistant fruits are produced all season long on plants that are unfazed by temperature extremes. The flavor is complex but sweet. Excellent holding quality makes this newer type outstanding for market. The bar just got higher! From Artisan Seeds. Pkt $2.75

SUNRISE BUMBLEBEE #TS150 *New!*

70 days. Chefs love the luminous swirls of reds and oranges, inside the fruits and out! Everyone loves the sweet, fruity taste, too! Oblong little fruits weigh

Violet Jasper

Nature's Riddle

Ananas Noire

barely an ounce, sometimes show a pronounced beak at the blossom end. Another member of the incredible new 'Artisan' series. Pkt $2.75

PINEAPPLE #TS103

75-95 days. Very large, up to 2 lbs each. The yellow fruit has red marbling through the flesh and is one of the most beautiful tomatoes we sell. The flavor is very sweet and fruity; good yields! A Gettle Family favorite. Pkt $2.50 *or 1/8 oz $8.50*

PINEAPPLE PIG #TS153 *New!*

90 days. Very large fruited variety reaches 1 lb or more! Fruits are creamy-ivory in hue, with some green striping or mottling, and a faint rose blush. Flavor is sweet and, of course, very low acid. A Brad Gates variety, released in 2013. Pkt (15 seeds) $3.00

PINK BOAR #TX120

80 days. This 4 ounce gem is pinkish-wine colored with meltallic green stripes. A great producer and is a definite winner if you want a smaller, juicy, sweet tomato. Pkt (15 seeds) $3.00

PINK TIGER #TS146

70 days. Here's another awesome member of Artisan Seeds'"Tiger" series. This one is striped in fire-engine red and gold. The elongated, 2-inch fruits resist cracking. Very striking appearance combines with reasonable earliness and excellent flavor! Thrives outdoors or in the greenhouse. A wonderful "Cherry-Roma". Pkt $2.75

PLUM TIGRIS #TS118

80 days. A pretty, plum-shaped variety that has shining red and yellow stripes; very unusual. Plants produce lots of 4 oz fruit that are of a very good flavor. This colorful tomato was sent to the USA by Andrey Baranovski, from Minsk, Belarus. Pkt $2.75

PORK CHOP #TX106

75-85 days. Indeterminate. While most "yellow" tomatoes are actually orange, this is a true yellow that starts off yellow with green stripes that ripen to gold. The medium sized, slightly flattened beefsteaks have sweet tomato flavor with hints of citrus. Wild Boar farmer Brad Gates says it is the "best yellow I have ever had." Pkt (15 seeds) $3.00

RED ZEBRA #TS107

75-85 days. Here is a red version of our popular Green Zebra. Fire-engine-red fruits are covered with bright yellow stripes. Sweet and flavorful, this variety should prove very popular for both home and specialty markets. Pkt $2.50

STRIPED CAVERN #TS106

80-100 days. Colorful, red fruit have vibrant yellow stripes. They are stunning! This variety has lobed fruit, like a bell pepper, and thick walls, making it perfect for stuffing. Good-sized fruit are fine-flavored, and they really draw attention at farmers' markets. Pkt $2.00

STRIPED ROMAN #TS105

80-90 days. Stunning and unique, these long, pointed, red fruit have wavy orange stripes! People were really excited about this one at our Heirloom Garden Show. It's a specialty grower's dream; just what chefs and today's buyers are looking for; a perfect midsize beauty with brilliant color, meaty flesh, and excellent flavor. This variety was developed by John Swenson. Pkt $2.50

Solar Flare

Pork Chop

Sweet Carneros Pink

Large Barred Boar

Green Copia

Green Bell Pepper

Tigerella

Green Zebra

SWEET CARNEROS PINK #TX103

This 2-4 ounce tomato is rose pink with gold colored stripes. It is not only great looking but also of excellent quality with its sweet tomato flavor. Another huge producing development from Brad Gates of Wild Boar Farms. Pkt (15 seeds) $3.00

SOLAR FLARE #TX107

This 6-10 ounce beefsteak is red with gold stripes and has very meaty flesh with luscious sweet red tomato flavor. Developed by Brad Gates and selected for flavor, production, increased earliness and scab resistance, he says the variety is one of his "work horses." Pkt (15 seeds) $3.00

TIGERELLA #TS113

55-75 days. Tasty, 2" round fruit are bright red with orange stripes. A quite beautiful and popular variety from England that is good for greenhouse production. The yields are high even in cool summers, and it starts producing very early. It also has good disease-resistance. So smooth, so pretty! Pkt $2.00 or 1/8 oz $8.50

TURKISH STRIPED MONASTERY #TS126

80-85 days. This variety was collected at a monastery garden just outside of Istanbul, Turkey. Small 2" fruit are beautifully striped, red and gold. One of the best flavored small striped tomatoes. Good production all summer. Just recently introduced to the USA. Pkt $2.25

VERNISSAGE BLACK #TP151

Here is a lovely "Black" tomato that is loaded with flavor as well as production. This 2 oz. tomato, along with it's other Vernissage cousins, is sure to make a big splash in the garden as well as the kitchen. These are perfect for rich tasting sauces. A "vernissage" is a special advance showing for an art exhibition, originating from a celebration of the completion of a piece of artwork. The Vernissage series is both a work of art and a celebration! Breeder Ruslan Dukhov is a young Ukrainian plant enthusiast and seedsman. Pkt (15 seeds) $2.50

VERNISSAGE GREEN #TG111

This little striped jewel is loaded with sublime sweetness and taste. A perfect addition to salads, salsas and even desserts! The small fruit have lovely light green flesh. Plants are quite productive over a long season. A new favorite at our farm. Pkt (15 seeds) $2.50

VERNISSAGE PINK #TK169

Gorgeous salad tomatoes to about 2 oz. These beauties are pink with usually faint green-to-orange stripes. Tasty and so productive! One of the exciting varieties this year that really is amazing looking! Grown from Ukrainian seed. Pkt (15 vseeds) $2.50

VERNISSAGE YELLOW #TY139

These beauties are yellow cherries to about 2 oz., with pale cream stripes. Fetching companion to Pink Vermissage when paired in salads or on relish trays! A tasty little tomato that comes to us from Ukraine. These really produce well. Pkt (15 seeds) $2.50

WILLIAMS STRIPED #TS114

Popular at farmer's markets, large fruit are 1 lb or more. Very beautiful exterior and interior of red and yellow colors. It is a favorite of many, having luscious tasting flesh. Pkt $2.50

Striped Cavern

Pineapple Pig

Pink Berkeley Tie Dye

Michael Pollan

Janet's Jacinthe Jewel

Blue Tomatoes

Blue Gold Berries

BLUE BERRIES #TX111 *New!*

75 days. Indeterminate. Here's a new, small cherry variety from Brad Gates, Wild Boar Farms. Very dark purple color, which means it's super-rich in anthocyanins. Unripe, the fruits are a glowing amethyst purple. At maturity they turn deep red where the fruit was shaded; the areas that received intense sunshine are a purple so deep it's almost black! The flavor is intensly fruity and sugar-sweet! Plants are very productive, yielding all season in elongated clusters that look so beautiful. A new favorite here at Baker Creek! Pkt (15 seeds) $3.00

BLUE GOLD BERRIES #TX121 *New!*

80 days--Incredibly beautiful cherry type in purple and yellow. Long clusters are packed with small, half-inch bright yellow cherry fruits. Each has indigo shoulders, bursting with loads of antioxidants, anthocyanin in this case. The flavor is very sweet and rich, and the plants are so productive. Sunburn and crack resistant, and the fruits hold well on the vine or in storage. A choice selection out of the original Wild Boar Blue Berries. Pkt (15 seeds) $3.00

BLUE BEAUTY TOMATO #TX110 *New!*

80 days. Indeterminate. This recent Brad Gates introduction was selected from a cross between 'Beauty King' and a blue tomato. Fruits are modest beefsteak-type slicers, weighing up to 8 ounces, and the flavor is as good as their outstanding anti-oxidant content! Gorgeous, deep blue-black shoulders make this unique among slicing types. Excellent potential for market, as the fruits hold well on the vine. Sunburn and crack resistance are a welcome bonus. Pkt (15 seeds) $3.00

INDIGO APPLE #TX108

75 days. Indeterminate. Immature fruits show deep purple, almost black coloration, which is caused by high anthocyanin (an anti-oxidant). The medium-sized fruit turn red when ripe, with purple shoulders and streaks, they have a good, sweet tomato flavor. The pendant clusters present a striking appearance in the garden! Resists sunscald and cracking, lasting long into cool autumn weather when others have quit. Shows disease tolerance and great shelf-life. A classic is born! This tomato ranked #1 for the largest amounts of Lycopene and Vitamin C, according to a recent study we conducted. Pkt (15 seeds) $2.75

WAGNER BLUE GREEN #TX122 *New!*

This great "Blue" tomato comes from renowned heirloom/OP breeder Tom Wagner. Color is an incredible blue, with green flesh! We were impressed with its beauty and great flavor! The round fruits are arround 3 inches in diameter, and are very smooth and blemish-free. Pkt (15 seeds) $3.00

Blue Berries

Indigo Apple

Wagner Blue Green

Blue Beauty

White Tomatoes

CREAM SAUSAGE #TW105

70-75 days. Determinate. Here is a new and stunning tomato, an elongated paste tomato that is creamy white to pale yellow in color. The sweet flavor should be a hit with gourmet chefs. Bushy plants are quite productive. Think of the new sauce colors this beauty will create! Pkt $2.50 *or 1/8 oz $8.50*

DUGGIN WHITE #TW110

80 days. A medium-sized, white beefsteak tomato that has a strong, fruity taste. This rare heirloom was sent to Dorothy Beiswenger by Lloyd Duggin. Pkt (20 seeds) $2.50

FANTOME DU LAOS #TW118

Glowing, creamy-white fruit have a hint of yellow, and are ribbed, flattened and of medium size. Sweet, low acid flavor will make this "ghostly" tomato a favorite of those looking for a mild variety. This attractive variety reputedly originates in Laos. Pkt (10 seeds) $2.00

GREAT WHITE #TW101

80-85 days. Large, 1-lb giant, creamy white fruit, this tomato is superbly wonderful. The flesh is so good and deliciously fruity, it reminds one of a mixture of fresh-cut pineapple, melon and guava. One of our favorite fresh-eating tomatoes! Fruit are smoother than most large beefsteak types, and yields can be very high. Introduced by Gleckler's Seedsmen. Pkt $2.50 *or 1/8 oz $8.50*

IVORY EGG #TW109

70-75 days. Sent to America by a seed saver in Sweden, this rare and attractive ivory cream-colored tomato is the shape and size of a chicken egg. The creamy flesh is both sweet and rich, great for making a lovely sauce or in salads. Plants are very productive. Pkt $2.25

IVORY PEAR #TW122

75-80 days. Cute little 1 oz fruits are ivory-cream in color, shaped like little pears. Plants are very high yielders! Charming when served combined with Yellow or Red Pear types. A new staff favorite. Pkt $2.50

TRANSPARENT #TW111

70-75 days. A very pale, creamy lemon-colored tomato which almost borders on translucent, giving this 3 oz wonder an exotic appearance indeed! Very mild and sweet, having a soft skin and smooth texture that makes it a delight for fresh eating. The vines set huge yields of this rare and delicious little tomato. Pkt $2.25

WEISSBEHAARTE TOMATO #TW120

We are proud to introduce this rare, old German heirloom that produces lovely, little 2 oz. cream to pale yellow jewels that are very juicy and sweet. Large vines set high yields, and tender fruit are globe shaped; skin is shiny and silky smooth. Pkt $2.25

Cream Sausage

Great White

WHITE BEAUTY OR SNOWBALL #TW108

80 days, indeterminate—Parchment-white tomatoes are extra smooth and beautiful. Renowned for their sweet, citrus taste that is richer and more complex than many white types. This variety is perfect for making a delicious white sauce or for eating fresh out of hand. In 1927 Isbell's Seed Co., of Jackson, Michigan, said that this was the best white variety that they had ever grown. Some sources say it may have been introduced as early as 1850. This eight-ounce variety is a wonderful piece of American history that is just too great to be lost. Chefs and market gardeners, take notice! Pkt $2.50

WHITE CHERRY #TW124 *New!*

70 days. Soft, creamy-yellow, little 1-ounce orbs are produced in nice clusters, right up to killing frost. Fruits are very sweet, juicy and delicious; quite possibly the best "white" cherry type we have ever trialed. (Those fruits that mature under leaf cover are the whitest white tomatoes around.) Lovely in salads, on relish trays or for snacking right in the garden! Prolific and very free from cracking. Pkt $2.50

WHITE TOMESOL #TW107

80 days. An amazing heirloom that is bursting with fragrance and natural goodness that's hard to beat. One of the best tomatoes I have tasted, being both sweet and rich. The cream colored fruit are beautiful, smooth and weigh about 8 ounces each. The vines set heavy yields of this rare treasure. It's sure to become a favorite of gourmet growers. Pkt (20 seeds) $2.50

WHITE WAX #TW115

75 days. Oblate, flattened fruit are medium-sized, cream-colored and waxy in appearance, hence the name. A unique and fun-to-grow heirloom, passed down to food historian William Woys Weaver from his Mennonite grandfather's seed collection. This variety was once grown for exhibiting at county fairs in Pennsylvania, according to Mr. Weaver. Fruit have a good, sweet flavor and yields are very high. Pkt $3.00

" The care of human life and happiness, and not their destruction, is the first and only object of good government."

-THOMAS JEFFERSON

Tomato Seed:

All varieties are believed to be 'indeterminate' (long vines), *unless specified* **'determinate' (short vines). The best tasting varieties tend to be indeterminate, as most of ours are unless otherwise noted. Packets contain a min. of 25 seeds (unless stated otherwise).**

Ivory Egg

Duggin White

Yellow Tomatoes

DIXIE GOLDEN GIANT #TY141

85 days. A huge, lemon-yellow beefsteak-type fruit, often with some blushing at the blossom end. The mild and sweet fruits often reach 2 lbs! Reputed to carry some disease-resistance. Old Amish type grown and preserved since at least as early as the 1930's. Very productive, as Amish-held varieties tend to be; deserves to be much more widely grown. Pkt $2.25

DOUCHOUA PEPPER TOMATO #TY146 *New!*

Graceful bell-pepper-shaped fruits, about the size of large plums, have a lovely cream white to yellow color. Flavor is good with just the right amount of acid, but fruit is not super juicy, being firm and quite crunchy, refreshing and delicious. Fruit very free of imperfections. The overall yield is strong. It would make an attractive and unique specialty market variety. Pkt (15 seeds) $2.75

DR. CAROLYN #TY116

65 days. Pale yellow cherries offer a burst of fresh, sweet flavor. They weigh about 1 oz each. This variety was named for our friend, Dr. Carolyn Male, who wrote the book *100 Heirloom Tomatoes*. The plants are hardy and heavy producers of velvety-feeling fruit. Pkt $2.00

EGG YOLK #TY114

80 days. The fruit are a lovely yellow color, being the shape, size and color of an egg yolk. A tantalizing taste treat just bursting with rich, fruity flavor and all of summer's sweetness. The extra-long vines really amazed us with their productiveness. Developed by Larry Pierce from a sport he found growing in his garden. Pkt $2.25

GOLDEN KING OF SIBERIA #TY128

This tomato is one of the real favorites here. Big, lemon-yellow fruit are a delightful heart shape. The flesh is smooth, creamy and has a nicely balanced sweet taste. I always find myself "snacking" on these one-pound beauties. Plants are very productive and seem to have some disease resistance. Thanks to Russia for this really great yellow type. Pkt $2.75

HARTMAN'S YELLOW GOOSEBERRY #TY142

Believed to be the same yellow cherry as listed by seedsmen since pre-1830's, this was reintroduced by John Hartman Seed Company. The very long vines bear clusters of 1-inch "Gooseberries" that are sweet, mild, tasty and light golden-yellow in color. One of the largest yielding tomatoes we have ever grown! Pkt $2.50

HSSIAO HIS HUNG SHIH #TY135

A delightful, yellow grape tomato that comes from historic China. This variety has been stored at the USDA since 1931, the same year it was collected in the East Market in Peiping, China. Crisp little, grape-sized nuggets are just right for snacking. Vines are hugely productive. Pkt $2.00

PILCER VESY #TY137

A classic, huge, yellow beefsteak type that we received from Russia. The fruit are a lovely lemon yellow and are flattened and ribbed. Fantastic flavor and thick flesh. This is now one of our favorite large tomatoes as they are also quite productive. Pkt $2.75

PLUM LEMON #TY110

80 days. Bright canary-yellow 3" fruit looks just like a fresh lemon. The perfect tomato for marketing (along with Green Zebra, Orange Banana, and Black Prince) to chefs and other gourmets. This variety was collected by Kent Whealy, co-founder Seed Savers Exchange, from an elderly seedsman at the Bird Market in Moscow. Delicious, sweet taste. Pkt $2.00

ROMAN CANDLE #TY101

85 days. Beautiful, neon yellow, banana-shaped fruits are bursting with intense sweetness and flavor. A wonderful

Golden King of Siberia

Pilcer Vesy

Topaz or Huan U

new tomato that originated as a "sport" from Mr. John Swenson's Speckled Roman. A new favorite of market growers, it is quite colorful. Pkt $2.25

TASMANIAN BLUSHING #TY125
85 days. Unusual yellow fruit, 5-6 ounces, occasionally larger; sometimes a trace of pink inside. Silky flesh. Very sweet, pronounced tomato flavor, yet mild like most yellows. Pkt (20 seeds) $2.25

TOPAZ OR HUAN U #TY132
Named for the beautiful yellow Topaz stone, this Chinese introduction is sure to please you with its beautiful and sparkling, 1-3 ounce fruit. Light yellow with golden speckles. Mild tasting, firm and good for snacking or salads. Like its sister "Violet Jasper" (see purple tomatoes), this variety is incredibly productive. Add some color this year. Pkt $3.00

WAPSIPINICON PEACH #TY106
80 days. Light, creamy-yellow, almost white fruit have superb taste and texture! One of the best tomatoes I have ever tried. The taste is complex, with its spicy, sweet, and very fruity flavor. The fruit are small, around 2", and the skin is slightly fuzzy like a peach! This Iowa heirloom is named after the Wapsipinicon River, a favorite fishing spot of mine. Pkt $2.50

YELLOW ICICLE #TY136
75 days Bright, lemon-yellow fruit are a little thicker in shape than the others in the Icicle series, being filled with cream-yellow colored flesh that is thick, sweet and perfect for paste and canning. It is a very pretty tomato and is one of the best yellow paste types you can grow, having a fine flavor and some juiciness; this variety also is incredible to eat fresh. Another variety of the icicle tomatoes that we have introduced from Ukraine. Pkt $2.50

YELLOW MORTGAGE LIFTER #TY133
90 days. A beautiful yellow version of the regular Mortgage Lifter. It has the same great size and taste except this one is bright yellow in color. Always popular with with our guests, this big heirloom is richly flavored and quite rare. A favorite! Pkt $2.75

YELLOW PEAR #TY122
78 days. Very sweet, 1½" yellow, pear-shaped fruit have a mild flavor, and are great for fresh eating or for making tomato preserves. Very productive plants are easy to grow. One of the first tomatoes I grew as a child. Pkt $2.50

YODER'S GERMAN YELLOW #TY140
80-90 days. This regular-leafed variety produces large yellow/pale orange beefsteak type fruit. Fairly crack resistant and can grow as large as 1 pound. Good flavor. From Amish lady Mrs. Yoder, whose family grew this tomato for over half a century in Tennessee and Kentucky. Pkt $2.00

"Uniformity is not nature's way; diversity is nature's way."
—VANDANA SHIVA

Plum Lemon

Wapsipinicon Peach

Roman Candle

Hartman's Yellow Gooseberry

Tasmanian Blushing

Douchoua Pepper Tomato

Turnip

(B. rapa) European crop, used for its leaves, roots, occasionally blossoms, and as a fodder crop since at least Roman times. Turnips are under-appreciated by today's gardeners, but, properly grown, they make a superb storage crop for use through the winter. They should be direct-sown in ordinary garden soil, well-worked and free of stones, about two months prior to first frost of autumn. Thin to stand 6 inches apart; thinnings may be used as greens. Roots are ready in from 35-70 days, depending upon the variety, and may be stored in the fridge, an unheated garage, root cellar, or right in the ground, if properly mulched. 600 seeds per packet

BOULE D'OR #TN113

The "Golden Ball" or "Orange Jelly" variety has been a mainstay of European turnips for over 150 years. This seed came to us from France where this old turnip is still cherished, written about and grown. It has a finer flavor than many of the white fleshed varieties as the yellow flesh is sweeter and milder. Lovely color. Pkt $2.00

EARLY FLAT WHITE #TN114

(Navet Blanc Plat Hatif) Described by Vilmorin as: *"Root exceedingly flat, like a broad disk in shape... four to five inches in its greatest diameter... flesh white, tender... and of good quality."* This is a very early variety and is quite tasty. Pkt $2.00

GOLDEN GLOBE #TN101

A tasty turnip with sweet, lightly golden flesh; fine flavored. A good turnip for spring or fall. Pkt $1.50 *or 1 oz $4.00*

"IDEAL" PURPLE TOP MILAN #TN104

An improved Milan turnip, the roots are very flat, white with purple tops. The flavor is sweet and mild. A good variety for marketing. Popular in Italy, the Milan turnip is a 19th-century Italian heirloom. Pkt $2.00 *or 1 oz $5.00*

NABO ROXO COMPRIDO #TN115

The name simply translates to purple turnip, but this elongated variety is white with a purple shoulder. Portuguese sources describe it as a fodder variety, but we thought it tasted fine. Foundation seed provided by our friend, collector Joao de Sousa Barroca of Portugal. Pkt (50 seeds) $2.25

NAVET DES VERTUS MARTEAU #TN106

The very tender, white roots are cylindrical, 5"-6" long and 2" wide with a mild and sweet flavor. This old French heirloom was one of the most popular varieties grown by French market growers in the late 1800s. Imported European seed. Pkt $1.75

NORFOLK A COLLETTO VIOLA #TN116

(Norfolk Purple Top) Late, globe- to barrel-shaped, purple top. This Italian variety may well be synonymous with Norfolk Red, of which Fearing Burr wrote in his 1863 tome, *"The Field and Garden Vegetables of America."* If so, it has been a market staple in England and parts of the Northeastern U.S. for generations, tracing back to at least the 18th century, and becoming increasingly rare of late. Pkt $2.25

Purple Top White Globe

Early Flat White

PETROWSKI #TN111

60 days A nice yellow turnip with sweet, flat roots that mature quickly. In 1916, Burpee's catalog stated: "A most distinct variety of early maturity. The flat roots average two and a half to three inches in diameter, and the skin is a rich deep orange-yellow, very smooth and entirely free from small rootlets. The firm solid flesh is fine-grained, crisp, light orange-yellow in color, and having a flavor which is much richer and sweeter than any of the early white-fleshed sorts." This old turnip was introduced to England in 1879 by Sutton's, who imported it from Germany, and around 1915 this variety was very important in Alaskan agriculture. A superior variety for home and market. Pkt $2.25

PURPLE TOP WHITE GLOBE #TN103

A popular market variety, heirloom (pre-1880), productive, and easy to grow. Skin is purple-white. Pkt $1.75 *or 1 oz $4.00*

SHOGOIN #TN109

A popular Japanese variety that has high quality, smooth white roots and delicious, mild-tasting greens. Perfect for steaming or frying. Harvest leaves in just 30 days. Pkt $1.50

SNOWBALL #TN107

Mentioned as the main market variety supplying the London, England markets, in "The vegetable Garden" by Vilmorin-Andrieux, 1920. Fine white roots have a mild flavor. Pkt $1.75

WHITE EGG #TN102

This very old pre-1880's heirloom was a top market variety in the US. A smooth, white turnip with quality, mild, white flesh; an early variety. Pkt $1.50

Boule d'Or

"Ideal" Purple Top Milan

Watermelon

(Citrullus vulgaris) We're #1 in watermelons—check our selection! Thrives in summer heat. A long-standing crop in the South where it was originally transported by slaves from Africa. 25-35 seeds per packet.

ALI BABA #WM152

Our favorite watermelon! We introduced this fine variety about 12 years ago after we were sent seed by Aziz Nael, an Iraqi gentleman who had collected this fantastic variety in Iraq. It is now nearly impossible to get seeds from this ancient country whose people have lost much of their genetic heritage in the long, bloody war. Now our corporate agriculture has been "kindly" suggested to native farmers who are losing thousands of years of plant breeding work. The 12-30 lb melons have hard light-green rinds that make them perfect for shipping and storage; the light color makes them resistant to sun burning. Plants are large, vigorous and give heavy yields of oblong fruit which do well in many conditions. The flavor is superb, being very sweet and luscious; and the texture is very crisp. This is a best seller and is a favorite of Dr. Amy Goldman and featured in her book "Melons for the Passionate Grower". Ali Baba has received much acclaim online "as the best tasting watermelon," and it will forever win a spot in any melon lover's heart. Pkt (15 seeds) $2.50 or 1 oz $8.50

ANCIENT #WM187

This melon has a green rind and succulent red flesh that is of excellent flavor and sweetness. This variety was found in a clay pot in a cave in the Southwest USA. It is a beautiful melon and a favorite on our farm, easy to grow and producing fruit up to 20 lbs. Pkt (15 seeds) $3.00

ARKANSAS BLACK WM189

85 days. Oblong fruits reach around 18 " in length, 15-20 lb, crimson flesh. Vigorous vines tolerated a lot of heat and drought in 2011. A local Arkansas variety sent in by a customer. Lovely, very dark green rinds really do look nearly black. Pkt $4.00

BLACK DIAMOND Yellow Belly Strain

#WM111 90 days. Sweet, red flesh; an old variety that can attain great size. Dark green rind; popular with many gardeners. Pkt $2.00

BLACKTAIL MOUNTAIN #WM129

70 days. One of the earliest watermelons we know of; superb for the North, but it also grows well in heat and drought. The flesh is red and deliciously sweet. Fruit have a dark rind and weigh 8-12 lbs each. This excellent variety was developed by our friend Glenn Drowns, owner of the Sand Hill Preservation Center in Iowa. A favorite of many gardeners across the USA. One of the best we have ever tried! Pkt $2.75 *or 1 oz $8.50*

CHARLESTON GRAY #WM117

87 days. This popular variety dates to 1954. The long gray-green fruit grow to 20-40 lbs; the red flesh is fiber-free and very tasty. Yields are very good, and melons are excellent for home or market. Pkt $2.00

Georgia Rattlesnake

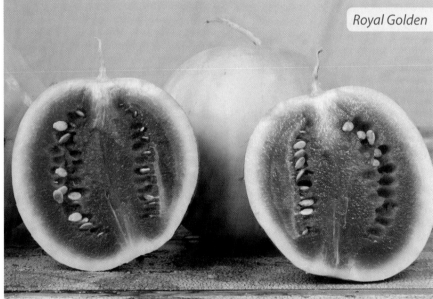

Royal Golden

Navajo Winter

"I thought this photo of my son would be a great addition to the catalog! He's holding half of an Orange-glo Watermelon grown from seeds I purchased from Baker Creek. It was delicious!!!!!"   *-Ashley Himes*

Golden Russian

Strawberry

White Wonder

CAROLINA CROSS 180 #WM199

90 days—One of the largest types we sell-- oblong fruits have reached 200 lbs! Bright red flesh is sweet and remarkably fine-grained for such a large melon. Needs a long hot summer to reach its full potential. Grow this one for bragging rights! Pkt $4.25

CHRIS CROSS #WM140

85-90 days. This heirloom was bred in Montrose, Iowa, in 1950 by "Chris" Christenson, and the "Cross" was Hawksbury crossed with Dixie Queen. 15 to 20-lb fruit have green striped rind and tasty, crisp red flesh. This variety is almost extinct. Pkt $2.50

COLORADO PRESERVING or RED SEEDED CITRON #WM142

This variety of melon was used in the 19th century for making preserves, candied citron, pies and more. The firm white flesh is not good for fresh eating but has many holiday uses in the kitchen. These are rock hard and keep for months. Citron-type melons are the ancestors to domestic watermelons and still grow wild in Africa. These are easy to grow, as they resist almost everything. Huge vines; 10-lb fruit have bright red seeds. Pkt $2.50

CONGO #WM124

90 days. Large 30 to 40-lb melons; very tough, striped rind. The flesh is deep red and very firm. Has a high sugar content and is an excellent, big tasty watermelon. AAS winner from 1950. Pkt $2.00

CREAM OF SASKATCHEWAN #WM133

80 days. A beautiful little melon with sweet, tasty, cream-colored flesh! An excellent variety for the North. Fruits around 8-10 lbs each with a striped, green rind. A favorite of those who grow it! An old heirloom. Pkt $2.50

CRIMSON SWEET #WM115

85 days. AAS Winner from 1964, very popular. Crisp and sweet, medium-red flesh, mild flavor. A good producing type that is still quite popular. Pkt $2.00

DAISY OR YELLOW SHIPPER #WM116

85 days. These incredibly delicious, golden-hued watermelons have tough rinds, making these one of the best yellow varieties for shipping and storage. Rinds are striped and flesh is bright yellow, crisp, sweet and very tasty! Fruit weigh 13-20 lbs. This variety was found growing in a field of watermelons by a customer of Burrell Seed Co. Pkt $2.50

DESERT KING #WM145

85 days. This watermelon produces 20-lb fruit that have a light pea-green rind that is resistant to sunburning. It is also one of the most drought-resistant varieties of watermelon known. It has sweet, yellow flesh and is very popular in the watermelon-growing areas of Arkansas. Good for storage. Pkt $2.00

DIXIE QUEEN #WM114

80 days. Pre-1935 variety, round in shape, can grow up to 50 lbs. Flesh is brilliant red, solid, and of a fine flavor. Skin is striped dark green and greenish ivory; uniform in shape, size, color, and quality. Pkt $2.00

EARLY MOONBEAM #WM197

75-80 days. Early and productive yellow-fleshed watermelon, very sweet and delicious! Bred by Dr. Alan Kapuler of Peace Seeds specifically for Oregon conditions, which often tend to be on the cool side, this variety delivers sweet watermelons in cool climates where others often fail. 5-8 lb fruit have thin rinds and an attractive light-green skin with darker-green stripes. Recommended for northern and higher-elevation gardens! Pkt (10 seeds) $2.25

GEORGIA RATTLESNAKE #WM113

90 days. A longtime Southern favorite, thought to have been developed in Georgia in the 1830's. Its stripes resemble those of a Rattlesnake, hence the name. Sweet, light crimson-colored flesh and large size. Used as a shipping melon; a great old variety. Pkt $2.50

GOLDEN HONEY #WM193

80-90 days. Dark green rind conceals the light golden-yellow flesh which is quite delicious. Listed in W. Atlee Burpee catalog before the turn of the 20th Century. Oblong, sweet fruits run 10-20 pounds. Pkt $2.50

GOLDEN MIDGET #WM107

70 days. A beautiful miniature watermelon that weighs around 3 lbs. It's easy to tell when they are ripe, as the rind turns a lovely golden yellow when ready for harvest, a very beautiful contrast with the salmon-pink-colored flesh. The taste is sweet and refreshing. Very early, matures in just 70 days. Developed by the late Dr. Elwyn Meader, UNH, in 1959. Unique. Pkt $2.50 *or 1 oz $8.00*

GOLDEN RUSSIAN #WM190 *New!*

A new introduction we received from our Ukrainian connection. It has a dark green skin with bright yellow flesh that is extremely flavorful and juicy. The size ranges from about 3 lb. to 12 lb. The smaller ones make great lunch-time melons for two people, with no leftovers. Pkt (15 seeds) $4.00

HOPI YELLOW #WM176

This variety from the Hopi people has bright, golden-yellow flesh that is very sweet, crisp and flavorful; medium to large size. We received this variety from Native Seeds Search. Pkt (15 seeds) $2.50

IRISH GREY #WM188

85 days. Oblong fruits of pale green are red-fleshed, sweet and so juicy! Fruits are moderately large to 15 pounds or so. The pale, light green ("gray") colored rind was favored around the turn of the 20th century, and this variety was listed as being a very popular Florida market type in the early 1920s. Very hard to find today. Pkt (10 seeds) $2.50

JANOSIK #WM204 *New!*

80 days. Yellow-fleshed Polish variety. Oblong fruits to about 10 lbs. The extra sweet, yellow flesh is lovely in contrast with the dark green rinds. Crisp and delicious! Beautiful, uniform fruit and one of the best eating bright yellow types! Pkt $3.00

JAPANESE CREAM FLESHED SUIKA

#WM168   85 days. A small Japanese type watermelon. 6-12 lb ice-box-sized fruit have crisp, cream-colored flesh, and an excellent

Orangeglo

"The true Southern watermelon is a boon apart, and not to be mentioned with commoner things. It is chief of this world's luxuries, king by the grace of God over all the fruits of the earth. When one has tasted it, he knows what the angels eat. It was not a Southern watermelon that Eve took; we know it because she repented."

—MARK TWAIN

refreshing taste with mild flavor. Best tasting cream-fleshed watermelon at Washington State University trials. Enjoyed by some with lime and salt, but I like them plain, straight from the patch! Productive and fairly early. Pkt (20 seeds) $3.00 *or 1 oz $8.50*

JUBILEE #WM130

90 days. Long, oval-shaped fruit with very sweet flesh that is deep red and very crisp. A popular old favorite. Large size. One of all-time best tasting melons! Pkt $2.50

JUBILEE BUSH #WM194

90 days. Bush-type plant spreads 3-5 feet. 10- to 13-pound oblong fruit containing crisp and juicy red flesh, with very high sugar content for a bush type. Some tolerance to anthracnose and fusarium wilt. Outstanding choice for gardeners who have limited space but who refuse to forego one of summer's most sublime delicacies! Pkt $2.50

KLECKLEY'S SWEET #WM106

85 days. Bright red, with a high sugar content, this heirloom has been a favorite ever since being introduced by W. Atlee Burpee in 1897. Fruit are large and somewhat oblong; rind is dark green. Not for shipping, but perfect for the kitchen garden. Pkt $2.50

KLONDIKE BLUE RIBBON STRIPED #WM125

85 days. Delicious red flesh that is very sweet and crisp; has been a family favorite of ours for many years. Medium-large size and a good shipper. A very good melon. Rare. Pkt $2.25

KOLB'S GEM or AMERICAN CHAMPION #WM102

100 days. Huge melons that have grown as large as 130 lbs! This variety dates back to at least the 1880's. The fruit are nearly round and have sweet, red flesh. Excellent choice if giant watermelons are desired. Pkt $2.50

MISSOURI HEIRLOOM YELLOW FLESH #WM159

We are excited to offer this great old variety from the "Show Me" state. It produces round, 20-lb melons with pale green skin and bright golden-yellow flesh that is crisp, sweet and refreshing. A really nice yellow type that is hard to find. Pkt (15 seeds) $3.00

MOON AND STARS #WM121

95 days. Legendary Heirloom Variety rediscovered in Macon, Missouri. Can grow to over 40 lbs. The dark green rind has bright yellow spots on it! Spots range in size from tiny to several inches across. Leaves are also specked in yellow. It has very sweet, brilliant red flesh. This is becoming one of the most popular Heirloom varieties, a winner! Originally introduced by Peter Henderson & Co. in 1926, it was called "SUN, MOON AND STARS." The catalog says, *"...an extraordinary variation...and that it has such a delicious taste."* It was sold then for 20 cents a pkt. Unique variety! Pkt $2.50

MOON AND STARS, YELLOW FLESHED #WM122

90-95 days. Rare, this is the yellow-meated strain of this fine heirloom; these are very delicious and have beautiful, yellow-orange meat that is very sweet. The large fruit can grow to 40 lbs, and they

Golden Midget

Tendergold

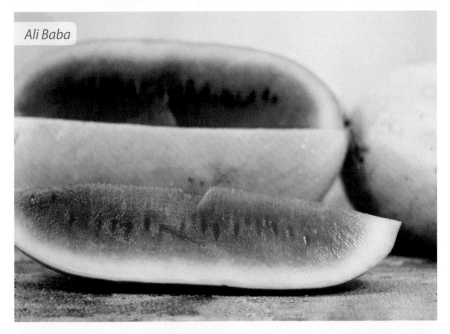

Ali Baba

Colorado Preserving

Moon and Stars, Yellow Fleshed

have large, yellow "Moons and Stars" covering their nearly black rinds. Our favorite variety of the planetary watermelons, it was a real favorite at our 2004 "Heirloom Garden Show". A great variety for farmers' markets. Pkt (15 seeds) $2.50

NAVAJO WINTER #WM185
85 days. Thick light green to striped rind, medium pink to red crisp, sweet flesh. Fruits have been known to keep for up to four months. Expect unusual drought tolerance from this eminent variety from the American Southwest. Pkt (10 seeds) $3.00

ORANGE FLESH TENDERSWEET #WM131
90 days. Excellent, deep orange flesh; very sweet and crisp, flavor lives up to its name! Delicious tasting! We prefer orange-fleshed types over most reds and yellows—they seem to yield better here than most others. A great variety for markets. Pkt $2.25

ORANGEGLO #WM127
85 days. Beautiful, deep orange flesh; very sweet, excellent, almost tropical flavor! The best-tasting of ALL orange varieties we tried—the favorite of many who tried it at our place. High yields. Very resistant to wilt and insects; strong healthy vines. These will sell at roadside stands & markets! Pkt $2.75 *or 1 oz $8.50*

PEACOCK STRIPED #WM126
87 days. Beautiful green mottled rind and crisp, sugary flesh makes it hard to stop eating this variety. A good-sized melon with fine-textured, bright red flesh; a great shipping variety that has become rare. Pkt $2.00

ROYAL GOLDEN #WM160
The most beautiful watermelon we carry; the rind of this heirloom turns brilliant golden-yellow when ripe! The distinctive color makes it a snap to know when to harvest and is so beautiful in your garden. The tasty pinkish-red flesh is sweet, crisp and refreshing. This variety is much larger than 'Golden Midget', with fruit weighing 8-25 lbs. We are so happy to offer seed for this great old melon that used to be offered by Willhite Seed of Poolville, Texas, until they discontinued it from their catalog in the 1970s and it almost became extinct. Pkt (10 seeds) $2.25

SCALY BARK #WM174
This truly historic variety was listed in the1885 Retail Catalogue of the notable James J.H. Gregory, who said, *"Skin somewhat rough, as the name denotes. Looks outside somewhat like Phinney's. Remains longer than usual in eating order after gathering."* This melon remained popular for many years, especially in the south. We are glad to see this great melon again in gardens. Named for the mottled, light and medium green rind that appears much like tree bark, very unique looking. The flesh is bright red, sweet and crisp; it also keeps very well, so you can enjoy melons over a long season. Pkt $4.00

STONE MOUNTAIN #WM164
A legendary commercial melon from the early 20th century. Stone Mountain was introduced in 1923 by Hastings Seed Company of Atlanta, Georgia, and went on to become one of the top commercial melons of the 1930's and 1940's, but now is almost extinct due to mass production

and hybrids. Nice-sized fruit weigh about 30 lbs, and have thick rinds that make them excel as shippers and storage melons. The red flesh is sweet, juicy and wonderful, bringing back memories of how watermelons used to taste. A classic Southern melon that we are proud to offer, thanks to seed collector Rodger Winn. Pkt (15 seeds) $3.00

STRAWBERRY #WM196
85 days. Flesh is a gorgeous strawberry pink, ripening to within a half-inch of the rind, and usually has very few seeds. Fine grained, distinctively flavored and super sweet, it is classed among the best-tasting by those who have tried it. The oblong, striped fruits reach 15-25 pounds. With moderate disease resistance, this variety deserves to be the star of your summer garden. Originally selected from a Florida heirloom by Walt Childs, and introduced in 1989 by our good friends at Southern Exposure Seed Exchange. Outstanding! Pkt (10 seeds) $2.75

SUGAR BABY #WM132
79 days. The most popular icebox-sized melon among gardeners! Early, 6 to 10-lb melons are great for the North and have sweet, deep red flesh. These also do well in the tropics. Pkt $2.50

SWEET DAKOTA ROSE #WM200 *New!*
The fruit are a medium-large size, with a Crimson Sweet appearance. It produces early and was one of the sweetest in the whole field last season. One of the best-tasting standard, commercial looking melons. Sunburn resistant, and has very few seeds. Thin, firm rind makes it a good market type and an excellent keeper! Developed decades ago by North Dakota farmer David Podoll, who stabilized a cross between Early Canada and Black Diamond. Very well adapted to short, cool seasons. Pkt $2.50

TENDERGOLD #WM195
80 days. A fairly early orange-fleshed variety that has great taste and texture. Its rind is hard and tough, making it a good orange variety for marketing. They are very uniform and weigh 22 lbs. Pkt $2.50

THAI ROM DAO #WM163
80 days Small fruit weigh about 5 lbs. A striped green rind and bright red flesh that is sweet and tasty. A fun little melon from Thailand. A great choice in hot, humid climates! Pkt $2.25

TOM WATSON #WM104
87 days. Large, 20 to 40-lb fruit with sweet, crisp, dark red flesh. The tough rind makes it a good shipping melon. A pre-1900 heirloom, popular with old-timers. It is getting hard to find as most sources have dropped it. Pkt $2.25

WILSON'S SWEET #WM161
80 days. Very unique spotted rind, with very crisp, sweet red flesh that bursts with rich, old time watermelon flavor! One of the best melons I've tried in the last few years. Truly a winner! It used to be grown commercially, and was offered by several seed companies in the 1960s, but has since become nearly extinct. A great variety for home and market gardeners, as it produces 15-to 20 lb fruit that keep well. Pkt (10 seeds) $2.50

WHITE SUGAR LUMP #WM166
We at last have a limited supply of seed for this

Sweet Dakota Rose

Golden Honey

Daisy

Kolb's Gem

Ancient

Peacock Striped

Cream of Saskatchewan

Crimson Sweet

Watermelon harvest at Baker Creek

very rare melon. The pale flesh is a creamy white color with a light, refreshingly sweet taste. Fruit weigh around 5-10 lbs each and ripen early. It was carried by the Henry Fields Seed Company in the 1950's and 1960's, and in 1956 they said "Sweet as sugar, that's why we call them Sugar Lumps." They offered these in three colors: red, yellow and white. Thin-striped rind. Pkt (15 seeds) $3.50

WHITE WONDER #WM150
80 days. Beautiful, snow-white flesh is so pale it's almost transparent! The flavor is unique, fruity, and so delicious. The small, round 3-8 lb icebox-sized fruit are very refreshing and perfect for gourmet growers wanting to target high-class markets. These will add contrast to any display and are sure to bring attention at farmers' markets. White-fleshed watermelons were common in the 1800's, but due to corporate agriculture, these genetic treasures are about to be lost. That is a shame, as white-fleshed varieties date back hundreds of years and were developed in Africa from wild strains. This early variety is not for shipping as it cracks easily, but you will enjoy its unique crispness, fresh from the garden. Pkt (15 seeds) $2.50

'Blessed are the peacemakers: for they shall be called the children of God.'
-MATTHEW 5:9

Blacktail Mountain

Tendergold

Watermelon Salad with Orange zest and Mint
By Chef Quintin

Its hard to fail when making a watermelon recipe. This is an easy salad to make. If you are throwing a party just skewer these and present.

INGREDIENTS
- 1 heirloom watermelon
- 1 T of sea salt
- Fresh mint (thin sliced)
- 1 T of honey
- 1 T of apple cider vinegar
- Zest of 1 orange

PREPARATION
1. Peel watermelon and de-seed as much as possible. Cut into 1 inch cubes
2. Whisk honey and vinegar until well mixed
3. Zest one orange with micro zester in a bowl and add to liquid
4. Season your watermelon with sea salt and drizzle sauce over the top and mix well
5. Upon serviing, sprinkle the mint onto the top of the salad

Aronia

Okinawa Spinach

Mulberry

Katuk

Live Plants

We are super excited to be offering a selection of live plants. These are produced for us by tissue culture, a natural process that produces plants that are generally high-quality and disease free. With some stunning new food crops in our plant listing, we hope you will try some of the exciting rare plants we offer this year. Pre-order now, as supplies on some of these will be limited. The plants we ship are small, but sturdy, and we offer a 30 day guarentee on live plants. Most plants will be 6"-12" in height. Plants will ship as available after the first of April to the end of June. We will ship orders to southern zones first. No guaranteed exact delivery dates. No orders shipped outside of the USA. No Extra shipping costs; you just pay our regular $3.50.

ARONIA VIKING #PL101 *New!*

(Aronia melancarpa) Viking is a beautiful small shrub with a very flavorful fruit when used in juices, jams, and wines. Aronia is high in flavonoid/anti-oxidants, as well as high in vitamins and minerals. The fall red foliage is incredibly striking. Aronia is a staple in Eastern Europe backyard gardens and has great potential in the US. We offer 2 small plants that have been propagated through tissue culture, a simple way to make small cuttings disease free. 2 plants for $13.00

OKINAWA SPINACH #PL102 *New!*

(Gynura crepiodies) Indonesian native takes full sun to partial shade; must have adequate water; perennial under frost-free conditions. Stunning leaves are green on top and magenta-purple on the underside and are appreciated for their pungent flavor. Delicious when used in salads; equally good as a potherb, in stir fry or tempura. (Do not overcook.) There is some evidence that this unusual herb can lower serum cholesterol levels. Makes an attractive, edible ground cover where the growing season is long enough. Be sure to take cuttings in fall to overwinter in frost-free location for next year's crop. 2 plants for $10.00

LONGEVITY SPINACH #PL103 *New!*

(Gynura procumbens) Related to Okinawan Spinach, but lower-growing and more spreading. Reputed to have anti-viral and anti-cancer properties, and to be beneficial in the treatment of diabetes and numerous other conditions. Cultivated throughout southern and eastern Asia. Can be used raw, juiced or cooked. Also frequently made into a tea. Grows in frost-free, warm conditions. Easy to propagate from cuttings. 2 plants for $10.00

GOJI BERRY #PL104 *New!*

(Lycium barbarum) Chinese native also known as Wolfberry. The red fruits are sweet and packed full of anti-oxidants and other nutients--rightly called a "superfood!" This relative of peppers and tomatoes is hardy to -15 degrees, F., prefers full sun and somewhat dry, well-drained soil. Plants reach to 6 feet tall and look stunning with their silvery, laurel-like foliage and small flowers like purple stars. Goji Berry should fruit starting in the second year after planting. 2 plants for $12.00

MULBERRY, DWARF EVERBEARING #PL105 *New!*

(Morus nigra) Morus nigra is a medium size black mulberry with a sweet tasty flavor. In pot culture it can be maintained as a dwarf with minor pruning. This ever-bearing mulberry will produce continuously in pots under warm and bright conditions. Mulberries have many health benefits: they strengthen the immune system and are good for eyesight. We offer 2 small plants that have been propagated through tissue culture, a simple way to make small cuttings disease free. 2 plants for $13.00

PANDAN #PL106 *New!*

(Pandanus amaryllifolius) Used widely in SE Asian cooking. Commonly known as Pandan leaves. Used to flavor jasmine rice, crackers and cakes. Thrives in sub-tropical and tropical climates, but can also be grown indoors. We just crave the delicious flavor of this lovely plant. We offer 2 small plants that have been propagated through tissue culture, a simple way to make small cuttings disease free. 2 plants for $10.00

POSSUM PURPLE PASSION FRUIT #PL107 *New!*

(Passiflora edulis) Self-fertile passion fruit that can be grown in containers, in the greenhouse, or outdoors in warmest climate zones. Prefers full sun, ample water. The delicious purple fruits are fine for eating out of hand, or processing into jellies, juices or desserts. The classic white, purple and cream-colored Passion flowers are stunning, especially when grown where they can be seen and appreciated close-up. Bees and butterflies love them

as well. Climbing plants will require staking. 2 plants for $12.00

COSTA RICAN OR JAMAICAN MINT #PL108 *New!*
(*Satureja viminea*) Potently minty, rather succulent leaves are produced all season long on this Caribbean native. A tropical plant, it is killed by frost, rendering it an annual in most of the country, so it's a great choice in gardens where common mint's aggressiveness isn't wanted! Also takes well to pot culture and can be overwintered indoors. Makes a large shrub where winter temps only rarely drop below freezing. 2 plants for $12.00

STEVENS' CRANBERRY #PL109 *New!*
(*Vaccinium macrocarpon*) Cranberry 'Stevens' is a self-fertile cranberry that produces large deep-red fruit. This evergreen likes acidic wet soils. Stevens is one of the most popular varieties in production. Cranberries can work well in home gardens as an edible ground cover where soils stay moist. They also can produce in containers and hanging baskets if a saucer of water is kept underneath. We offer 2 small plants that have been propagated through tissue culture, a simple way to make small cuttings disease free. 2 plants for $12.00

EDIBLE GINGER ROOT #PL110 *New!*
(*Zingiber officinale*) Ginger root is the rhizome or underground stem of this Asian plant. Ginger root can be harvested at any time, but plants require several months of hot and fairly humid conditions to make the maximum yield. Plants may reach 4 feet in height. Mature roots are plump and sleek outside, white, juicy and aromatic within. May be grown outdoors in full sun in most of the country, lifting mature roots before ground freezes in autumn. Replant smaller roots next spring, preferably starting early in a sunny windowsill or greenhouse. 2 plants for $10.00

KATUK #PL111 *New!*
(*Sauropus androgynus*) A wonderful tropical plant that has leaves that have delicious peanut-like flavor and almost 10% protein! This amazing herb is used widely in Asia as both a cooking and salad green! Hard to find, it can be grown outdoors in the deep south if protected from frost. In Northern Vietnam the plants overwinter after being trimmed back to about 15 inches; the nights there do get close to freezing. In subtropical areas it forms a small shrub. For gardeners in the north it can be grown as an annual or taken inside in the winter, or even cultivated in a greenhouse or sun porch. But you can grow it as an annual or year around in a greenhouse. The tender shoots are what is harvested; regular pruning and watering assures a constant harvest. Even though the plant is completely edible raw, it is highly recommended that it is cooked if large quantities are consumed. 2 plants for $10.00

AFRICAN POTATO MINT #PL112 *New!*
(*Plectranthus esculentus*) Also known as Kaffir Potato. This mint relative is grown for its potato-like tuber. These tubers can get very large, up to 4 lbs., are very high in protein, carbohydrate, iron and calcium. A so-called "lost crop" of Africa that in fact is of immense value today! Thrives in hot and fairly dry conditions. Requires 6 months of warm to hot growing conditions to yield mature tubers; in most of the nation we recommend starting plants indoors in containers and setting outdoors after weather has warmed in late spring. 2 plants for $10.00

YACON #PL113 *New!*
(*Smallanthus sonchifolius*) Here's a delicious and unusual South American relative of Dahlia and Jerusalem Artichoke. Sweet-potato-like tubers weigh up to 3 lbs and are produced in 3-5 months from planting. Yacon plants reach 4-5 feet in height, and occasionally bloom, bearing small yellow daisies. Two types of tubers are produced: propagation tubers, at the center of the root mass, which can be divided and replanted in the spring, and the edible tubers, which grow outside the central ones. The flavor is like a crisp apple combined with Asian pear. The roots contain insulin (may be useful to diabetics), and possess anti-oxidant and pro-biotic qualities. 2 plants for $14.00

VARIEGATED TAPICOA #PL114 *New!*
(*Manihot esculenta*) Spectacular, dark-green palmate foliage is richly variegated in lime green and creamy-white. Tropical plant grows quickly enough to be appreciated as an annual, or grow in greenhouse or in containers and overwinter indoors. Perennial in frost-free zones. Plants get 3-6 feet tall, take full sun or partial shade. Thrives in heat with average water. The roots yield tapioca. CAUTION: roots are poisonous when raw and must be processed properly to render them safe to eat. 2 plants for $12.00

Yacon

African Potato Mint

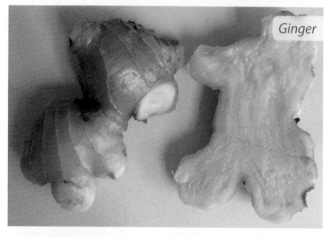
Ginger

Variegated Tapicoa

TRULY TINY BANANA #PL119 *New!*

(Musa) We believe this to be the smallest edible banana variety anywhere! "Truly tiny" plants mature at just 2-4 feet tall, making them ideal for greenhouse culture or containers, which is how it should be grown in most of the country. Leaves are very ornamental, with purple-red splashes. Yield a small dessert-type banana. This crop is easy to grow in the south, and produces fruit rather quickly for such a large plant. . You can grow these as far north as zone 8 with protection or in heated greenhouses of sun-rooms farther north. We love growing bananas in our Missouri greenhouse and get a crop in under a year. 2 plants for $15.00

Edgar's Baby Dragon Fruit

EDGAR'S BABY DRAGON FRUIT #PL120 *New! (Hylocereus hybrid)* Flavor of the magenta fleshed fruits is very well balanced, a perfect blend of sweet and tart. Named in honor of the breeder, Edgar Valdivia, the ripe fruits had a Brix of 18º! According to Joe the best tasting Dragonfruit in the world! Grow outdoors in a sub-tropical climate or grow as an amazing greenhouse plant. It may take a few years to start producing, but when it does be prepared for super delicious, magenta fleshed fruit! Plants need little water and produce lovely blooms, too. We offer 2 small plants for $15.00

Live Plants

We are super excited to be offering a selection of live plant collections, these are produced for us by tissue culture, a natural process that produces plants that are high-quality.

RARE FIG ASSORTMENT #PL121 *New!*

(Ficus) An assortment of some of the world's most amazing and delicious fig varieties, with flavorful pink, green, or red flesh. Fruit will vary in size depending on variety. Figs are super easy to grow and most thrive outside in zones 7-11 and many people grow them farther north with protection. We get massive amounts of fruit each year in our small Missouri greenhouse. Figs are delicious for fresh eating but also make incredible jams, jellies, desserts, and are delicious in salads and main dishes as well! Young fig plants may need some protection even in zones 7-8 if the winter is harsh until they are well developed, but this can be easily done by either bringing them inside or wrapping them in cloth or landscape fabric. We offer 3 assorted small plants for $15.00

MUSA 'BASJOO' BANANA #PL122 *New!*

The world's hardiest banana! Documented to survive temps to -20 degrees F., when mulched! At only 8-14 feet tall, it works well in containers, too. Cultivated in Japan for the fibers harvested from the leaves. Produces attractive fruits that are not considered edible. Yet it's a great choice for the garden or ornamental landscape. Bragging rights, anyone? 2 plants for $15.00

MUSA 'DWARF NAM WA' BANANA #PL123 *New!* Widely regarded as one of the best-tasting varieties! Seldom exceeds 10 feet in height, making it workable for container-growing, as well as less prone to wind damage. Sweet "lady finger" type fruits are delicious eaten out of hand or cooked, carrying a definite hint of vanilla. Plants produce large bunches, ripening to a classic soft yellow. Male flower bud is also edible. Indonesian variety known by many other names, famous as "Pisang Awak." Pink to red trunk is attractive in contrast with the brilliant green leaves. 2 plants for $15.00

Grow delicious figs

ELEPHANT EAR OR TARO COLLECTION
#PL124 *New!*

(Colocasia) One of the original "Canoe" plants of the ancient Hawaiians, it is both an incredible food plant and rich source of ornamental beauty in the garden. (Warning: only eat this plant with proper preparations as it can be poisonous otherwise.) We offer an incredible assortment of beautiful varieties that are generally hardy in zones 8-11, but are easy to grow almost anywhere with winter protection. The Gettle family spent the winter in Hawaii and has become fascinated by the incredible diversity and usefulness of this amazing plant. We especially love the cooked greens! Grow well in moist soil and love warmth. Some of these may only produce small tubers, but all produce abundant leaves! We offer 3 assorted small plants for $15.00

THAILAND CALADIUM COLLECTION
#PL125 *New!*

The most beautiful Thailand Caladiums produce a wide, glossy leaf and come in some of the most stunning colors known to man! Tissue culture produces superior Thailand Caladiums. This easy-to-grow plant thrives in warm, tropical and sub-topical climates but can easily be grown anywhere with a warm summer. Wonderful for containers. We offer 3 assorted small plants for $15.00

LOUSIANA IRIS COLLECTION   #PL126
New!

(Also known as Swamp Iris) A complex of about four species, native to the Mississippi River valley and Gulf Coast, which interbreed freely, has given rise to the Louisiana Iris. The plants take heat, humidity and moist soil, as you might expect given their geographic point of origin. Great for pond edges. Plants get very large, a few to 4 feet in height, and come in a stunning range of colors. The flowers tend to be large and super-showy, many opening very flat, and the range of colors is incredible: Pinks, whites, reds, violets, copper, bicolors, veins, stripes, blotches--you name it, it's probably in the mix. Hardy to about 5 degrees F, possibly lower with protection. We offer 3 assorted small plants for $15.00

DWARF BANANA COLLECTION   #PL127

New! Dwarf types with fruits ranging from dessert types to plantain (cooking) types. Height ranges from 6- 12 feet in most cases, making these suitable for container culture. This crop is easy to grow in the south, and produces fruit rather quickly. Some varieties have green fruit and some red. You can grow these as far north as zone 8 with protection or in heated greenhouses or sun-rooms farther north. We love growing bananas in our Missouri greenhouse and get a crop in under a year. We offer 3 assorted small plants for $15.00

DRAGON FRUIT COLLECTION #PL123

New! Grow outdoors in a sub-tropical climate or grow as an amazing greenhouse plant. It may take a few years to start producing, but when it does, be prepared for super delicious, pink fleshed fruit; yields year-round where conditions are right! Plants need little water and produce lovely blooms, too. (Most varieties are night-blooming; be prepared to hand-pollinate indoor-grown specimens.) We offer 3 assorted small plants for $15.00

HARDY KIWI COLLECTION   #PL128

New! (Actinidia arguta) These kiwis are good producers of bite-sized kiwis. It has a tremendous cold hardiness and is easy to grow. Besides its rock-solid hardiness, one key element that makes this kiwi so special is its pineapple-like flavor! Use Actinidia agruta 'Hardy Male' as a pollinator. For zones 5-9. We offer 3 assorted plants(1 male & 2 female) plants for $15.00

Sweet Potato

(Ipomea batatas) The sweet potato is a drought and heat tolerant, warm season vegetable that it is actually related to the morning glory. Although sweet potatoes are usually thought of as a southern staple, they can be grown in the north. Sweet potatoes are grown from slips, which are shoots from last season's tubers. Plant in rich well-drained soil with plenty of composted manure.

Sweet potatoes are a nutritionally dense root crop with a wide breadth of culinary uses. A tasty heirloom sweet potato crop will be the cornerstone of your winter pantry, filling pies and lending carotene-rich, orange hues to soups and breads. Try a purple sweet potato variety to take advantage of a sweet, natural source of anthocyanins, a nutrient shown to reduce cardiovascular disease. A superbly sustainable choice, sweet potato tubers can be saved for next season's slips. We use tissue culture to propagate our sweet potatoes in order to ensure that you have a disease free crop. This is a more expensive process, but well worth the cost because in the future you can save your own plants easily if you like.

MOLOKAI PURPLE, SWEET POTATO
#PL115 *New! (Ipomoea batatas)*
Purple-fleshed type that is a locally-developed, signature type on the islands, but seldom offered elsewhere. Much higher in antioxidants than orange-fleshed types. Very sweet-fleshed and creamy, with overtones of chestnut in the flavor. Perfect as-is when baked or roasted, needing no further adornment. Deep purple flesh and skins. 3 plants for $9.00

JERSEY YELLOW, SWEET POTATO #PL116
New! (Ipomoea batatas) Plump, drier-fleshed type is medium creamy-golden skinned with cream-colored flesh. Remains firm and solid even when cooked. A delicious type for curries, stews and perfect as sweet potato fries; an old fashioned favorite that has appeared on the tables of the New Jersey families since 1780. 3 plants for $9.00

OKINAWAN PURPLE, SWEET POTATO
#PL117 *New! (Ipomoea batatas)*
Descended from the first sweet potatoes to reach Japan, prior to 1500. The purple coloration is connected with the high anthocyanin content. This one is documented to contain more of the potent anti-oxidant than even blueberries! Ivory-colored skin, brilliant purple flesh. 3 plants for $9.00

OMANI PINK, SWEET POTATO #PL118
New! (Ipomoea batatas) A lovely pink skinned sweet potato from the deserts of Oman, a beautiful country on the Arabian peninsula. Found in a remote oasis in the Northern mountains. This rare variety has a delicious dry flesh that is a nice cream color. Super good tasting and did well here in Missouri. 3 plants for $9.00

Omani Pink

Jersey Yellow

Molokai Purple Hash with Toasted Pistachios

INGREDIENTS

1 Molokai purple potato
1 T Olive Oil
1 Heirloom carrots small chopped
1 Garlic Clove
1 Heirloom apple small chopped
½ Onion small chopped
Sea Salt and Pepper to taste
1 t Lemon zest
1 Rib of celery small chopped
1 t Ground Sumac
Drizzle of aged balsamic vinegar
Sprig fresh thyme
Drizzle of Truffle Oil
1 t of Pistachios
1 T Dried cranberries

PREPARATION

Peel and small chop sweet potatoes

Small dice onions, garlic, carrots, apples and celery

Heat sauté pan on high heat and caramelize potatoes; pull and reserve

Drizzle more olive oil and sauté the rest of ingredients on high heat until well browned

Mix all ingredients in bowl and add picked thyme leaf

Top dish with fresh chopped pistachios

Herb Seed

We offer a great selection of flavorful culinary types and popular medicinal varieties. Everyone should experience the joy of having fresh herbs. Notice: All statements listed in our catalog are for historical information only and are not approved by the FDA. Seek the advice of a qualified health professional before using any herbs for medicinal purposes.

ANISE #HB217
Tender perennial usually grown as an annual to 20 inches. An ancient herbal favorite, hailing from the eastern Mediterranean region and cultivated at least since the days of ancient Egypt! Lacy umbels of delicate white flowers give rise to the seeds, which are the part usually used. Widely appreciated for flavoring baked goods and liqueurs. Also great for use in soups, sauces, stews and salads. Pkt $2.25 (200 seeds)

BASIL, BLUE SPICE #HB200
(Ocimum basilicum) Vigorous plant with dense spikes of light purple flowers enclosed in showy deep purple bracts, making for an especially fine appearance in pots or in the garden. Heavy fragrance with spicy vanilla overtones that makes a pleasant contribution to both fruit salads and savory dishes. The most fragrant basil. Pkt (75 seeds) $2.50

BASIL, CARDINAL #HB224
At last, someone has bred a basil to accentuate the stunning flower heads! Still a culinary basil, but the rich purple flower heads are huge! Use the flowers in arrangements, the leaves in your favorite recipes. Very new and very choice—a milestone of conventional plant breeding! Pkt (100 seeds) $3.00

BASIL, CINNAMON #HB104
Spicy flavor, Mexican variety iwth a distinct cinnamon like taste. Pkt (50 seeds) $1.75

BASIL, CORSICAN #HB206
Mediterranean heirloom type from Napoleon's island birthplace off the French and Italian coasts. This versatile type comes in varying degrees of green to purple, often spectacularly mottled in both. A competent culinary type that makes a scintillating contribution in the border as well. Recommended! Pkt (75 seeds) $2.50

BASIL, DARK PURPLE OPAL #HB106
A beautiful and ornamental variety; deep purple. Pkt (75 seeds) $2.50

BASIL, EMILY #HB194
Compact version of the classic Genovese type that is superior for pot culture, having shorter stem-length between leaf nodes. Widely recognized to be longer-lasting when cut, all of which make "Emily" a better subject for market growers and home gardeners. Pkt (150 seeds) $2.50

BASIL, FINE VERDE #HB110
Very small, fine leaves on compact bushes; great for containers. Perfect rich, spicy basil flavor that Italians love. Pkt (75 seeds) $1.75

BASIL, GENOVESE #HB101
68 days. The famous Italian heirloom is very popular with many cooks. Pkt (40 seeds) $2.50 or 1 oz $8.00

BASIL, GENOVESE RED FREDDY #HB219
The same large, deeply pleated leaves as Genovese that everyone loves, but instead of green, Red Freddy boasts deep Roman purple. Pkt $2.50 (100 seeds)

BASIL, GREEK DWARF #HB144
Cute little compact plants are only 6" tall and are great for growing in containers. It has a spicy, slightly anise flavor and is a must for Greek cooking. Pkt (100 seeds) $1.75

BASIL, LEMON #HB107
Wonderful lemon fragrance & taste, a real culinary delight. Pkt (100 seeds) $2.00

BASIL, LETTUCE LEAF #HB108
Huge 3"-5" leaves; Japanese basil with a great flavor. Pkt (100 seeds) $2.00

BASIL, LICORICE #HB105
Has a strong licorice scent and flavor. Unique. Pkt (100 seeds) $1.75

BASIL, LIME #HB103
A unique lime-flavored basil from Thailand. Popular variety for fresh market! Pkt (40 seeds) $2.50

BASIL, PERSIAN #HB207
Really interesting and flavorful! Known as Reyhan throughout the varied nations of southwestern Asia. Has a distinctive aroma, both lemony and spicelike. Pkt (75 seeds) $2.50

BASIL, RED RUBIN #HB232 *New!*
Deep burgundy leaves and a compact habit (to only about 12 inches!) are the first things you notice about this exciting variety. But the fragrance and taste will exceed all expectations! Nice large flat to slightly blousy leaves are fully as delicious as the standard green types--spicy and intensely aromatic! The size and coloration make this plant suitable for edging a border, or for containers. Pkt (75 seeds) $2.50

BASIL, SIAM QUEEN THAI #HB102
Very strong, clove-scented basil. This is a must for curry and all Thai cooking. This selection has beautiful flowers. Very tasty. This improved variety produces very large and lovely flowerheads. Pkt (100 seeds) $2.50

BASIL, THAI HAIRY LEMON #HB185
(Ocimum canum) This basil has slightly fuzzy stems, hence the name. Delicious flavor that lends itself well to many Oriental dishes. Popular in Thailand. Pkt (100 seeds) $2.50

BASIL, THAI HOLY "KAPRAO" #HB142
A popular herb in Thai cuisine, the fragrant purplish-green leaves can be used in potpourri and have a spicy, sweet, clove-like flavor. A religious herb of the Hindus. Pkt (75 seeds) $2.25

BASIL, THAI SWEET #HB166
Popular sweet, spicy basil that is essential in Thai cuisine. Very flavorful with a nice licorice taste. Pkt (100 seeds) $2.50

BEE BALM, LEMON #HB124
(Monarda citriodora) An annual, lemon-flavored variety. Superb tea plant; striking pink-purple flowers, beautiful and tasty. Pkt (100 seeds) $2.25

Dark Purple Opal Basil

Emily Basil

Red Rubin Basil

Siam Queen Basil

Genovese Red Freddy Basil

Greek Dwarf Basil

BORAGE #HB139

(*Borago officinalis*) Cucumber-flavored fresh leaves are added to salads, cooked, or made into a cooling drink. The blue flowers are used as a garnish. Makes a good honey plant. Also used medicinally. Pkt (60 seeds) $2.00 *or 1 oz $5.00*

BURDOCK, GREAT #HB197

(*Arctium lappa*) Renowned traditional medicinal plant in Europe, North America and China, resorted to at one time or another as a diuretic. It has also been used in cases of snakebite, skin diseases and burns, fevers, and women's complaints. Rhubarb-like leaves yield nutritious stalks that are cooked like celery; young roots are eaten raw or prepared like parsnips. The stickery seeds can be sprouted and have been used as buttons! How much more can one plant offer? Pkt (100 seeds) $2.50

CARAWAY #HB150

(*Carum carvi*). Delicious seeds are used for flavoring many dishes, from desserts to soups. The leaves are used in salads, stews, and sauces. Also medicinal. Pkt (100 seeds) $2.50

CATMINT, GRANDVIEW #HB187

(*Nepeta subsessilis*) Mounds of fine, aromatic foliage gives way in early summer to fantastic whorls of tubular flowers running the gamut from palest blue through violet. If spent blooms are removed, the show lasts into autumn. This is a choice variety for the middle of the border, and is a favorite of hummingbirds, bees and butterflies as well. Pkt (125 seeds) $2.25

CATNIP #HB127

(*Nepeta cataria*) The herb that drives cats wild is also medicinal; used in a tasty herbal tea for colds and flu. Vigorous plant. (200 seeds) Pkt $2.00

CATNIP LEMON #HB212

(*Nepeta cataria*) Perennial. Sturdy, nearly indestructible and very distinct variant of regular catnip. This one boasts white to pale pink flowers and a lemony scent, but with the same elegant silvery foliage. Plants reach occasionally to 4 feet, typically much shorter. Not a favorite with the feline set, possibly due to its citrus scent, and may not have identical herbal properties to regular catnip. (100 seeds) Pkt $2.50

CHAMOMILE, GERMAN #HB118

(*Matricaria recutita*) Beautiful, small flowers; makes a relaxing tea with a sweet, fruity fragrance; medicinal. Attractive plants. Pkt (300 seeds) $2.25

CHERVIL #HB188

(*Anthriscus cerefolium*) Traditionally used in French cooking, where the slightly anise-like flavor of the leaves is appreciated when added to eggs, vegetable and fish dishes. Leaves are added at the very last minute of cooking, to preserve the delicate flavor. Small white flowers atop 15-20 inch stems. Also known as French parsley. Pkt (400 seeds) $1.75

CHIA, CROWN JEWELS #HB182

(*Salvia columbariae*) A different Salvia species with a long history, as it was grown as a staple food crop by Native Americans years ago. It has a high nutrition value. Called Chia in Mexico

and other Central American countries, it is also a special ornamental plant which forms a clump of decorative grey-green leaves and colorful purplish flowers. Chia seeds are now a popular natural health product. Pkt (100 seeds) $2.50

CHINESE CHIVES #HB111

(*Allium tuberosum*) These winter-tolerant chives are great for greenhouse production. They have great garlic flavor and are popular with Asian chefs. We love 'em. Pkt (300 seeds) $1.75

CHINESE MOTHERWORT #HB140

(*Leonuris artemisia*) Hard-to-find medicinal herb, related to Lion's Tail but having whorls of delicate purple flowers. Space 3' tall plants about 1' apart; easy to grow. It is used in Asia for many health problems, including to help lower blood pressure. Pkt (50 seeds) $2.50

CHIVES, COMMON #HB135

Wonderful, mild onion flavor. These long, thin chives are excellent in many meals; great raw or cooked. Lavender flowers. Pkt (300 seeds) $2.50

CILANTRO #HB125

(*Coriandrum sativum*) Popular in Mexican cuisine, this herb is a must for all salsa and chili recipes; delicious and flavorful. Pkt (100 seeds) $2.00 *or 1 oz $5.00*

CILANTRO, SLO-BOLT #HB143

(*Coriandrum sativum*) This is a slow-bolting version of Cilantro/Coriander that produces flavorful leaves over a longer period. Pkt (100 seeds) $2.50

CORIANDER, LARGE SEEDED #HB205

(*Coriandrum sativum*) Early-bolting seed type is intended for use of the seed, which are true coriander; however the leaves may be harvested sparingly for cilantro. Very productive, and fresh coriander is so much nicer than the dried seeds in cooking! Pkt (50 seeds) $2.25

CORIANDER, MOROCCAN #HB236 *New!*

We are excited to offer this wonderful coriander from Morocco. This types seed has a more mellow, sweeter and slightly citrus-like flavor, making it perfect for a variety of dishes. The leaves are also good as cilantro. Pkt (50 seeds) $2.50

CUMIN #HB152

(*Cuminum cyminum*) The flavorful seeds are an important ingredient in many Mexican dishes; also used in bread and cakes. Small, tender, crawling plants reach about 6" tall. Pkt (100 seeds) $1.75

DILL, BOUQUET #HB126

(*Anethum graveolens*) Early to flower with large seed heads. Excellent in pickles and used to flavor many other foods. Easy to grow. Pkt (300 seeds) $2.50

DILL, ELEPHANT #HB180

A very aromatic, late-flowering variety that has nice green color and is productive. Pkt (300 seeds) $2.00

DILL, VIERLING #HB176

Deep, blue-green color and finely cut foliage. A good late flower strain for commercial leaf production; it is also used as a cut flower, as it produces attractive, light greenish flowers. Pkt (300 seeds) $2.00

Rosemary, Rosy

Stinging Nettle

Marshmallow

Tansy

Basil Cardinal

Milk Thistle

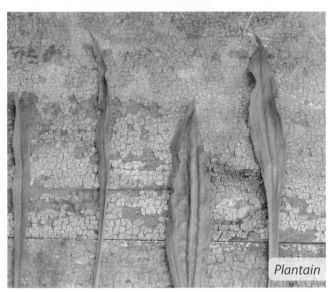

Plantain

Lion's Tail or Wild Dagga

DOCK, BLOODY (RED SORREL) #HB189

(*Rumex sanguineus*) Stunning foliage plant with elongated, medium green leaves, exquisitely veined in a brilliant burgundy-purple. A hardy perennial, it quickly forms an attractive clump, which sends up red flower-clusters in early summer, followed by brown seed heads. A superb, deer-resistant accent plant. Pkt (100 seeds) $2.50

ECHINACEA PARADOXA OR OZARK YELLOW CONEFLOWER #HB171

Like the pale purple coneflower, but these are a bright golden-yellow color. Brilliant blooms do well in fairly dry, rocky soil like is found on many of the Ozark hills here in Missouri and Arkansas; this is the region where this unique coneflower is native. Used by Native Americans as a traditional medicine, it is being researched today for its herbal uses. It can be hard to find even here in Southern Missouri, but is rather easy to grow. Pkt (30 seeds) $2.50

ECHINACEA PURPUREA #HB119

A beautiful, purple wildflower and well-known medicinal herb with numerous uses. Excellent. Pkt (50 seeds) $2.50

ECHINACEA TENNEESSEENSIIS #HB238

New! Tennessee Purple Coneflower. Perennial. Here's a chance to grow a really rare native species! This species is almost extinct in the wild, being native only to dry glades in the hills and mountains of Tennessee. Appearance is similar to the commoner types of Purple Coneflowers, except that the ray flower petals tend to be narrow and not usually reflexed. This makes the starlike flowers unusually showy in an understated way. Flower heads reach 18-30 inches in height. The plants take dry soil and fairly hot-summer conditions. Great for dry banks and roadside plantings. Pkt (30 seeds) $3.00

FENNEL, BRONZE #HB198

(*Foeniculum vulgare*) Very decorative bronze-hued lacy foliage. Its unusual color makes a striking accent plant, a sophisticated addition in salads, or an elegant garnish. Seeds may, of course, be used like those of any fennel. Pkt (50 seeds) $2.50

FENNEL, FLORENCE #HB128

(*Foeniculum vulgare*) Plant grows like dill. Used in Italian cooking; tasty. Very easy to grow. Pkt (200 seeds) $2.00

FENUGREEK #HB136

(*Trigonella foenum-graecum*) The aromatic leaves are a popular potherb in India. Also used in curry powder, in imitation flavorings, and as a coffee substitute. The seeds make a tasty tea. Popular in western Asia and the Mediterranean. Pkt (75 seeds) $1.75

FEVERFEW #HB158

(*Chrysanthemum parthenium*) This herb produces pretty daisy-like flowers; it is used to repel insects and traditionally used by many for migraines, arthritis and as a digestive aid. Very easy to grow. Pkt (125 seeds) $2.00

HYSSOP, BLUE #HB123

(*Hyssopus officinalis*) Excellent for attracting bees and butterflies, bright blue flowers; a superb antiviral plant that many use to treat flus, etc. Pkt (125 seeds) $1.50

HYSSOP, ANISE #HB122

(*Agastache foeniculum*) This herb is used to make one of the best herb teas; the leaves possess a naturally sweet, wonderful anise taste and fragrance. Lovely purple flowers that bees love; many uses, including medicinal. Pkt (125 seeds) $2.50

HYSSOP, KOREAN #HB208

(*Agastache rugosa*) Perennial, more robust relative to Anise Hyssop, with similar flavor and overall appearance except that, at four feet tall, it is very much larger. One of the 50 Fundamental Herbs in Chinese traditional medicine, this plant has been studied in recent times for antibacterial properties. Makes a wonderful base for herbal tea blends; makes a definitive statement in the garden! Pkt (100 seeds) $2.50

LAVENDER #HB112

(*Lavandula vera*) Famous for fragrance, the lavender-colored blossoms are used in potpourris, soaps, etc. A great old-time cottage garden plant. Pkt (100 seeds) $2.25

MUNSTEAD STRAIN LAVENDER #HB213

(*Lavandula vera*) Perennial. Compact, superior Northern-hardy strain. The plants seldom exceed a foot in height. Use the fragrant spikes as you would any lavender—potpourris, sachets, dried arrangements, etc. The silvery-gray foliage is elegant even when out of flower. A reliable as well as beautiful old-fashioned garden favorite. Pkt (100 seeds) $2.75

LEMON BALM #HB117

(*Melissa officinalis*) Deliciously lemon-flavored; great in tea. A vigorous, hardy plant. Pkt (300 seeds) $2.50

LEMONGRASS #HB162

(*Cymbopogon citratus*) The famous, tropical lemon-flavored herb of Thai cuisine. It has long, slender, pale green stems that are thick and fleshy. I just love the wonderful flavor this herb adds to soups, curries and stir-fries. We enjoy cooking with it often. This perennial must be grown in warm weather or inside to keep from freezing. We are pleased to offer this rare and much requested seed. Pkt (60 seeds) $3.00

LION'S TAIL OR WILD DAGGA #HB167

New! (*Leonotis nepetifolia*) A member of the mint family, it is native to Southern Africa and is used as a folk medicine among the native peoples for treating numerous ailments, and has shown some promise in studies. Tall, evergreen tropical plant produces loads of stunning peachy-orange flowers. Caution: this plant is a mild narcotic. Pkt (15 seeds) $3.00

LOVAGE #HB153

(*Levisticum officinalis*) Flavorful, dark green leaves and yellow flowers; the leaves and seeds are used for flavoring stews, soups, salads, pickles, and more. Nice celery taste. The hardy plants can be grown in most of the North. Pkt (200 seeds) $2.00

MARJORAM #HB137

(*Majorana hortensis*) A fragrant and flavorful herb that is a popular seasoning. Easy to grow. Pkt (800 seeds) $2.50

MARSHMALLOW #HB190

(*Althaea officinalis*) African native. The original source of an Egyptian confection which evolved

Echinacea Purpurea

Shungiku

Parsley, Giant of Italy

Sorrel, Green de Belleville

Tootheache Plant (Spilanthes)

Yarrow, Cerise Queen

Dock, Bloody

into today's marshmallows. The roots and velvety leaves have been eaten as a vegetable for centuries, often fried with onion and garlic. 3-4 foot stems of 1-2 inch, white-to-pink flowers are reminiscent of hollyhocks, to which this plant is related. The plant is also renowned in various folk cultures for its medicinal properties. Pkt (35 seeds) $2.25

MILK THISTLE #HB168
(*Silybum marianum*) This biennial is a lovely plant with glossy green leaves with silver veins. Historically used for many tonics, and is said to be good for the liver. Pkt (40 seeds)$1.75

MILKWEED - SUNSET FLOWER #HB169
(*Asclepias curassavica*) There are beautiful reddish-orange flower clusters on this tropical milkweed that grows as an annual here. This plant is used in traditional medicine of Central America and the Caribbean. **Warning: Can be toxic, only for use by medical professionals.** Pkt (30 seeds) $2.50

MILKWEED– BUTTERFLY WEED #HB228
New! (*A. Tuberosa*) Perennial. The hardy native Milkweed essential to the survival of Monarch butterflies. Mature butterflies feed on the nectar produced in the flowers, while the foliage provides food for their larvae. The brilliant orange and yellow flowers are showy in massed plantings, but fascinating up close, with their intricate detail. The three-foot plant is native throughout the eastern and southern regions of the country, usually preferring drier sites, and should be hardy except at very high elevations. Very durable and long-lived once established, and may gently increase on its own in favorable locations. (CAUTION: The milky sap is poisonous if ingested in large quantities, and contact with the skin may cause dermatitis in sensitive individuals.) Pkt (40 seeds) $2.50

MILKWEED – RED OR SWAMP #HB229
New! (*Asclepias incarnata*) Perennial. Rosy-pink-flowered Milkweed that is the best choice for moist locations, as it is native to wet ground throughout much of North America. Supports the Monarch and other butterfly populations as well as bees and hummingbirds. The sweet vanilla fragrance, and large numbers of flowers, support the gardener's enjoyment as well. May reach 5 feet tall in favored locations. (CAUTION: The milky sap is poisonous if ingested in large quantities, and contact with the skin may cause dermatitis in sensitive individuals.) Pkt (40 seeds) $2.50

MILKWEED– MEXICAN WHORLED
#HB230 *New!* (*Asclepias fascicularis*) Perennial. Native to the Western regions of the US, and a great choice for use in this region, where it constitutes a vital food source for the Monarch butterflies and their relatives, as well as bees. Individual plants are often short-lived but reseeds itself freely, with the potential to become invasive in moist locations, so it's best grown on drier sites. (CAUTION: The milky sap is poisonous if ingested in large quantities, and contact with the skin may cause dermatitis in sensitive individuals.) Pkt (40 seeds) $2.50

MOLDAVIAN BALM, DRAGONHEAD
#HB204 (*Dracocephalum moldavicum*)

Eurasian native that has been cultivated for centuries. The minty-lemony leaves and large purple flowers have long been used in a tea for reputed herbal benefits, including "lightening a discouraged heart." Beloved by bees, like all the mint tribe. Pkt (75 seeds) $2.75

MUGWORT #HB116
(*Artemisia vulgaris*) A popular woman's medicinal herb from Asia. A large plant. Pkt (125 seeds) $2.00

OREGANO, VULGARE #HB131
(*Origanum vulgare*) This is a beautiful and delicious Italian flavoring herb. Also medicinal. Great for Italian and Greek cooking. Pkt (400 seeds) $2.25

OREGANO, WILD ZAATAR #HB174
(*Origanum syriaca*) We offer seeds from Israel for this plant that grows wild in Israel, Jordan and surrounding areas. Doubtless a common herb in Bible times, and still one of the tastiest! It has great flavor that blends hints of Oregano, Thyme and Marjoram. A favorite. Pkt (75 seeds) $2.50

PARSLEY A GROSSE RACINE GROS HATIF
#HB183   Grown for its flavorful large, long roots, a French selection that is early. Pkt (400 seeds) $1.75

PARSLEY DEMI LONG ROOT #HB177
This French rooted variety makes shorter, fatter roots that are better for heavy soil; this old vegetable is delicious grated into salads or sliced into soups. Pkt (400 seeds) $1.75

PARSLEY, GIANT OF ITALY #HB133
A very large Italian strain of parsley with great flavor. Perfect for sauces. Pkt (400 seeds) $2.00

PARSLEY, HAMBURG ROOTED #HB134
This heirloom dates to the pre-1600s and is grown for its large roots that make superb soups and stews. Leaves are also delicious. Pkt (400 seeds) $1.50 *or 1 oz $5.00*

PLANTAIN #HB201
English Plantain (*Plantago lanceolata*). Legendary herb used for centuries, many benefits having been ascribed to this plant. The leaves sometimes cooked for greens. Plants form a low rosette of leaves,10-20" in diameter. In time a bare, tall flower-stem emerges from the crown, reminiscent in a way of tiny cattails. Some small birds relish the seeds in season, and the plant hosts several species of moths. This common plant has naturalized widely but we offer an improved strain. Pkt (100 seeds) $2.00

PENNYROYAL #HB216
(*Mentha pulegium*) Perennial. Short, spreading plant with clusters of lilac flowers. Leaves have a strong minty aroma, have traditionally been used in cooking and medicinally. However, recent studies have indicated that this herb may have toxic effects. We offer it as an ornamental only, and caution against taking this herb internally. Pkt (100 seeds) $2.50

PURSLANE, GREEN #HB151
(*Portulaca oleracea*) Low, crawling plant produces tender stems and juicy leaves that are excellent added to salads. A popular green in Mexico that was favored by my Hispanic grandmother. Also used in herbal healing plans.

Pkt (300 seeds) $2.00

ROSEMARY, ROSY #HB218
(*Rosmarina officinalis*) Tender perennial to 30 inches. The plant has been used for centuries both medicinally and in the kitchen. Small evergreen shrub is covered with needle-like aromatic leaves and a myriad of tiny pink or blue flowers in summer. Perennial in mild-winter climates; elsewhere, grow in containers for overwintering indoors. The dark green leaves may be used fresh or dried. Flowers are beloved by bees. We offer select seed, that is easier to start, but it still can be somewhat challenging to start, but the plants are lovely and can live for years with proper care. Pkt (35 seeds) $3.00

RUE, HERB O' GRACE #HB191
(*Ruta graveolens*) Historic herb whose use dates back to ancient times—rue is mentioned in the New Testament. The evergreen plants are a rich sea-green, quite distinctive even from a distance, forming a compact mound in the herb garden. Thrives in poor sandy soils and hot, dry sites. Pkt (100 seeds) $1.75

SAGE, BROAD LEAF #HB147
(*Salvia officinalis*) Used in Europe and America to flavor many meats, stuffings, vinegars, and more! Fragrant leaves are also used in potpourri. 20"-tall gray-green plants are quite attractive. Pkt (75 seeds) $2.00

SHEEP'S SORREL #HB130
(*Rumex acestosella*) Tasty, sour, clover-like leaves; pretty plant and flowers. Pkt (150 seeds) $1.50

SHISHO or PERILLA "PURPLE ZI SU"
#HB155 (*Perilla frutescens*) A beautiful and delicious plant that is very popular in Asia. The purple-red leaves are used to color and flavor vinegar and to make beautiful pink rice. They are great in salads; flavor is a mix of basil and mint. Pkt (75 seeds)$2.50

SHUNGIKU EDIBLE CHRYSANTHEMUM
#HB129 (*Chrysanthemum coronarium*) Delicious green leaves are great in salads and stir-fries. The brilliant yellow flowers are also tasty! A beautiful Oriental heirloom, very colorful. Pkt (125 seeds) $2.50

SORREL, GREEN DE BELLEVILLE
#HB202 (*Rumex acetosa*) Sorrel is appreciated in native cuisines throughout Europe and in many parts of Asia and Africa as well. A perennial, it is available in early spring, before many annual crops have even been sown! The lemony tartness of the young succulent leaves gives a tangy twist to salads. Widely used in soups; combine with spinach for an authentic spanakopita. This cultivated variety with clear green leaves is much slower bolting than the wild species. Pkt (200 seeds) $2.00

SPEARMINT #HB199
(*Mentha spicata*) Here is the true species spearmint, used to flavor everything from jellies to chewing gum, teas to toothpaste! This old favorite reaches to 2 feet tall, grows in sun or shade. The lilac-pink flowers make wonderful food for bees. It has many documented medicinal effects, including antiandrogenic properties. Easy from seed. Pkt (125 seeds) $2.00

Hyssop, Korean

Shisho or Perilla "Purple Zi Su"

Stevia

STEVIA #HB175

(*Stevia rebaudiana*) A hard-to-find herb that is grown for the famous Stevia leaves which, when dried, are used to sweeten drinks and desserts. Much sweeter than sugar; stevia powder is reported to be 300 times sweeter! Not winter-hardy, except in zones 8-10. From Brazil and Paraguay. The chemical companies who make artificial sweeteners hate this plant, and have tried to make it illegal. But I just love it! Pkt (15 seeds) $2.75

SWEETIE STAR STEVIA #HB223

Sweetie Star has finer leaves than common Stevia strains. We believe this strain is the sweetest Stevia on the market from seeds. Pkt Pkt (15 seeds) $4.00

STINGING NETTLE #HB203

(*Urtica dioica*) Yes, it's the very same plant that causes unwary hikers such discomfort! But drying or cooking eliminates the sting, and the attractive plants have a long history of use in herbal medicine, as a medicinal shampoo and reputed to alleviate symptoms in cases of arthritis, enlarged prostate, and many other complaints. Also used in salt-reduced diets. Young shoots taste like spinach and are rich in vitamins and iron. Nettle is one of the foundations of Biodynamic practices. Pkt (800 seeds) $2.00

SUMMER SAVORY #HB138

(*Satureja hortensis*) Delicious peppery flavor that is popular in beans and many other dishes; also used medicinally. Pkt (250 seeds)$1.75

TANSY #HB220

(*Tanacetum vulgare*) Perennial, to 4 feet. Fern-like, aromatic leaves, with a fragrance reminiscent of camphor and rosemary. Mature plants produce heads of attractive yellow button-like flowers, interesting when grown at the back of an herb border. Dried tansy has historically been used to repel insects like moths and ants; the plant also yields a traditional green dye. Not recommended for culinary use. Pkt (100 seeds) $2.50

TARRAGON, RUSSIAN #HB145

A flavorful herb that is used to season salads, meats, and other dishes; hardy plants grow to 40". Used fresh or dried. Pkt (175 seeds) $2.00

THYME #HB113

(*T. vulgaris*) Very aromatic and flavorful; not winter hardy. Pkt (800 seeds) $2.50

THYME, WILD #HB214

(*Thymus pulegioides*) Perennial. (Also known as creeping thyme) Spreading perennial that forms thick mats with tight clusters of rose-purple flowers. Very fragrant; useful for planting between stepping stones and at the edge of walks, where its vigorous growth habit is a virtue. Used in cooking and for medicinal purposes; anti-fungal action has been documented for this species. Pkt (200 seeds) $2.25

TOOTHACHE PLANT #HB160

(*Spilanthes acmella*) Pretty yellow and red cone-shaped flowers and leaves have properties similar to Echinacea; said to enhance the immune system, improve digestion and help nausea.

The name toothache plant comes from the numbing properties it produces when the leaves and flowers are chewed, and it is used by many herbalists for this purpose. It is a tender perennial but can be grown as an annual in most areas. Pkt (75 seeds) $2.50

VALERIAN #HB221

(*Valeriana officinalis*) Perennial. (Also known as Garden Heliotrope) Delicate-looking, low-growing plants give rise to 4-foot, charming clusters of tiny pale pink flowers June-September; very attractive in borders or herb gardens. Extracted fragrance of the flowers was used in perfumes in the Renaissance. Valerian was touted for its medicinal properties for centuries, and modern research has confirmed its value. The root has been the part most used, having been recommended as a pain reliever, sedative, and to allay migraine, but most importantly, to relieve insomnia. (We make no recommendation and any use of herbs should be undertaken only under medical supervision.) Pkt (100 seeds) $2.00

VIETNAMESE MINT OR BALM #HB172

A flavorful herb that has a lemon-like taste, that goes well in many dishes as well as making a great tea, which in Vietnam is used medicinally. A fast-growing plant that is similar to mint. Pkt (50 seeds) $2.25

WHITE HOREHOUND #HB192

(*Marrubium vulgare*) This is the traditional remedy for coughs, having earned its place in the herb garden! Mounds of silvery foliage, around 18 inches tall and somewhat broader, last all season long in most climates. White flowers in season are pretty but not really showy. Pkt (100 seeds) $2.00

WORMWOOD #HB115

(*Artemisia absinthium*) Silvery-grey leaves, a beautiful plant; ornamental. Used to expel worms, and as a bitter tonic; hardy. Pkt (500 seeds) $2.00

YARROW #HB114

(*Achillea millefolium*) Beautiful when used as a dried flower. Also popular as an herb; used for colds, fevers, and for healing wounds. Pkt (800 seeds) $2.00

YARROW, CERISE QUEEN #234 *New!*

(*Achillea millefolium*) Perennial--Brilliant pink flowers, borne in typical yarrow fashion: hundreds of tiny blooms, in flat clusters, are produced with abandon until late autumn. Same carefree ways as white yarrow, and the same foot-tall plants with fernlike foliage, but the color really makes an impression! Pkt $2.00

YARROW, COLORADO MIX #HB235

New! Perennial—Mix of blood red, cerise, cream, yellow and white. All the good traits of yarrow, but in an irresistible blend of colors. The large flower clusters are in reality made up of scores of tiny daisies, last a long time and bloom until very cold weather. Pkt $2.00

Oregano Vulgare

Lemongrass

"Wars are not paid for in wartime, the bill comes later."
—BENJAMIN FRANKLIN

Dill, Elephant

Hyssop, Blue

Bee Balm, Lemon

Chamomile, German

Borage

Flower Seed

We are glad to be able to offer a good selection of old cottage garden flower varieties. Flowers bring so much joy and beauty to any garden. The old flowers seem to have disappeared even faster than their vegetable cousins. Today we can only dream about many of the superbly beautiful and fragrant flower varieties the Victorians grew. Warning: some are very poisonous. Do not use for food unless you are sure they are edible.

FLOWERS: Should all be grown in full sun, in moderately rich, moist soil except as noted.

ANNUALS: Seed should be started in spring. Most can be started indoors and plants set out after danger of frost is past. Or sow in place after frost season.

BIENNIAL: Plants usually grow one year to flower in the second year. Many occasionally live over as short-lived perennials.

HARDY ANNUALS: Seed may be started in the spring or sown outdoors or in cold frames the previous autumn.

HARDY PERENNIALS: May be sown spring or fall. Many will bloom from the second year on.

TENDER PERENNIALS: True perennials in their mild native climates; not winter hardy in temperate zone climates and therefore usually grown like annuals. Preferably started very early in the spring for transplanting after warm spring weather has arrived.

Why Flowers? By Shannon McCabe

Flowers; More Than Just Good Looks

Growing flowers in your garden will add happiness and color to your life as well as create a welcoming space for family and friends. The benefits of growing flowers go far beyond stunning beauty and intoxicating fragrance; they are capable of repelling and killing garden pests as well as attracting pollinators, and quite a few flower varieties are edible.

Flowers have been scientifically proven to enhance your mood and to overall benefit a person's feeling of well being. Studies have shown that people who had taken a moment to enjoy flowers each morning reported an immediate positive impact on their happiness level and their interactions with others. Flowers in the garden and cut flowers in the home also create a more inviting shared space for family and company.

Flowers are an open invitation for the best garden company of all: beneficial insects!

Butterflies, bees and hummingbirds are welcome garden guests. Honeybee populations are in danger; it is important to grow flowers that honeybees feed off of to support the population. This action will benefit you; honeybees are helpful in pollinating your vegetable garden to ensure that certain plants set fruit. For example, if you have a lack of pollinators in your garden, you may find that your cucumbers aren't fruiting. Butterflies and humming birds will brighten up your day, and they also complete an important part of the plant's life cycle by pollinating their flowers.

Not all of our garden critters are welcome guests; insect pests can ravage your vegetable garden and leave you desperate enough to resort to harsh pesticides. However, before launch all out chemical warfare, consider planting a trained assassin among your vulnerable vegetables. Certain flower varieties will lure insect pests but contain toxins in their foliage that kills the insect when they eat the flowers' leaves. Other flowers simply act as a trap by distracting pests from your prized vegetables.

Many flowers are even edible! They are a great way to jazz up a salad or to garnish a cake or other baked good. Just be sure the flowers have not been sprayed with pesticides that aren't safe to use on food crops.

With a bit of research, you can choose flowers that are nice to look at and will work for you! All edible flowers in this season's Baker Creek catalogue are marked so you can pick your favorite looking tasty variety.

ABUTILON (FLOWERING MAPLE) (Edible)

BELLVUE MIXED #FL904

(Abution X) South American native often called "Flowering Maple" for the shape of the delicate-looking leaves. Ours flowers in shades of muted orange, red and yellow; the large, crepe-like blooms look like miniature hibiscus flowers, to which it is related. Charming pot or container plant. An old-fashioned favorite! Pkt (25 seeds) $2.25

AGROSTEMMA - CORN COCKLE

MILAS MIXED #FL125 *New!*

Annual. Old-fashioned cottage-garden favorite, native to the eastern Mediterranean. Dapper 5-petaled flowers are extravagantly produced atop 3-foot stems in summer and fall. Each satiny blossom is two inches across in the most cheerful pink imaginable, grading to white at the center. Contrasting darker striping sets off the color scheme splendidly. Spectacular at the rear of the border or in front of a stone wall. Makes a fine cut flower, too! [Cannot ship to AR or SC.] Pkt (125 seeds) $2.00

ASTERS-CHINA

(Callistephus chinensis) Asters originated in China. Annual. (200 seeds per Pkt)

ANDRELLA SUPER MIX #FL104

Large, open, single flowers are daisy-like and come in a myriad of bright colors. Great for a cutting or bedding flower. Blooms summer to first frost. Grows 24" tall. A real beauty. Pkt $2.00

CREGO MIX #FL103

This heirloom was introduced around 1900. Large, 4" flowers really stand out in their many brilliant colors; very handsome and vigorous. Pkt $2.50

DOUBLE RAINBOW MIX #FL102

Colorful, double blooms come in a large variety of colors. Strong stems make this one of the top choices for cut flower growers nationwide. Pkt $1.50

GIANT PERFECTION MIX #FL101

Beautiful, long-lasting cut flowers, an old-fashioned favorite. Peony-type, extra-large flowers that are great for cutting. This formula mix has all the best colors. This variety is popular with home and market growers. Pkt $1.50

GIANTS OF CALIFORNIA MIX #FL105

A long-stemmed ostrich-feathered type that has unique curled petals. These come in a variety of typical aster colors. Attractive and unique. Pkt $2.00

BACHELOR'S BUTTON (Edible)

(Centaurea cyanus) Hardy annual. Often self-sows. Bachelor's Buttons were brought to America in the 17th century. (150 seeds per pkt)

BLACK BOY #FL162

Lovely, nearly black flowers are perfect for the old-fashioned cottage garden. This rare heirloom was listed in Buist's 1942 catalog. Colorful and unique. Pkt $2.00

BLUE BOY #FL160
Colorful blue, double flowers on tall 3' plants, bloom all season. Very easy to grow. It is a self-seeding annual, so you will not have to replant. Pkt $2.50

CLASSIC ARTISTIC MIX #FL157 *New!*
Hardy annual. Balanced formula-mix of assorted Bachelor Buttons of mostly two-toned color patterns. The spectrum runs from sky blue through royal blue, deep burgundy to reds, rose, pinks, and white. Lends wonderful color to beds, borders and especially to old-style cottage garden designs, and makes a perfect cut flower too! Truly an artistic new spin to an old classic favorite. Pkt $2.75

POLKA DOT MIX #FL163
A semi-dwarf mixture of many brilliant colors: plum, red, blue, lavender, pink, and white. Easy to grow, with a long blooming period. Pkt $1.75

TALL MIXED COLORS #FL161
An old-fashioned mix of tall types. Many beautiful colors: purple, violet, light and dark blue, rose, white, lavender, pink, and more! Very easy to grow. Pkt $1.75

BABY'S BREATH
Annual. Succession plant to prolong season, well-limed soils. (700 seeds per pkt)

COVENT GARDEN #FL110
(*Gypsophila elegans*) A lovely annual, single-flowered type that produces clouds of small pure white flowers on each stem. A cottage garden favorite that is perfect for fresh or dried floral arrangements. Pkt $1.50

Where Have All The Flowers Gone?
Since the year 1900, we have lost nearly every flower variety offered in catalogs of that era. That is why our catalog will feature more flowers! They are super important for a healthy garden and a happy you.

BALSAM (Edible)
(Impatiens balsamina) Annual. Thrives in heat. (65 seeds)

CAMELIA FLOWERED MIX #FL120
Pre-1870 heirloom. Beautiful rose-shaped blooms in many colors: Pink, Lavender, Red, Rose, White, and more. Short bushy plants have large bright green leaves. Very easy to grow. A must for Victorian gardeners. Pkt $2.00 *or 1 oz $7.00*

PEPPERMINT STICKS #FL121
A lovely red and white mottled balsam variety that really makes a beautiful statement in the garden. Splashy color over a long period on upright 2' tall lovely plants. Fast blooming direct from seed. Pkt $2.00

BELLS OF IRELAND   Hardy annual.

BELLS OF IRELAND #FL140
(*Moluccella laevis*) Tiny white flowers in large green bell-shaped calyxes. Great as a cut flower, fresh or dried. This old-time plant has been cultivated since 1570. Very easy to grow. Pkt (125 seeds) $2.50

BLACK-EYED SUSAN VINE

BLACK-EYED SUSAN VINE MIX #FL917 *New!* (*Thunbergia alata*)
Tender perennial grown as an annual. Trumpet-shaped, 5-petaled tubular flowers in a warm mix of yellows, oranges and golds. Bearing 2-inch flowers with dark purple-black throats, this East African native is showy trained up a trellis, in hanging baskets, or in pots. Mature plants grown in a frost-free environment may climb 20 feet; expect 6- to 8-foot plants when grown as an annual. Pkt (25 seeds) $3.00

BROWALLIA Annual.

BROWALLIA BLUE LADY #FL168 (*Browallia americana*)
Lovely blue flowering annual with attractive, deep green leaves. This plant bears numerous 1"- wide clear blue flowers with a cream center. Native of South America, it is easy to grow in full sun or partial shade. Plants reach 2' in height and bloom till frost. A must for those that love blue flowers. Poisonious. Pkt (250 seeds) $2.50

BRUGMANSIA OR ANGEL'S TRUMPET

Tender perennial. Grow like eggplant or peppers. Overwinter in frost-free location.

PINK ANGEL'S TRUMPET #FL171

(*Brugmansia suaveolens*) Amazing, fragrant, trumpet-shaped flowers can grow up to 1 foot long! This variety is a beautiful blushing pink color and makes a really eye-popping display that will give the whole area a sweet aroma. One of my favorite flowers that is somewhat frost hardy. It will bloom nearly all year long in warm coastal climates, with temperatures between 50-80 degrees being perfect for this plant. Can be grown in sunlight or semi-shade. In cooler climates this plant can be grown in a large pot or directly in the ground as long as the plants are brought in before winter. *Warning: the seeds and plants are very poisonous.* Pkt (10 seeds) $4.00

CACTUS

CACTI MIXED #FL909 *New!*
Formula mix featuring diverse plant habits, flower forms and colors. Fascinating subjects for houseplant or greenhouse. Cacti are usually slow growers and very long-lived in suitable conditions. Pkt (25 seeds) $2.75

CAPE MARIGOLD Annual.

MIXED COLORS #FL295

(*Dimorphotheca aurantiaca*) Annual--Sunny, yellow to orange single daisies arrive in profusion all summer long! Two-inch flowers on rugged, foot-tall stems keep their cool even in heat and drought. South African native but naturalized in the Southwestern US. Stunning in massed plantings! Pkt $2.50

CALENDULA (Edible)

(*Calendula officinalis*) Hardy annual. Often self-sows. (125 seeds per pkt)

BALL'S IMPROVED ORANGE #FL205
Pretty, double, 3" flowers are a deep orange color. They are great as cut flowers or as a tasty garnish in salads and add color to many dishes. Pkt $1.75

DOUBLE WHITE SHADES (Availiable In 2016)

(*Calendula officinalis*) Hardy annual--There's no true white calendula, but this mix does include some of the palest to be found! Produces fully double blossoms in warm tones ranging from old ivory to tangerine. Blooms all summer in cool summer areas, late spring to summer elsewhere. Classic calendula proportions. Makes a fine cut flower, too! (Availiable in 2016)

FIESTA GITANA #FL211 *New!*
Hardy annual. Dwarf selection of an old favorite, with plants reaching only about 10" in height. Fully double flowers; color is a wide mix, running from pale cream through soft yellow, bright yellow to apricot and deep, intense orange, with some bicolors. Bred in the 1970's, this selection still answers the need for a calendula suited to the front of borders, and makes an excellent container variety. Pkt $2.75

INDIAN PRINCE #FL207
This traditional variety had become very popular by the 1930's. Tall plants produce stunning two-tone flowers. Deep orange petals are backed by crimson, making this a stunning cut flower. Pkt $2.00

KABLOONA #FL204
Lavish display of flowers in tones from cream to gold and yellow to orange, with the centers of the daisy-like flower often in contrasting shades and textures. Fine for cut flowers. Calendula petals have been used as a substitute for saffron. A care-free plant blooming in late spring to early summer; excellent in cottage gardens. Pkt $2.25

ORANGE KING #FL208
Massive, double calendula flowers in a beautiful shade of brilliant orange make this variety a true king of calendulas. Pkt $1.75

ORANGE PORCUPINE #FL202
A beautiful selection of the old "Radio" variety, this one has beautiful quilled petals, bright orange in color. Unique. Pkt $2.50

PACIFIC BEAUTY MIX #FL200
Lovely flowers up to 4" in colors of orange, apricot, yellow, peach, and cream. A historic heirloom garden plant that was known as "Pot Marigold." A colorful addition to any garden. Pkt $1.75 *or 1 oz $6.00*

PINK SURPRISE #FL201
A lovely calendula with apricot flowers tinged with pink; truly something new and exciting. Frilly flowers bloom over a long season. Pkt $2.25

RADIO #FL206
This 1930's introduction celebrated the invention of the radio. The glowing orange flowers have pointed, quilled petals. Blooms over a long season and can easily be grown in pots. Pkt $2.00

CANTERBURY BELLS

CANTERBURY BELLS MIXED #FL150
(Campanula) Tall spikes of long-lasting, bell-shaped flowers, in rich tones of purple, lavender, reds, pinks, yellows and white to cream. A cottage-garden staple for centuries. Makes a fine cut flower. It was offered by Comstock, Ferre & Co. in 1856. Pkt (500 seeds) $2.00

RESINA #FL210 *New!*
Bright yellow medium-sized daisies, with an occasional orange bloom just to keep things lively! This variety has the highest concentration of resins of any known type, which makes it the most potent for any of Calendula's many herbal uses! The yellow flowers also make a renowned yellow traditional dye. Pkt (50 seeds) $2.75

YELLOW GEM #FL209
Annual—Dwarf Calendula reaches only about a foot in height. Perky, clear yellow semi-double blooms. Adds a cheerful touch in late spring-early summer. Pkt $2.25

CANDYTUFT
Hardy perennial. (125 seeds per pkt)

CANDYTUFT TALL #FL001
(Iberis umbellata) This is a lovely, taller type which produces that simple, charming look that has been lost in modern gardens. Having lovely pastel shades, it is easy to grow, as it even grows in rather poor soil. Pkt $1.75

FAIRYLAND DWARF MIX #FL002
(Iberis umbellata) This dwarf plant adds an old-fashioned charm to the garden, with its lovely flowers in candy-colored shades of red, pink, lavender and white. This plant flowers quickly and makes pretty dried seed heads. Pkt $1.75

CASTOR BEAN
(Ricinus communis) Annual. Persists as a shrub in very mild-winter climates. **Poisonous!** (20 seeds per pkt)

IMPALA #FL284 *New!* ↑
(*Ricinus communis*) Here's a dwarf castor bean variety, ideal for smaller gardens that simply cannot accommodate the more exuberant sort! 'Impala' seldom exceeds 6 feet in height, a great improvement over full-sized types where space is tight. The palmate leaves start out bronzy burgundy, mature to a deep green. Large leaves and burgundy seed heads lend a tropical feel to borders or patio plantings! Pkt $3.00

GARDEN MIX #FL280
Castor Beans were introduced in the 16th century. We offer a mix of reds, pinks, greens, and burgundy. Tall, 8'-12' plants are tropical looking, have colored flower pods, and are easy to grow. **Warning: the seeds and plants are very poisonous.** Pkt $2.50

GIANT ZANZIBARIENSIS #FL281
This giant castor bean will take center stage in any garden. Magnificent plants can grow over 15' in the first season, and the leaves can reach 3' across! A true monster that gets big in most climates and really huge in warm climates. Provides a quick, tropical-like shade. **Warning: the seeds and plants are very poisonous.** Pkt $3.50

GIBSONII #FL282
This old-favorite type produces lovely reddish-bronze leaves and stunning scarlet seed heads. One of the most colorful, it adds a tropical touch to gardens anywhere. **Warning: the seeds and plants are very poisonous.** Pkt $2.75

RED GIANT #FL175 *New!*
Large, dusky-red leaves have bright-red veining and stems. Dark seed pods are very exotic looking, being covered in deep red spikes. Warning: the seeds and plants are very poisonous. Pkt $3.50

CANNA

CANNA INDICA, INDIAN SHOT CANNA #FLI142 (Edible) *New!*
A lovely species canna you can grow from seed. It produces lovely green plants with tropical foliage and smaller red to orange blooms. Easy to grow and is native to the Southern USA. The small black seeds are quite hard, and it is said that during a 19th century Indian Mutiny that soldiers resorted to using the seeds from this canna when they ran out of bullets in the wilderness. Grow as an annual or move inside in cooler climates. Pkt $3.50

CELOSIA, FOREST FIRE #FL176 *New!*
Vivid bright scarlet flower heads really are reminiscent of flame! This plume-type Celosia makes enormous blooms that fairly cover the entire top portion of each 30" plant. Attractive foliage is tinged with burgundy. Fine for drying, supplying some of the most brilliant color attainable to dried arrangements. Dazzling! Pkt (125 seeds) $2.00

COCKSCOMB, DWARF CORAL GARDEN MIX #FL266
Beautiful color on short, dwarf plants, these can produce large heads that sometimes reach 8" across, although they vary. A perfect bedding plant that adds vibrant colors to any garden; even the smallest can fit in a few of these. Pkt (125 seeds) $2.00

CELOSIA, PAMPAS PLUME MIX #FL905
(*Celosia plumosa)* To 28-48 inches. Full-sized plume-type celosia. The soft, feathery plumes come in the range of colors. Arresting at the back of the border; sensational in arrangements. Holds color well as a dried flower. Summer garden workhorse thrives in heat and dry conditions. Pkt (125 seeds) $2.00

CELOSIA, ORANGE PEACH #FL269
Annual, to 48". Stunning, large, very deeply folded crested-type cockcombs in shades from apricot to coral pink. Gorgeous at the back of a mixed border; also makes a nice dried flower. Pkt (100 seeds) $2.75

COCKSCOMB, AMISH #FL262
Orral and Joan Craig discovered this variety growing in an Amish garden near Arthur, Illinois. Beautiful, large red heads on compact 1'-tall plants. I first saw this variety growing at Seed Savers in Iowa and was taken aback by its color and beauty. Pkt (100 seeds) $2.50

COCKSCOMB, AMISH WHITE #FL268
This lovely cockscomb comes from an Amish seed collector. It produces large cream-colored flowers that are quite unique. This stately variety has

COCKSCOMB, TALL MIXED #FL267
These tall cockscombs are hard to find, but offer a gorgeous display of flashy color in shades of pink, red, and yellow. The extra-tall plants are great for borders and group plantings for massive displays of color. Great as cut flowers, they sell well at market. Pkt (125 seeds) $2.75

EDIBLE FLOWERS

In recent years much has been written about eating flowers, but it really isn't a new idea--flowers have always been enjoyed for the colors, fragrances and flavors they bring to the table. They are usually most valued as a garnish, in salads, or anywhere that they may be employed without cooking. (Cooking would spoil the brilliant colors and amazing visual forms!) Although some species like dahlias produce edible tubers that can be great cooked, and celosia that is great cooked green, etc, etc!

While many flowers may be used in this fashion, here is a list of some of the most widely used types:

Herbs--any edible herb species will have edible flowers if allowed to bloom. Some commonly used ones include: basil, borage, hyssop, anise or Korean hyssop, chamomile, lavender, shungiku or garland chrysanthemum.

Ornamentals--Calendula, Dahlia, Dianthus including Carnations, Nasturtium, Pansies, Sunflower.

Caution: Not all flowers are edible, and some are downright poisonous. Before eating any flowers, be certain that you have a solid identification, and then proceed cautiously. Even edible types could cause an allergic reaction in some sensitive individuals.

CHRYSANTHEMUM (Edible)

GOLDEN BALL #FL177 *New!*

(Chrysanthemum parthenium, also known as Tanacetum parthenium) Perennial--Equally appropriate to the herb- or flower garden! This highly ornamental form of feverfew boasts attractive bright yellow flowers all season long. The flower form is nearly spherical, made up of very closely packed petals. The plants are very compact, reaching to 18" tall and wide. The lemon-yellow blooms are produced non-stop until the weather turns really cold, and look so chipper with their backdrop of the textured gray-green foliage. Takes a fairly hot, dry location once established. Pkt $2.50

COLEUS

Tender perennial. Overwinter indoors, or grow as an annual, starting indoors in early spring.

RAINBOW FLORIST STRAIN MIX #FL225

This old-fashioned plant is perfect for any shady spot. The heart-shaped leaves come in many bright colors, great for containers and borders. This plant evokes the spirit of Victorian gardens. Start inside and don't cover seeds. Leaves are cooked in some Asian cultures. Pkt (100 seeds) $2.00

CHINESE HOUSES

CHINESE HOUSES #WF130 *New!*

(Collinsia heterophylla) Annual. One of the showiest of native California flowers! Spectacular flowers are bicolored in amethyst and white, produced in whorls on two-foot stems. Each tier of blooms is smaller than the one below, giving the flower spikes a fanciful resemblance to pagodas. Traditionally used in Native American herbal medicine. Pkt (500 seeds) $2.00

COREOPSIS COREOPSIS

DWARF RED PLAINS COREOPSIS #WF127 *New!*

Annual. Extravagant deep maroon version of a widely occurring native wildflower. Single blooms seem to float above one- to two-foot plants. Easy from seed, prefers dry soils. Plains Coreopsis is used by the Zuni people of the Southwest to make a mahogany dye. Pkt (1000 seeds) $1.50

GOLDEN GLOBE #FL179 *New!*

(Coreopsis grandiflora) Perennial--Very double type, ray-flowers deeply pleated or even conical in shape. Each delicate-looking bloom is like a brilliant sunburst. Stocky plants branch freely from the base, reach just 2 feet in height. Superb form and color, all season long! A truly choice native perennial. Pkt (100 seeds) $2.75

PLAINS COREOPSIS #WF104

(Coreopsis tinctoria) Hardy annual. Occasionally self-sows. Prefers a drier soil. Lovely red and yellow daisy-like flower, this prairie annual blooms in the summer or fall; brilliant color. Pkt $1.50 *or 1 oz $6.50*

ROULETTE #WF137 *New!*

(Coreopsis tinctoria) Hardy annual--Large blooms of velvety dark mahogany-red, having an inner row of smaller petals in pale gold. The effect is very intricate and rich! Elegant refinement to a native old-favorite; equally splendid in drifts in borders or as cut flowers. Free-flowering, drought-tolerant plants reach above two feet in heght, adding wonderful color to sunny, rather dry locations. Seldom bothered by deer, blooms early summer to frost. Pkt (100 seeds) $2.75

CONVOLVULUS

CONVOLVULUS TRICOLOR MIXED #FL130 *New!*

Annual, to 12 inches high--Non-vining morning glory relative grows like a small, prostrate bush. Miniature morning glory flowers are an inch and a half across. And the colors are wild! Concentric star-like rings of pinks, rose and dark purple alternate with white, while the throat of each trumpet-shaped flower glows in sunny yellow. All we can promise is that each flower has three colors! The lax habit makes this superb in planters or pots. Stunning! Pkt (150 seeds) $2.50

COSMOS (Edible)

Hardy annual. Great for salads and garnishing. Often self-sows.

BRIGHT LIGHTS #FL241

(Cosmos sulphureus) Brilliant flowers in shades of orange, yellow, and flame-red, the plants are early to bloom and produce profusely. Colorful and easy to grow. Pkt (100 seeds) $1.75

COSIMO COLLARETTE #FL249 *New!*

Enchanting semi-double Cosmos in subtle stripes of shell-pink and white. The inner petals are smaller than the primary ones, forming a ruffled "collar!" This is very slight on some of the blooms, pronounced on others. The overall effect is very appealing. Dwarf habit (compared to standard Cosmos) at 20-24 inches tall, makes this variety great for smaller borders, for bedding or as a patio plant. Pkt (30 seeds) $2.50

COSIMO RED-WHITE #FL250 *New!*

Annual—Sumptuous, well-behaved dwarf cosmos, barely 2 feet tall, combined with a dramatic, bicolor sunburst appearance. Each petal is white toward the center, deep red to the edges. Early flowering on compact, sturdy plants are choice candidates for containers. A great cut-flower, too! Pkt (30 seeds) $2.50

INDONESIAN KENNIKURA #FL243

(*C. sulphureus*) Beautiful and tasty. Popular in Indonesian cuisine and is used as a garnish. The lovely 3" flowers are bright yellow and orange; this variety blooms over a long season and is very colorful. Pkt (40 seeds) $2.75

SENSATION MIX #FL240

(*C. bipinnatus*) Beautiful shades of pink, crimson, white, and rose. Tall bush plants are very easy to grow, providing colorful blooms all summer. Pkt (100 seeds) $2.50

RUBENZA #FL248 *New!*

Deep rich ruby-red color is very unusual in a cosmos! Single blooms are a luxuriant, deep burgundy when they open, fading gradually to old rose as they mature. The contrast with the burnished gold of the centers is striking and very regal! Very compact plants reaching only to 2 feet. Superb for cutting, like all cosmos. Pkt (30 seeds) $2.50

SEA SHELLS #FL247

(*Cosmos bipinnatus*) Here's something unusual for cottage gardens or for cut-flowers: the ray flowers of this charming cosmos are tubular or cone-shaped rather than flat, giving the blooms an intricate look. Three-inch flowers are produced abundantly all summer until frost, in the usual cosmos shades of deep rose, shell pink and pure, snowy white. Plants reach 3-4 feet; like most cosmos, tolerates poor and dry soils, hot conditions. Pkt (50 seeds) $2.50

SENSATION CANDY STRIPE #FL246

(*C. bipinnatus*) Bushy border plant with ferny foliage and stunning large flowers of white with rose petal edges. Colorful, unique selection. Traditional cottage garden subject. Pkt $2.00

DAHLIA (Edible) (Also see page 334 for dahlia tubers)

Annual. Tubers may be lifted and stored for planting the following spring. Flowers and tubers are both useful as food.

CACTUS FLOWERED MIX #FL301

(*Dahlia variabilis*) Full-sized Dahlia plants, reaching 4 ft tall, cover themselves in sumptuous, large, quilled, fully double flowers spanning the range that Dahlia has to offer—jewel tones of scarlet, lemon yellow and pinks. Gorgeous at the back of the border, or a fine candidate for the cutting garden. Enormous blooms to 4 inches in diameter. Pkt (30 seeds) $2.50

MIGNON SINGLE MIX #FL184 *New!*

Compact, rounded plants are a useful size, reaching about 20 inches—perfect for bedding, large enough to make a real showing in containers or window boxes. Flowers are single, large at 3-4", with petals of unusually heavy substance. Colors are perky Dahlia tones of white, pinks, soft yellows, and reds. Pkt (30 seeds) $2.50

COLTNESS MIX #FL305

(*Dahlia variabilis*) Single flowers of this variety make a charming counterpoint to the exuberance of the more popular double types. Color range is a bit unusual, running from yellow and orange, through pink and to rather somber maroons, but with a twist: a few of the flowers are two-tone or picotee. Compact plants reach just two feet. Pkt (30 seeds) $2.50

RED SKIN MIX #FL302

(*Dahlia variabilis*) Rich bronze-red foliage makes this a standout! Semi-to fully double flowers, petals very wide and full, in hues of crimson, scarlet, orange, yellow and cream. Compact plants reaching 20 inches or so. All-America Award winner for 1975. Pkt (30 seeds) $2.50

SHOWPIECE DOUBLE MIX #FL303

(*Dahlia variabilis*) Very uniform classic Dahlia-type flowers in pale yellow, red, carmine, lavender and salmon. Flowers are full-sized; form is very double. Vigorous, carefree plants reach to 4 feet in height. Fine for cutting or in the border—wherever a riot of color is wanted. Very choice! Pkt (30 seeds) $3.00

STARLIGHT MIX #FL306

(*Dahlia variabilis*) Single, star-like flowers are held above plants seldom reaching 18 inches in height. The recurved petals create a stunning effect. Pkt (30 seeds) $3.00

UNWINS MIX #FL300 ↑ (*Dahlia hybrida*) Colorful mix of rose, orange, yellow, crimson, purple, and brick red. Single and semi-double flowers; a popular garden flower. A classic dahlia mix that has greeted several generations of gardeners each summer. Easy to grow. Pkt (50 seeds) $2.25

DAISY (Various Species)
DOUBLE FLOWERED MIX, ENGLISH DAISY #FL296

(*Bellis perennis*) Biennial or perennial. To 6". Petite, double daisy flowers, about an inch across, atop 5-6-inch stems, in reds, pinks and pure white. Was often planted to add a pop of color in old-fashioned lawns. Often naturalizes or grows as a perennial in lawns. A quaint, nostalgic reminder of the gardens of yesteryear.Pkt (300 seeds) $2.25

GARLAND DAISY #FL299 *New!* (*Chrysanthemum coronarium*)

Annual. Single to fully double daisies, 1-2 inches in diameter, are constantly renewed over a very long season, making this a great addition to the border. But it is equally at home in the vegetable patch, since it is the same species as Shungiku, with the same deeply cut, delicious, spicy foliage. Either way, the upbeat, sunny tones of buttercup through bright yellow are welcome wherever they are found. And yes, you can string the flowers into garlands! Pkt (200 seeds $2.00

LITTLE MISSY #FL294 *New!* (*Brachycome iberidifolia*)

Petite little clumps of dainty, charming little daisies. Each single, violet-blue flower has a center of pale gold, surrounded by a halo of snowy white. Breathtaking in close up! Great for containers, or mass plant for a soothing effect--the flowers look so serene and cool floating above the lacy dark-green foliage. At its best in cool summer regions, or started early to bloom late spring to early summer. Pkt (200 seeds $2.00

ROSE BALL ENGLISH DAISY #FL297

(*Bellis perennis*) Biennial or perennial. To 6". Super-double pompons in a delicate carnation pink. Very large flowers for an English Daisy; look just like miniature dahlias or chrysanthemums. Pkt (300 seeds) $2.25

ALASKA SHASTA DAISY #WF117 (*Chrysanthemum maximum*)

Hardy perennial. This easy to grow daisy has large white daisy flowers with bright yellow centers, great for your cottage garden and perfect for a cut flower. Pkt $1.50

SWAN RIVER DAISY MIXED #FL298 (*Brachycome iberidifolia*)

Annual. Single, one-inch daisies in shades of violet, lavender-pink and white add a much-needed cool note in the late spring or summer landscape. Small stature of these carefree plants makes them ideal for pots, rock gardens, or at the front of summer borders. Blooms over a long period; tolerant to hot conditions and dry soils. Native of western Australia, but widely grown and appreciated outside the Land of Oz. Pkt (300 seeds) $2.25

DATURA

Tender perennial: Grow like eggplant or peppers. Overwinter in frost-free location. Warning: Poisonous!

BALLERINA MIX #FL310

(*Datura metel*) A wonderful dwarf version of this lovely plant, growing to about 20" tall if grown in containers. The beautiful, large trumpet-shaped flowers can be creamy yellow and purple, bi-color or pure white. Truly a show stopper! Rare and hard-to-find. **Caution: all parts of these plants are very poisonous.** Pkt (10 seeds) $4.00

DELPHINIUM & LARKSPUR

CARMINE KING #FL375 *New!*

Biennial or hardy annual--Truly massive spikes of densely-packed, brilliant, carmine-rose blooms. When well grown these reach 3 feet in height! Selected out of the Giant Imperials strain,"Carmine King" makes a superlative cut flower! Prefers partial shade, especially in hot-summer climates. Warning: It is poisonous! Pkt (300 seeds) $2.50

GIANT IMPERIAL MIXED LARKSPUR #FL371

(*D. ambigua*) Beautiful flower spikes on plants that can grow to 4' tall, covered with lovely flowers in shades of pink, lilac, white, blue and rose. This old favorite is also called *Annual delphinium*, and is perfect to grow along a fence. Warning: It is poisonous! Pkt (300 seeds) $2.00

PINK QUEEN #FL374 *New!*

Biennial or hardy annual—Another selection from the old favorite, Giant Imperials. This one is in chaste apple-blossom pink. Incredible, 3-foot flower spikes provide great structure to the early-summer border. Excels as a cut flower, naturally. Prefers partial shade, especially in hot-summer climates. Warning: It is poisonous! Pkt (300 seeds) $2.50

DAME'S ROCKET   (Edible)

EVENING DAME'S ROCKET #WF118
(*Hesperis matronalis*) This plant has naturalized in many parts of the US since it was introduced in the 1700s. Pretty, large, flower spikes of lilac-colored blooms that are fragrant at night. Pkt $1.75

DIANTHUS (CARNATIONS AND PINKS)
(Edible)   Perennial. Direct sow in spring. (100 seeds per pkt)

BABY DOLL #FL320
(*Dianthus chinensis*) A lovely compact plant that produces an array of bright pink, white, and crimson flowers; good for pots. A popular old-time garden plant. Pkt $1.75

CHABAUD LA FRANCE CARNATION #FL324
(*Dianthus caryophyllus*) True florist's strain for cut-flower use. Frilly, fully double blooms, in a chaste shell pink, are held aloft on sturdy, wiry stems. Light clove fragrance completes the picture of floral perfection. Pkt $2.00

BLACK AND WHITE MINSTRALS #FL329   ↑
Hardy annual. Dainty, fully double blooms in deepest maroon, almost black, edged in brilliant white. The margins of the petals are heavily frilled, and the overall effect is one of great dignity and refinement, yet stunning beauty. The one-inch blooms are sweetly fragrant. Makes a fine cut flower but really shines in a massed planting. Compact plants, the flowers are held above the grass-like foliage, reaching about a foot in height. Pkt (50 seeds) $3.00

CHABAUD ORANGE SHERBET #FL906 Large double flowers are borne on strong, long stems. Fragrant, fringed blooms are pale orange splashed liberally with much more intense reddish-orange. Excellent cut-flower strain. Perennial in warmer climates. Pkt $2.75

CHABAUD RED AND YELLOW CARNATION #FL187 *New!* Saucy blend of cream, salmon, and deep rose-pink petals splashed and streaked with scarlet. Thin to largest bud on each stem for fully double florist style blooms. Pkt $2.75

FLAX

BRIGHT EYES #WF141 *New!*
(*Linum grandiflorum rubrum*) Hardy annual. Charming plant for rock gardens, borders, and meadow plantings. The 5-petaled blooms seem to float 12-18 inches above the gray-green foliage, but are actually held there by wiry stems. Flower color is pure white with a striking and unusual red center. Easy from seed, very free-flowering and self-sows readily while never becoming a nuisance. Native to Algeria. Pkt $1.75

BLUE FLAX #WF120
(*Linum perenne*) This perennial flower was discovered on the Lewis & Clark Expedition, and hence the species was named "lewisii". Lovely blue flowers on 24" plants, beautiful and easy to grow. Pkt $1.50

SCARLET FLAX #WF115
(*Linum grandiflorum rubrum*) Often self-sows. This species can be grown in hot and dry conditions. The plants produce loads of lovely, scarlet-red flowers. This plant is native to southern Europe and northern Africa. A hardy annual. Pkt $1.50

FOXGLOVE
Biennial. Direct sow spring or autumn. Self-sows freely where contented.

APRICOT BEAUTY #FL340
(*Digitalis purpurea*) Lovely, peachy apricot flower spikes. These grow to 30" and are quite lovely. **Please remember that the seeds and all parts of this plant are poisonous.** Pkt (800 seeds) $2.25

CHABAUD PICOTEE FANTASY MIX CARNATION #FL327
(*Dianthus caryophyllus*) A wide mix of carnation colors—cardinal red, pinks, violets, crimson, salmon, whites and yellows—all "fantastically" striped or edged in brilliant contrasting tones. Large, fully double, sweetly scented blooms make great cut flowers. Reaches about 2 feet in height. Pkt $2.75

DWARF PERSIAN CARPET MIXED #FL325
(*Dianthus chinensis*) Cheerful single blooms in many different shades from white to pale pink to carmine red. Blooms are steadily produced until frost. Pkt $1.75

GRENADIN KING OF THE BLACKS CARNATION #FL326
(*Dianthus caryophyllus*) Rich, dark burgundy-red, double flowers are lavishly produced, contrasting smartly with blue-green, mounded foliage. Border-type carnation that nevertheless makes a wonderful cut flower. Lightly fragrant blooms reach 15 inches tall atop wiry stems; the clove-like scent comes as a bonus. A real show-stopper! Pkt $2.25

SWEET WILLIAM, TALL SINGLE MIXED #FL322
(*D. barbatus*) Biennial. Plant spring or summer for blooms the following year. A colorful garden flower that is fragrant. The 4 inch flower heads cover 18" tall plants. A native of Europe that is often grown as an annual cut flower. Pkt $1.50

CHABAUD LEGION OF HONOUR #FL328
Perennial. Large, double blooms in clear warm red shades. Wiry stems make Chabaud types great for cutting, but they are just as effective in the border. May be grown as an annual if started very early indoors. Plants reach to 2 feet or a bit more. Pkt (100 seeds) $2.50

CHABAUD ENFANT DE NICE #FL330
Perennial. Very full double flowers in tones from burgundy red through to white. Somewhat shorter and more compact than Chabaud types, with plants reaching not quite 2 ft in height. Makes an equally fine cut flower or border specimen. May be grown as an annual if started early indoors. Pkt (100 seeds) $2.50

"It is thus with farming, if you do one thing late, you will be late in all your work." -CATO THE ELDER

GOMPHRENA

GLOBOSA MIXED #FL189 *New!*

Annual—Often called Globe Amaranth, and it is an amaranth relative, but petite by comparison—plants seldom exceed 2 feet in height. And the thimble-shaped, papery flower heads are just an inch across, produced in great numbers. Colors are tones of white, pink, and rosy reds. Great for cut-flower use, fine for drying. Also well proportioned for containers, where it makes an unusually long-lasting display. Takes heat and drought, too. Beloved old-fashioned garden plant that is finding renewed favor! Pkt (75 seeds) $2.00

GILIA

GILIA GLOBE #WF135 *New!*

Hardy annual. Globe-shaped, tightly-packed clusters of sky-blue to violet flowers are sweetly scented. Held about 15" above the ground, the flowers come over a long season. Very attractive to butterflies and bees and makes great forage for these precious and beautiful insects. This West Coast native prefers hot and dry conditions. Perfect for roadside plantings, meadows and, of course, flower borders. Makes a fine cut flower; self-sows freely where the environment suits it. Pkt (800 seeds) $1.75

BIRD'S EYES #WF107

(*Gila tricolor*) Hardy annual. Often self-sows. Attractive tricolored flowers, white with edges blushed in lilac—centers are purplish black! Very unique-looking annual that likes a dry, sunny area. Pkt $1.50

GAILARDIA

GAILLARDIA INDIAN BLANKET #WF111

Hardy annual. Often self-sows. Lovely, yellow, daisy-like flowers with red centers, this annual is easy to grow. Great for sunny, dry areas. Pkt $1.50

HOLLYHOCK (Edible)

(Alcea rosea except as noted) Biennial. Delicious petals are perfect for salads. (35 seeds per pkt)

FIG-LEAFED HOLLYHOCK #FL428

(*A. ficifolia*) Species form of the common hollyhock, that is not bothered by rust. Deeply indented leaves, 5-petaled, single flowers, mixed colors. Old-fashioned plant cultivated since at least the 1600's and known for its beautiful flowers that add a certain Victorian charm to any fence row. Pkt $2.25

INDIAN SPRING #FL420

Wonderful shades of soft to bright pink flowers. Tall plants produce old-fashioned single flowers. Hardy and easy to grow, this variety blooms the first year. Beautiful! Pkt $2.25

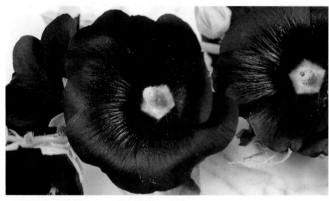

JET BLACK OR NIGRA #FL421

This variety was mentioned in 1629 and was planted in the gardens at Monticello by Thomas Jefferson. This traditional variety is shockingly beautiful with its near-black flowers and just a hint of red. Gorgeous planted out by the old white outhouse or in the back of your flower bed. A must for historical gardens. You'll love this richly-colored variety. Pkt $2.75

DWARF QUEENY MIXED #FL429

Compact form, 2-3 feet high, is ideal for bedding use, small enough to grow in pots! Huge, fully double blooms held all along the stems. Contains the full range of hollyhock colors: purple, red, rose, pink, salmon, yellow and white. These bloom very quickly from seed, about 65 days. Pkt $2.50

MAJORETTE DOUBLE CHAMPAGNE #FL423

Romantic, soft, blushing pink flowers with darker pink centers, this dwarf variety produces fully double, large "powderpuff" type flowers. Such a lovely color and easy to grow as an annual or biennial. Pkt (30 seeds) $2.75

MAJORETTE DOUBLE YELLOW #FL424

A hard-to-find variety with pretty, canary-yellow blooms. This dwarf variety produces fully double, large "powderpuff" type flowers. Add some "Sunshine'" with this easy to grow annual or biennial. Pkt $2.50

QUEENY LILAC-ROSE #FL425

A beautiful dwarf variety in the "Queeny" series developed by Dr. Zoltan Kovacs of Budapest, Hungary. Compact stalks produce loads of lilac-rose colored, double blooms that are so cute! Now you can even grow annual hollyhocks in pots or small spaces for a wonderful old-fashioned look. Pkt $2.50

SUMMER CARNIVAL, MIXED #FL426

This All-America Winner is sure to add color to even the most faded outhouse or border. Big, brilliant, double blooms in many shades. The tall stems make this perfect as a cut flower, and it is easy to grow as an annual or biennial. A great mix of tall Carnival colors. Pkt $2.00

ZEBRINA #FL427

(*Malva sylvestris*) Not a true hollyhock, but growing much the same, this Malva was widely planted in Victorian cottage gardens. It is one of the most beautiful plants we offer and one of the most popular heirloom plants at historic gardens. The flower spikes bloom profusely with lovely lavender flowers that have stunning deep purple stripes. Looks like a small, single hollyhock. Pkt $2.00

DOUBLE CARNIVAL ROSY RED #FL192 *New!*

Annual or biennial—Fantastic, showy 3- to 4-inch blooms are of deep rose. This one is superb in massed plantings, or as an accent plant, adding height and structure to the garden lay-out. Plants reach 6-7 feet in height and really crank out the color all season long! Pkt $2.50

DOUBLE MAJORETTE BROWN RED #FL193 *New!*

Annual or biennial—Flowers are double, but more of a collarette type, opening rather flat with a ruff of smaller petals in the center. The color is so much lovelier than the prosaic name suggests: the satiny petals are deep garnet to burgundy. Plants are comparatively compact at only 3-4 feet tall. Pkt $2.75

DOUBLE MAJORETTE DARK ROSE #FL194 *New!*

Annual or biennial—Similar compact plants to other varieties of the Majorette series, but the elegant double flowers are a clear medium pink. A really choice border plant! Pkt $2.50

QUEENY SALMON #FL195 *New!*

Annual or biennial--Very double, light coral pink powder-puff flowers on the smallest hollyhocks we offer—the Queeny series seldom exceeds 2 feet tall! Their smaller stature frees these choice plants from the back of the border, allowing you to grow them were the elaborate blooms can be appreciated close-up. Pkt $2.50

QUEENY WHITE #FL196 *New!*

Annual or biennial--Bushy plants reach only 2 feet in height, clothe themselves in paper-white double blooms. The huge flowers, reaching 3 inches in diameter are at the center gently suffused with buttercup yellow. Rather more elegance than is commonly expected in a hollyhock! Pkt $2.50

QUEENY YELLOW #FL197 *New!*

Annual or biennial—Soft pastel yellow to almost ivory flowers. Compact proportions and habit like others of the Queeny series. The subtle hues are curiously restful and refreshing to the eye, especially when planted alongside "Queeny 'White' ". Pkt $2.50

DOUBLE CARNIVAL BLUSH PINK #FL191 *New!*

Annual or biennial—Stunning, carnation-pink blooms on 6- to 7-foot spires. Makes a screen in no time, which is the classic cottage garden use for hollyhocks. Heavenly combined with "Carnival 'Rosy Red'" ! The Carnival series offers big plants, good double flower form, and flower placement toward the lower portions of the plants which makes the plants so much more graceful. Pkt $2.50

HYPOESTES

PINK POLKA DOT #FL236 *New!*

Tender perennial, usually grown as an annual—8-inch foliage plants. Leaves are teardrop shaped, shiny dark green. But each leaf is covered in confetti-like flecks of bright carnation pink. Plants are very easy and reliable from seed and begin providing color with their very first leaf. Often seen as a houseplant, but superb outdoors in shade. Stunning for edging the border. Wild! Pkt (25 seeds) $3.00

HYSSOP - AGASTACHE (Edible)

ARCADO PINK #FL126 *New!*

(*Agastache X hyb.*) Think Anise hyssop with a twist--this variety blooms in clear pink rather than the more usual lavender-purple. Incredibly free flowering on compact plants, early summer right through to hard frost, and the bees, butterflies and hummingbirds love it! Pkt (25 seeds) $3.00

ICEPLANT (Edible)

SUCCULENT ICEPLANT #FL919
(*Mesembryanthemum crystallinum*) (Also known as Hottentot Fig) Annual or biennial, to 10 inches--Prolific production of daisy-like white to pink flowers in summer. A bed of Iceplant is oddly reminiscent of an undersea stand of sea anemones! The glistening, succulent leaves are tinged with bronze, making a delicious, slightly tart spinach substitute. At one time the leaves were used to treat scurvy on long voyages, which explains its occurrence worldwide, seeds being present in soil dropped by ships in ballast dumps. Has naturalized along the California coast where it is something of a trademark, even though it's native to southern and western Africa.   Pkt (100 seeds) $2.50

KISS-ME-OVER-THE-GARDEN-GATE
Perennial. Direct sow in spring. Slow germinator.

KISS-ME-OVER-THE-GARDEN-GATE #FL360
(*Polygonum orientale*) Exotic, long, flowing flower heads are a cerise-pink in color. Plants are over 6' tall and produce many hanging, rope-like flowers. We are happy to offer this rare and colorful heirloom from the gardens of yesteryear. Freeze seeds for a week before planting, and plant very early in the spring or late winter. A nice cut or dried flower. Pkt (25 seeds) $2.50

LAVATERA (Edible)

PATIO PINK #FL608 *New!*
Annual. Lavatera is also known as Tree Mallow, and can reach 6 feet tall! But Patio Pink is smaller and more manageable for today's smaller gardens, seldom exceeding 28 inches. The large, stunning flowers come on all summer long, shimmering in shades of clear, satiny pink. The size makes this one perfect for borders and bedding, but it is equally at home in containers, patio plantings, and more. Pkt (30 seeds) $2.50

LINARIA OR TOADFLAX

FAIRY BOUQUET MIX #FL791 *New!*
Hardy annual--Small snap-dragon type flowers are held over lacy foliage, attracts butterflies and bees. The color range is sublime, in soft, not-quite-pastel tones of cream, buttercup, rose and lavender. Arresting in rock gardens, containers and hanging baskets, and positively breathtaking in massed plantings! Flowers to about 9 inches in height come quickly from seed, bloom over a long season. All America Award winner for 1934. Prefers cool-summer conditions, or may be grown spring and fall in warmer zones. Charming! Pkt (500 seeds) $1.75

NORTHERN LIGHTS #FL139 *New!*
Hardy annual. Taller than Fairy Bouquet Mix, reaching sometimes to 20". The color range is similar, but in more intense shades, including reds, oranges, yellows, and bicolors. Native to Morocco. Attracts butterflies and bees. Pkt (500 seeds) $2.00

LOVE-IN-A-MIST (Edible)
Hardy annual. Direct sow early spring or late autumn. (200 seeds/pkt)

MISS JEKYLL MIX #FL221 *New!*
Hardy annual--If the foliage is like filigree, the star-like blooms are like smoky gems, in mellow jewel-tones of rose, sky blue, dark blue, and crystalline white. A standard since at least as far back as the 1930's, and still among the very finest late-spring flowering plants.   Pkt $2.50

DELFT BLUE #FL138

(*Nigella papillosa*) A mix of pastel to true Delft blue, the color range is reminiscent of the Dutch pottery style of its namesake. Stunningly beautiful! Pkt $2.75

MIXED COLORS #FL400

(*Nigella hispanica*) HHA. A splendid mix of colors with wispy, feathery foliage surrounding the beautiful blue, white, pink, and purplish-blue blooms. Love-in-a-mist dates back to English gardens of the 1570's. A very attractive flowering plant. Pkt $2.50

TRANSFORMER #FL142

Nigella orientalis—Bizarre flower form starts out with wildly exaggerated stamens, then yields strange seed pods. These are turned inside-out to make a curious dried specimen! Pkt $2.50

LUPINE

ARROYO LUPINE #FL143   *New!*

The most moisture-tolerant of all Lupines, preferring heavy, fairly moist soils. Spires of ravishing pea flowers medium blue-violet and white, can reach 4 ft in favored locations. Has been used in erosion control. Native to the Pacific slopes of the West, but can be grown throughout most of the country. Warning: Poisonous! Pkt $2.00

PIXIE DELIGHT MIX LUPINE #WF124   (*Lupinus hartwigii*) Annual.

Diminutive plants with flower spikes barely exceeding a foot tall. Charming mix in dark blue, medium-pale blues, lavender, pinks, rose and white. Bees love the mildly fragrant blooms. Makes a fine cut flower, small enough for a ground cover or massed planting in sun or part shade. Summer flowers from a spring sowing. Native to Mexico and the American Southwest. Warning: Poisonous. Pkt $2.00

TEXAS BLUEBONNET #WF103

(*Lupinus texensis*) Perennial. Soak seeds 24 hours before planting. This popular, bright-blue wild flower is the Texas State Flower. An easy annual to grow. Warning: Poisonous! Pkt $1.50

RUSSELL MIX LUPINE #WF105

(*Lupinus polyphyllus*) Hardy perennial. Best in cooler climates. Soak seeds 24 hours before planting. Tall stems are covered with beautiful flowers in colors of pink, red, peach, blue, burgundy, and brown. This fine flower will naturalize. Warning: Poisonous! Pkt $1.50

AUREUS YELLOW LUPINE #WF110

(*Lupinus densiflorus*) Perennial. Soak seeds 24 hours before planting. A stunning, yellow Lupine; 30" stalks are covered with brilliant flowers. Warning: Poisonous! Pkt $1.50

LYCHNIS

MALTESE CROSS #WF119

(*Lychnis chalcedonica*) Large 3'-4' tall spikes produce stunning neon flame-red colored clusters of blooms. This perennial often blooms the first year, if started very early. Was grown by Thomas Jefferson in 1807, and it still is one of the showiest flowers of early summer! Pkt $2.00

MARIGOLDS   (Edible)

(*Tagetes patula*) Annual. Great in salads! Thrives in heat.

GOLDEN AGE #FL214   *New!*

Annual Here's the first scentless marigold variety! Medium gold flowers are fully double, come in at about 15" in height. The virtually odorless foliage is a big advantage to gardeners who love marigolds' sunny, generous summertime nature, but their scent, not so much. Who says you can't have it both ways? Pkt (100 seeds) $2.50

MARY HELEN #FL467

Tall plants reach 3 feet. Large, bright yellow blooms are produced in profusion. Blooms are very double—spectacular in arrangements or at the back of the border. Carefree plants flower all summer. Pkt (200 seeds) $2.25

QUEEN SOPHIA #FL215 *New!*

Annual Gorgeous to the point of excess! Double, deep orange-to-russet flowers reach 2.5" in diameter. They have a tidy, geometric look because the petals occur in neat concentric rings. Each petal lays nearly flat, without crowding its neighbors, showing to advantage the intricate edging, penciled in pure gold. Foot-high plants are great for bedding, edging the border, or in window boxes or pots. Pkt (100 seeds) $2.50

SIERRA FORMULA MIX #FL216 *New!*

Annual A nice mix of lemon yellow, yellow-gold, and deep pure orange flowers. Robust plants to 30". The deeply ruffled, very double flowers are especially nice for cutting, appearing on long, sturdy stems. Also suitable for cottage gardens. Pkt (75 seeds) $2.50

BROCADE MIX #FL471

This lovely variety produces large 2" flowers on dwarf plants. A brilliant mix of red, gold and orange, it is very pretty and helps repel some insects and nematodes. Pkt (200 seeds) $1.75

COURT JESTER   #FL476

This little marigold has stunning, yellow and burgundy striped single blooms. Very fancy and attractive looking on the dwarf plants. Pkt $2.00

CRACKERJACK MIX #FL470

The giant African type that is popular with gardeners coast-to -coast; the big double blooms come in shades of lemon yellow to deep orange, and the 30" plants are profuse. Pkt $2.50 *or 1 oz $10.00*

ESKIMO #FL477

(*T. erecta nana*) Knee-high plants bear graceful, large, fully double flowers. The soft cream-colored petals make an arresting contrast to the dark green foliage. Blooms late spring until frost if spent flowers are removed. Spectacular in a massed planting! One of the best white selections. Pkt (30 seeds)$3.00

GYPSY SUNSHINE #FL472

Dwarf, bushy plants are loaded with pretty golden-yellow, double flowers. A great all-yellow variety for pots or flower beds. Pkt (150 seeds) $1.75

HARLEQUIN #FL464

This antique variety dates back to 1870 and has recently become popular again. It is quite unique with its yellow-and-red-striped flowers that are both charming and flashy. It makes a good cut flower, too! Pkt (75 seeds) $2.50

KILIMANJARO WHITE #FL473

We finally have added a unique white marigold; this variety has lovely 2" creamy-white blooms that really stand out in a crowd. White marigolds were long in the making; in fact, Burpee Seed Company spent 56 years of searching and breeding before finding success. After years of trying, David Burpee offered $10,000 to the first home gardener who sent in the right seeds to help make a real white variety; thousands of gardeners responded for years. One lady, Alice Vonk of Sully, Iowa, sent seeds for 21 years, and in 1975, Burpee awarded her the coveted prize for her work— after the company had spent 56 years and $250,000 testing during the contest years. Now there are several white varieties, including this beauty. Pkt (30 seeds) $3.00

ORANGE HAWAII #FL462

Large, deep-orange flowers are 4" across, very striking and beautiful. Plants grow to 3'. Orange Hawaii is used as a natural feed additive to brighten the yolks of eggs. Pkt (200 seeds) $2.25

LEGION OF HONOR #FL908

Dwarf charmer reaches only 12"; ideal for the front of the bed or border! Single flowers of clear sunny gold with clean lines present a very neat appearance, accentuated by the restrained brown to maroon blotch that embellishes each ray petal near the flowers' centers. Introduced about 150 years ago. Different and very pretty! Pkt (150 seeds) $2.25

PETITE MIX #FL474

Very dwarf mixture of the crested French Marigolds; plants only grow to 10"-12" tall. Bright colors. Easy to grow, even in small pots. Pkt (200 seeds) $1.75

RED CHERRY #FL475

This dwarf variety produces distinctive mahogany-red flowers, which are large in size and fully double. A great variety that flowers very early, making them among the first flowers of summer. Pkt (100 seeds) $2.00

SPUN GOLD #FL469

Outstanding strain of Mexican Marigold boasts fully-double pale gold flowers. The petals are quilled and look just like chrysanthemums! Blooms all summer long on 16 inch plants. Superb border plant, great for cut flowers! Pkt $2.50

SPUN ORANGE #FL920

Extra large, attractive, super-double flowers with tubular petals. The color is a pleasing, clear orange rather than the harsh orange-brown so often seen in African marigolds. Plants are rather compact, seldom exceeding 20 inches. Very uniform series is ideal for cutting, yet earns its keep in the border. Pkt (100 seeds) $2.50

SWEET MACE OR MEXICAN MINT #FL465

(*Tagetes lucida*) Enjoy this late-blooming marigold in teas and other drinks; a great flavoring for many dishes. This old Hispanic heirloom is hard to find nowadays, but is still a great garden plant that is easy to grow and quite flavorful. Pkt (50 seeds) $2.50

MALLOW & MALOPE (Edible)

Start indoors 3-4 weeks before setting out after frost, or sow seeds in place at about the last frost date of spring. In either case, sow in fine, moist soil and cover lightly.

PINK MUSK MALLOW #FL914

(*Malva moschata*) Hardy perennial. Its name comes from the mild, musky aroma that fills the air when the plants are brushed or bruised. Clouds of pretty, one-inch wide, pink blooms are produced all season. Easy from seed, blooms first year from an early sowing. Deeply cut leaves on plants that reach 30 inches on this Mediterranean native. Pkt (75 seeds) $2.25

CARMINE ROSE #FL915

(*Malope trifida*) Annual. To 3 feet. Old-time favorite, beloved by the gardeners of yesteryear. Plants grow quickly to about three feet in height, clothing themselves with satiny flowers of intense carmine to cerise, with darker veining. Five-petaled blooms reach about 3" in diameter, and are reminiscent of Rose of Sharon, hollyhock and hibiscus, all close relatives to Malope. Pkt (75 seeds) $2.25

MALOPE MIX #FL916

(*Malope trifida*) Annual. To 3 feet. Trumpet-shaped flowers in violet, pink or white, the petals often heavily veined in purple. The satiny-textured flowers contrast handsomely with the fuzzy leaves. Formerly, Malope was widely grown as a cottage garden plant but it has become very rare. Well grown, flowers in only six weeks from sowing. Pkt (75 seeds) $2.25

MARVEL OF PERU or FOUR O'CLOCK

(Mirabilis jalapa) Tubers may be lifted and stored for planting the following spring. Discovered in the 16th century, the flowers open at approximately 4:00 PM. Fragrant flowers come in a wide range of colors, such as pink, magenta, yellow, white, and more. Very bright and attractive. Makes another great flower for night gardens. One of the easiest flowers to grow! (*Warning Poisonous*)

MARBLES MIXED #FL448

Extravagant mixture contains all of the various colors and patterns of the "Marbles" series! Yellows, reds, oranges and whites, each flower uniquely striped and splashed with contrasting hues. Pkt (25 seeds) $2.50

MARBLES WHITE-YELLOW #FL445 ↑
The mellow member of the "Marbles" clan. The plants are smothered in sunny yellow and white blooms. Pkt (25 seeds) $2.50

SALMON SUNSET #FL447 →
True salmon-colored trumpets with a pale pink star at the center of each flower. A sophisticated addition to the garden. Pkt (25 seeds) $2.50

STARS AND STRIPES #FL440
Here is a glorious mix of bi-colored and splashed flowers in the colors of yellow, white, rose, red, and blue. Very unique and colorful. Pkt (35 seeds) $2.00

SWEET FOUR O'CLOCK #FL443
(*Mirabilis longiflora*) This unique species of Four O'Clock is quite striking with 4" long trumpet like flowers that are creamy white; but the amazing part is the delightful, exotic fragrance that fills the air as these flowers open each afternoon. Easy to grow and can be left in the ground to regrow each year in warm areas or can be grown as an attractive annual in cold climates. This attractive plant comes from the American Southwest and Mexico. Pkt (25 seeds) $2.25

"it isn't enough to talk about peace. One must believe in it. And it isn't enough to believe in it. One must work at it."

-ELEANOR ROOSEVELT

MORNING GLORY, IPOMOEA

Annual, Easy to grow vine, this is an amazing plant that was refined in 9th century Japan. Jere's favorite vine, colorful and so easy to grow! (35 seeds per Pkt)

CARDINAL CLIMBER #FL480

(*Ipomoea x multifida*) Beautiful, small, bright red flowers; the vines have lovely foliage. Long vines are excellent for ornamental covering. Pkt $1.75

CARNEVALE DI VENEZIA #FL496

(*Ipomoea purpurea*) A truly stunning mix of two types of flowers. They come white with rose-pink or with purple-blue stripes! Amazing looking and sure to be the highlinght of any garden. A hard to find variety from Europe. Pkt $2.75

CHOCOLATE #FL490

(*Ipomoea nil*) The Japanese started selecting morning glories in the 9th century, and this selection is one of their most stunning. Huge, 5"-6" blooms are in the loveliest creamy, chocolate-pink color. Large plants produce loads of these beauties that are so rare and unique. Imperial Japanese morning glories were quite popular in America during Victorian times, and we plan to make them popular here once again. Pkt (10 seeds) $3.00

CHOCOLATE WHITE EDGE #FL854

Soft red-brown with a delicate white edge to the flowers. Very large flowered Imperial Japanese type. Very showy even before it flowers, as the leaves are often splashed with pale green to nearly white variegations. Very unusual and choice! Pkt (10 seeds) $3.00

CLARK'S HEAVENLY BLUE #FL481

(*Ipomoea purpurea*) Lovely, 4" pale-blue flowers; this heirloom dates to the 1920s. Produces long 12' vines, and flowers the full season. Pkt $2.50

CRIMSON RAMBLER #FL482

(*Ipomoea purpurea*) Beautiful, deep rose color, with white throats, marked with a deep red star running though them. Excellent. Pkt $1.75

DACAPO LIGHT BLUE #FL491

(*Ipomoea purpurea*) A new variety of this well-known and easy-to-grow climber has eye-catching clear blue flowers with a darker purple-blue star. This stunning variety is early to bloom and is sure to stand out on any garden fence. Pkt $2.50

HAZELWOOD BLUES #FL492

(*Ipomoea purpurea*) A lovely mixture of many delightful shades of blue, from creamy pale blue to almost as dark as night. These also have attractive star-like markings. A must for the cottage garden and perfect for any fence or trellis that needs to be covered in pure beauty. Pkt $2.50

FERINGA #FL497

(*Ipomoea purpurea*) Gorgeous burgundy-colored flowers make an electrifying contrast with the dark-green, angular, lobed leaves. Vigorous vines bloom all summer until frost. You'll love this easy to grow and stunning variety. Pkt $2.25

FLYING SAUCERS #FL485

(Ipomoea purpurea) Huge 6" blooms are pure white with bright blue stripes! Too beautiful to describe; very spectacular looking. One of our favorite varieties. Introduced in 1960. Pkt $2.00

FEATHER MIX #FL922

(Cypress Vine) Annual to 10 feet. Feathery foliage crowned by brilliant-hued small flowers that look like 5-pointed stars! The blooms span a stunning range from white through pink to deep, oxblood red. Attracts hummingbirds. Very unusual and very choice! Pkt $2.25

GRANDPA OTT'S #FL486

(Ipomoea purpurea) Small, deep-purple blooms, with a bright red star in their throats; very colorful and unique. This Bavarian heirloom was one of the original varieties that gave the Whealys the idea to start Seed Savers Exchange. We were really impressed by its beauty. Pkt $2.50

KIKYOZAKI, MIXED #FL493

(Ipomoea nil) Kikyozaki morning glories are popular in Japan, and this is a cool mix of many colors. These are star-shaped and many will be semi-double. Fantastic looking and much sought after, this is a true botanic treasure that we are proud to offer. Pkt (10 seeds) $3.00

LA VIE EN ROSE #FL494

(Ipomoea purpurea) This mixture is loaded with many pretty shades of red and pink, from crimson to rose, and even cotton candy-colored blooms that make this selection a favorite in the best gardens of Europe and now America. I love morning glories, and pink shades are always a favorite. Pkt $2.50

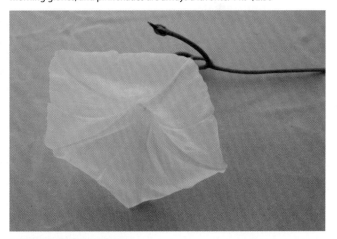

MOONFLOWER #FL483

(Ipomoea alba) Long, vigorous vines grow to 20'; giant fragrant white "Glory"-type flowers. Excellent for planting in night gardens. Pkt (20 seeds) $2.50

RED PICOTEE #FL495

(Ipomoea nil) This stunning Japanese Kikyozaki variety offers a whole new dimension. Imagine star-shaped morning glories in shades of carmine-red and trimmed in creamy white. The lovely vines also have heart-shaped leaves. A must for those who like unique beauty. We were so excited to find seed for several of these priceless Japanese selections. Pkt (10 seeds) $3.00

ROSE FEATHER #FL488

(*Ipomoea quamoclit*) Here is a stunning new variety with lovely pink, star-shaped flowers that are so unique! The vines have feathery, cut-leaf foliage that is quite beautiful. This is an excellent variety that is hard to find. Pkt $2.50

SCARLET O'HARA #FL484

(*Ipomoea purpurea*) A beautiful rose-and-red heirloom, the vines produce loads of large blooms. Perfect to grow on a fence or trellis. Pkt $2.00

SPLIT SECOND #FL902

(*Ipomoea purpurea*) Shell-pink to almost coral, fully double flowers have individual petals—gone is the trumpet form of regular morning glories! The margins of these individual petals are notched and frillied; the overall effect is that of a peony, or parrot-tulip, yet the vigorous vines easily climb 4-6 feet! Pkt (10 seeds) $3.00

SUNRISE SERENADE #FL489

(*Ipomoea purpurea*) Our most asked-for flower in our 2008 trial gardens. A few vines covered the arbor over our garden gate. The flowers are so unique and stunning: they're true, double morning glories! They are fully double and uniquely shaped, plus they come in the most lovely shades of ruby-rose. This historic heirloom has long been out of catalogs due to the introduction of modern varieties, but this variety proves that some things can't be improved! Pkt (25 seeds) $2.75

AOMURASK ZYOUHANTEN FL923 New!

[Ao muraski zyouhanten shibori] Incredibly lovely product of centuries of traditional Japanese breeding work! Medium-large flat blooms are crystal white with varying streaks and patches of violet-blue. Each flower is unique—no two are alike. Pkt (15 seeds) $4.00

BABY BLUE SKY FL924 New!

Cute, tiny blue blooms on long vines that spread everywhere. A pretty little variety that is quite charming and hard to find. Pkt (15 seeds) $2.25

ASAHI RISING SUN FL925 New!

[Asahi Rising Sun, Morning Light] Giant blooms are a rosy-pink to cherry red. The startlingly white throat is the "sun", the "rays" are the white streaks radiating from the center to the edge of the flower. Stunningly beautiful! Pkt (10 seeds) $5.00

WISTERIA GIRL FL926 New!

[Wisteria Girl also known as Fuji Musume] A wonderfully beautiful Japanese variety. Large lavender to plum-colored blooms are crisply edged in snow white. Elegant and subtle. Pkt (10 seeds) $5.00

NASTURTIUM (Edible)

(Tropaeolum majus) Annual. Sow where plants are to grow. Delicous flowers and leaves, perfect for salads! (25 seeds per Pkt)

ALASKA MIX #FL500

Beautiful, variegated, green-and-white foliage, with stunning red, yellow and orange flowers. Superbly unique and colorful. Pkt $2.50

ALASKA RED SHADES #FL217 *New!*

Annual. Stunning round-leafed nasturtium foliage is brightly variegated. The velvety, deep maroon blooms come as a bonus. A bit somber and very dramatic! Dwarf, upright plants. Pkt $3.00

DWARF JEWEL MIX #FL503

Bright, sunny colors: yellow, pink, red, and orange. The edible flowers are popular for salads and as a garnish; the peppery leaves are also very flavorful. A colorful garden favorite. Pkt $2.50 *or 1 oz $6.00*

GLOBE OF FIRE #FL218 *New!*

Annual--Semi-double and double, searing scarlet, spurred blooms held well above the foliage, pertly facing upward. Compact, non-trailing plants. Pkt $2.50

EMPRESS OF INDIA #FL508

A very unique old heirloom with dark foliage and brilliant fire-red blossoms that are delicious in salads. It was popular in Victorian times. Pkt $2.50

JEWEL PEACH MELBA #FL507

This jewel of nasturtium breeding produces blossoms in a lovely shade of primrose-cream with pearly-red spots. Dwarf plants are great for pots and superb in salads. Pkt $2.50

KING THEODORE #FL514

Fashionable, dark green plants have mahogany-red blooms with chocolate overtones. Stunning and flashy. You'll love this heirloom from the 1890's with its compact, beautiful plants. Pkt $2.00

MILKMAID #FL505

Here is a most unique nasturtium that is a pale, creamy color that is quite beautiful; hard-to-find seeds from Europe. Pkt $3.00

MOONLIGHT #FL509

Wonderful trailing vines can grow to 7' and makes a great ground cover or is stunning in large hanging baskets. The flowers are a glowing creamy-yellow, pale and beautiful. Quite tasty. Pkt $2.50

ORANGE TROIKA #FL930 *New!*

Annual. The tangerine blossoms are very pretty, but lots of nasturtiums come in tints of orange. What make 'Troika' special is the foliage: tropical-looking leaves are fantastically splashed, striped and spotted in white and pale green! Semi-trailing habit and the exquisite detail on each leaf make this variety a knockout in hanging baskets; equally stunning in your summer salads! Pkt $3.00

SAHIN'S PASO DOUBLE #FL219 *New!*

Annual—The flowers are conspicuously displayed above lush bright green foliage, so each can be savored! Dwarf plants in a range of vibrant colors of deep reds, golds and apricots. Pkt $3.00

SPITFIRE #FL510

Long, trailing vines produce a cascade of fiery, red-orange blooms. Great for growing over a garden wall or in a window box. A stunning color of the great vining types that have become hard to find in recent years. Still has that American cottage garden charm. Pkt $2.00

TALL TRAILING MIX #FL511

This heirloom favorite grows up to 10' in a season and is perfect for covering walls, arbors and tall fences. Bright and cheery flowers come in shades of yellow, orange and red. The flowers are spicy and flavorful, making the most beautiful salad. Pkt $2.50

YELLOW CANARY CREEPER #FL515

(Topaeolum peregrinum) Exotic South American native vine reaches 15 feet, yet is no harder to grow than its cousin, the garden nasturtium. Round, deeply lobed leaves are edible; bizarre, bright yellow orchid-like flowers are produced all summer long; must be seen to be believed. Pkt $2.75

YETI #FL513

Named after the ape-like rare creature that legend says inhabits the Himalayas, these white nasturtiums are rare indeed. Not just things of folklore, here is a creamy-white flowering variety that blooms on long trailing vines that have large leaves. Pkt $3.00

NEMOPHILA

FIVE SPOT #WF139 *New!*

Annual. *(Nemophila maculata)* White and purple cousin to Baby Blue Eyes. But this one features snow-white petals with a delicate tracery of purple veining. The name comes from the large purple spot at the distal end of each of the five petals. A low-growing, cool-season annual that does best in cooler summer weather. Pkt (300) $2.25

BABY BLUE EYES #WF132 *New!*
Annual. Charming and unusual wildflower. Blooms are an inch across, in tones of the truest sky-blue with white centers. Easy from seed! The sprawling plants are pretty at the front of borders, or sown as filler beneath spring-blooming bulbs. Native to the West from Baja to Oregon, takes many different environments but at its best in cool, moist conditions. Pkt (300 seeds) $1.75

NICOTIANA and TOBACCO
(*Nicotiana alata* except as noted) Annual. Container-sowing indoors in early spring preferred. ***Caution: Poisonous.***

CRIMSON BEDDER #FL220 *New!*
Annual. Full-sized Flowering Tobacco plants are robust. Flower spikes exceed 2 feet, and bear cherry red 2" trumpets until hard frost. The uniform color makes this one especially nice in mass plantings, or paired with Aztec Sweet Scent. Pkt (600 seeds)$2.50

DELAWARE INDIAN SACRED #FL525
(*N. rustica*) Dwarf 15" plants produce clusters of light-green flowers. A cute little plant for borders; this is a ceremonial tobacco to the Delaware Lenape tribe of Indians. A rare Native American heirloom that is pretty and unique. Caution: poisonous. Pkt (100 seeds) $2.50

HOPI TOBACCO #FL527
(*N. rustica*) Traditional ceremonial variety used for centuries by the gentle people of the Four Corners country. A typical Indian type tobacco, reaching to 24 inches in height. Fragrant green flowers in perhaps more compact spikes than some. Pkt (100 seeds) $2.50

LANGSDORF #FL526
(*Nicotiana langsdorffii*) Well-known green flowering Nicotiana for high borders. This tall species from Brazil and Chile produces lovely apple-green blooms that add a unique splash of color to any garden. Perfect great for arranging. Pkt (400 seeds) $2.25

LIME GREEN #FL521
A truly amazing and wonderful shade of bright lime-green, these are a standout in the cottage garden. Lovely and hard to find. Pkt (600 seeds) $2.50

PANSY (Edible)

(Viola) Annual. Spring-plant for summer bloom in cool-summer climates; plant late summer for autumn bloom in warmer zones. Grows and blooms best when cooler conditions prevail.

ALPENGLOW #FL223 *New!*
Annual. Here's a selection out of the Swiss Giants series that is sure to please: vivid deep cherry red, very flat-faced pansy blooms, reaching over three inches across! Dark chocolate markings with even darker venation complete the picture. Very different and very desirable! Pkt (200 seeds) $2.50

LOUISIANA PIROQUE #FL524
(*N. tabacum*) Named for the traditional flat-bottom boat that is used by the Cajuns in the swamps of Louisiana. This old heirloom was given by the Indians to the Cajuns and passed down through the years. Given by a Creole man to Kurt Bridges, who then supplied us with some seed. We grow the plants for their beauty, as they grow 4' tall, have big, wide leaves and produce loads of gorgeous sunset-pink flowers. Traditionally used by the Cajuns, but it is poisonous along with all tobacco. Pkt (100 seeds) $3.00

LAURA #FL546
Jewel-tone rosy-lilac blooms to 3 inches have a velvety texture and deep, nearly black splotches. One of the Swiss Giants that were bred around the beginning of the 20th Century. Pkt (200 seeds) $1.75

SCENTSATION MIXED #FL522
Nicotianas were popular in early America and were planted by Thomas Jefferson. This tall variety produces flowers that open in the day; color range: pink, red, lavender, rose, and white. These are easy to grow and cause a splash of color. Pkt (800 seeds) $2.50

ORANGE SUN #FL547
Fancy, tangerine-orange colored blossoms are really stunning on the bright green plants. A very pretty, large variety of the Swiss Giants family. Pkt (200 seeds) $1.75

SUPER BEACONSFIELD #FL276 *New!*
Annual. A stunning bicolor type: velvety lower petals in darkest purple are complemented by upper petals of white to palest lavender. The effect is one of incredible richness! Another selection from the Swiss Giants series, which is still yielding new material decades after its creation.   Pkt (200 seeds) $2.50

SWISS GIANTS MIX #FL541
An old standard in pansies, large flowers come in many bright and attractive colors. The flowers have long stems and add an old-fashioned touch to any garden. Pkt (350 seeds) $2.50

BOWLES' BLACK #FL545
This old-fashioned garden favorite has small viola flowers that are nearly black in color with a pale yellow eye. It blooms all summer long and will come back every year in your garden. Pkt (200 seeds) $2.50

MORNING DEW #FL271 *New!*
Cheerful, little pansy flowers in a range of colors including burgundy, lavender, gold and art-shades. But they all have a rosy blush, and they all have the cutest little frowny "faces." They look like little cartoon pansies, as though they were about to burst into song! Pkt (35 seeds) $3.00

OXALIS

OXALIS VALDIVIENSIS #FL938 *New!*
Tender perennial usually grown as annual (Also known as Wood Sorrel) Andean relative of a common North American weed. Three-leafed "shamrock" leaves peep jauntily from behind richly buttercup yellow, five-petaled flowers, stunning in their simplicity. Makes a long-lived container- or houseplant when overwintered indoors.   Pkt (50 seeds) $2.50

PETUNIA (Flowers Edible)
Annual. Early start indoors recommended.

BALCONY MIX #FL562
This old petunia was popular with gardeners throughout much of the first part of the twentieth century, but has nearly been lost to cultivation because of seed companies' interests in selling newer varieties. This variety has delightfully fragrant blooms in shades of rose, lavender and purple. Trailing plants are perfect for adding color and fragrance to window boxes and hanging baskets. Pkt (800 seeds) $2.50

DWARF BEDDING MIX #FL561
Here is the old standard petunia that graced American gardens in the 1950s. Dwarf plants produce loads of brightly -colored flowers in shades of mostly, lavender, purple and cream. A must for all who want to re-create a vintage American garden. Pkt (800 seeds) $2.50

FIRE CHIEF #FL563
An All-America Selections Winner in 1950, but this old winner has nearly suffered the sad fate of all the 50 or so other petunia varieties that were once so popular in the 1950's. Bred by Bodger Seed Company of Lompoc, California, this variety set the standard in the 1950's for red petunias, being rich red and fading to a soft red color; unlike modern petunias, these are fragrant. These come from a time when people watched "I Love Lucy" and every family had a cottage garden. Pkt (200 seeds) $2.50

ALDERMAN #FL567 *New!*
Annual. Classic funnel-shaped petunia flowers, straight from the gardens of yesteryear! The blooms are very showy in deep lavender-purple. Their rich, velvety texture completes the picture of lush garden opulence. Plants reach about 12 inches in height, bloom all summer if spent blooms are removed occasionally. A 1950's favorite. Pkt (200 seeds) $2.50

SALMON CORAL #FL566 *New!*
Annual. Call the brilliant color salmon, or call it coral--either way, you've got a winner! Show-stopping, 5-lobed, single trumpets are produced constantly until frost. Pair it with white Alyssum for a season-long bouquet, right in your garden. So sophisticated! Pkt (200 seeds) $2.50

SNOWBALL #FL568 *New!* ↑
Annual. Extra-large petunia flowers reach 4 inches across, are of the whitest white. The plants are robust for petunias as well, frequently exceeding 15 inches tall. The chaste white funnel-shaped blooms are often fringed along the margins, look like soft, pillowy clouds as they float above the velvety green foliage. A cheerful cornerstone to the summer garden! A favorite from the mid-20th century. Pkt (200 seeds) $2.50

TWINKLES DWARF MIX #FL233 *New!* ↑
Annual. Deeply fringed or indented petal margins give the impression of far more than the 5 petals that are actually present. Diversity of streaks, stripes and zoning makes "Twinkles" really shine. Widest possible range of phlox colors, too! Compact plants rarely exceed 9 inches, are perfect for edging. Makes a superior container variety, when situated so that the intricate details of each unique flower can be appreciated up close. Pkt (200 seeds) $2.50

BEAUTY FORMULA MIX PHLOX #FL570
(*P. drummondii*) A formula mix of crimson, lavender, white, scarlet and yellow. Dwarf compact, annual plants, selected for beautiful flowers. Pkt (200 seeds) $2.50

CECILY MIX #FL229 *New!*
Annual. Range of dainty summer pastel tones evokes images of watercolor paintings. Delicate tones of shell-pinks, rose, mauves and purest snowy white are so pretty, cool and refreshing—relief for the eye, at least, when summer weather is at its most torrid! Compact plants rach about a foot tall. Pkt (200 seeds) $2.50

MOUNTAIN PHLOX #WF108
(*Linanthus Grandiflorus*) Hardy annual. Often self-sows. Pastel lavender-pink flowers. This native annual is a very beautiful favorite! Pkt (100 seeds) $1.50

SCARLET PHLOX #FL231 *New!*
Annual--Gorgeous tight clusters of vibrant, pure scarlet, 5-petaled flowers with a deep maroon, almost black eye at the center. Keep coming all summer long! Stocky plants often reach 20 inches in height, making this a great variety for the middle of the border. Also top-notch in containers and window boxes. Very choice and carefree! Pkt (200 seeds) $2.50

POPPY
ORIENTAL SCARLET: Perennial. SOMNIFERUM TYPES: Hardy annual.

AMERICAN LEGION #FL585
(*Papaver rhoeas*) This Flanders poppy grew in Europe in World War II, and the name "American Legion" honors the soldiers who died. Bright red blooms cover plants; grows and blooms very easily. Annual. Pkt (600 seeds) $2.25

BALLERINA DOUBLE MIX CALIFORNIA POPPY #FL593
(*Eschsholzia californica*) A graceful mixture of the colors available in California Poppies—warm orange, of course, but also sulfur yellow, white, carmine rose, lilac and scarlet. Double to semi-double, crepe-like flowers reaching about 14 inches in height. Such a cheery mix for naturalizing or the border! Pkt (600 seeds) $2.25

BLACK SWAN #FL591
(*Papaver somniferum*) Gorgeous double flowers have exotic, frilly cut petals of burgundy to almost black. One of the most unique and stunning varieties you can grow! Pkt (600 seeds) $3.00

BLACK PEONY #FL582
(*Papaver somniferum*) We offer pure seed for this truly amazing, deep purple-black colored poppy. The flowers are fully double, ruffled and so large! This elegant beauty will be the winner in any garden. The seedpods make a wonderful addition to dried flower arrangements. This poppy is very easy to grow but does better in cooler regions. Pkt (600 seeds) $3.00

EASTERN HORNED #FL588
(*Dicranostigma franchetianum*) A rare, yellow-flowering member of the Poppy family. Upright growing plant with decorative grey-green leaves and deep yellow half-nodding flowers. Like most other poppies, best when direct seeded on a light soil with sufficient moisture in full sun or partial shade. Hardy annual and even may be biennial in the right conditions. This native brightens the hills of southwest China. Pkt (300 seeds) $3.00

HUNGARIAN BLUE BREADSEED #FL581
(*Papaver somniferum*) Beautiful, 3"-4" purple-blue blooms make this variety very unique and wonderful. After the flowers, there are the attractive, large seed pods that are great for crafts and are traditionally used for their delicious, culinary seeds that are great in bread and cakes. This fantastic variety is easy to grow. Self-seeding annual. Pkt (200 seeds) $3.00

MISSION BELLS CALIFORNIA POPPY #FL584
(*Eschsholzia californica*) Lovely semi-double and double flowers in shades of yellow, gold, salmon, red, pink and cherry. This annual adds a space of color to any sunny spot! So pretty. Pkt (600 seeds) $2.00

GOLDEN WEST CALIFORNIA POPPY #WF138 *New!*
(*Eschscholzia californica*) Bright yellow-gold, four-petaled flowers sport true orange centers. First introduced in 1907. Self-sows in most climates. Easy and carefree, like all California poppies! Pkt (600 seeds) $2.00

LILAC POMPOM #FL590 ↑
(*P. somniferum*) Amazing double and semi-double lanciniata-type flowers in delicate lilac color. The large, frilly blooms are truly eye-catching when they contrast to the blue-grey foliage of the plants. Just scatter the seeds of this hardy annual in early spring and wait for the colorful blooms. One of the most unique and beautiful poppies you can grow. Pkt (600 seeds) $3.00

ORIENTAL SCARLET #FL580
(*Papaver orientale*) A charming Asian variety, with large, glowing red-orange flowers—attractive and old-fashioned. This type of poppy has been popular in the Orient for centuries. Perennial. Pkt (600 seeds) $2.25

PURPLE PEONY #FL592
(*P. somniferum*) Large, double poppy flowers are of a stunning, bright, grape-purple color. These big beauties really make a statement in your cottage garden. The seed pods produce lots of great poppy seeds for baking. This annual with its big peony-like flowers is among the most lovely you can grow. Pkt (600 seeds) $2.75

ROSE PEONY #FL587
(*Papaver somniferum*) Brilliant rose-colored blooms are among the largest of all poppies. They are double and 4-5" across. A unique color in poppies so pretty that makes this variety's blooms look like massive rose blossoms. A sturdy annual plant that often self-seeds. Pkt (500 seeds) $2.50

MOTHER OF PEARL #FL589
(*Papaver rhoeas*) A lovely mixture of misty and subtle shades. The late Sir Cedric Morris, painter and gardener, presumably years ago selected and named this mixture of pale and smoky colors as grey, lilac, mauve, pink, soft orange and white. Various flowers have flecking in the same tones and some delightful picotees. This refined mixture has a good balance of pastel colors. It is one of the most subtle poppy mixtures to grow in the garden. Easy, direct seeding on almost any soil, full sun or partial shade. Stunning! Pkt (600 seeds) $3.00

BRIDAL SILK #FL594 *New!*
Hardy annual—Finally, someone has come up with an all-white strain of Flanders Poppy! Snow-white blooms on wiry stems look like little circles of crepe paper. Easy and reliable, like all Flanders poppies. Pkt (500 seeds) $2.50

DANISH FLAG #FL595 *New!*

Annual. Enormous flowers reach six inches across. Each one is intricately crinkled and feathered or frilled, of unbelievably vivid scarlet, and at the center of each is a large, snow-white Greek cross. The variety does indeed resemble the national flag of Denmark, which consists of a white cross on a scarlet field. Flowers attain a height of about 30". Breathtaking in mass plantings! Pkt (600 seeds) $2.50

FLORIST PEPPERBOX #FL596 *New!* ↑

Annual. Breadseed-type poppy in shades of red, purple, and pink. The papery blooms are so large and showy! And after blooming is done, large pods yield blue-gray poppy seeds, ideal for use in baking and confections. Simply sake the seeds out and store them; then use the empty pods in dried arrangements. At 3-4 feet in height, the brilliant flowers and prickly, gray-green foliage are quite a sight! Pkt (600 seeds) $3.00

LAUREN'S GRAPE #FL249 *New!*

Hardy annual. 3-4-inch wide blooms, atop 3-foot stems, in a choice and vibrant color—plum purple, almost raspberry. This one is an absolute show stopper! Pkt (600 seeds) $3.00

PRICKLY POPPY #FL597 *New!*

(Argemone albiflora) Annual. Gardeners don't have that many options for white poppies, but here's a choice one from western North America. Solitary white flowers appear in late summer, atop wiry 3- to 4-foot stems. Cup-shaped, single six-petaled flowers are huge—to 6 inches across, reminiscent of crinkled crepe paper. Bees love the pale golden centers. Plants are gray-green and, wait for it: prickly. Tolerates rather hot and dry conditions, poor but well-drained soils. Pkt (300 seeds) $3.00

CALIFORNIA POPPY, ORANGE #WF106

(Eschscholzia californica) Hardy annual. Often self-sows. Early. The brilliant orange, small poppy from parts of California. This easy-to-grow, spring bloomer makes a splash of color. Pkt $1.25 *or 1 oz $6.50*

CALIFORNIA POPPY, PURPLE GLEAM #WF122

(Eschscholzia californica) Light purple-pink to dusky rose, single version of the state flower of the Golden State. Blooms in spring from a fall sowing, or in summer from a spring sowing. Superb in meadows or native gardens. Pkt $1.75

IVORY CASTLE #WF175 *New!*

(Eschscholzia californica) Each creamy white, four-petaled single bloom is punctuated with a sunny yellow center. Showy enough for a specimen plant, yet easy enough for mass planting. Or sow it into meadows, which are its original home in nature anyhow. Perfectly glorious! Pkt 2.00

PARTRIDGE PEA

PARTRIDGE PEA #FL132 *New!*
Annual. Fern-like compound leaves on reddish stems, to 2 feet tall. Showy yellow pea flowers are marked with red, blooming abundantly from midsummer to hard frost. Native from the Plains eastward, where it is an important winter food for deer, quail, pheasants and other wildlife. Also a major bee forage—the bees harvest nectar not from the flowers but from nectaries along the stems. Sensitive leaves partially fold when disturbed. Takes drought and poor soil, which it improves by fixing atmospheric nitrogen. Has been used in erosion control. Choice subject for meadows, dry banks and wild gardens. (Caution: may be poisonous to cattle and other livestock.) Pkt $3.00

PUNCHING BALLS

PUNCHING BALLS #FL133 *New!* ↑
(*Polygonum Capitatum*) Perennial. Spreading plant is mostly used as a groundcover, but is also superb in planters and hanging baskets. Burgundy-tinged leaves spring to fall (year-round in mild winter areas), are surmounted by curious, small, nearly-round flower heads in shades of pale shell pink. Drought tolerance and ability to take sun or shade make this an interesting choice for banks, roadsides and other wild areas. Be careful where you plant this, as it readily reseeds itself. Pkt $2.50

PINCUSHION FLOWER - SCABIOSA (Edible)

IMPERIAL MIX #FL612 *New!*
Hardy annual. Glorious "pincushions" in the widest possible array of Scabiosa colors: white, palest pink, lavender and deep burgundy red. Scabiosas are so long-lasting when cut, and this variety blooms over such a long season, that no cottage- or cut-flower garden is quite complete without it. Sweetly fragrant, too! Pkt $2.50

PORTULACA (Edible)

MOSS ROSE, DOUBLE FLOWERED MIX #FL918
Trailing or sprawling annual to 5 inches in height--Super-dwarf plants are ideal for xeriscaping, edging the front of borders, or nestled into cracks between stones in rock gardens. Completely unfazed by heat and drought that wither most plants; the small, succulent leaves always look fresh and healthy! Provides an endless succession of large (2-inch), fully double cup-shaped flowers in vibrant jewel tones. A care-free, old-fashioned favorite that deserves to be rediscovered by modern gardeners! Pkt (600 seeds) $2.00

MOSS ROSE, SINGLE MIX #FL251 *New!*
Annual. Heat-tolerant mix of brilliant Portulaca colors in single flowers—cerise, scarlet, tangerine, sunflower yellow. Low-growing color, ideal for dry banks, edging, or in pots.   Pkt (600 seeds) $2.00

MOSS ROSE, ORANGE EXTRA DOUBLE #FL252 *New!*
Annual. Splendid, consistently double blooms in deep orange. The intense heat and sunshine that Portulaca favors makes the flowers' color all the more searing. (Sunscreen not included!)   Pkt (600 seeds) $3.00

PRIMROSE (Edible)

EVENING PRIMROSE #WF102
(*Oenothera lamarckiana*) Biennial. Beautiful, yellow native flower. Pkt $1.50

SHOWY EVENING PRIMROSE #WF129 *New!* ↑
Perennial. Here's a stunning addition to the wild garden, meadow plantings and more! Delicate-looking, four-petaled flowers are generously produced all summer long. Two- to four-inch blooms are in soft pink, with very narrow lines or veins in darker pink, set off by buttercup-yellow throats. Flowers bloom in the evening and are great habitat for moths, but often remain open the following day. Plants reach 2 feet tall in favored locations. Spreads slowly by underground runners, hardy in all but the coldest one-third of the country. Native to the southern Plains states. Pkt $2.25

RATIBIDA - PRAIRIE CONEFLOWER (Edible)

RED MEXICAN HAT #WF121
(*Ratibida columnifera*) Perennial. This flower is colorful with its red flowers that look like Mexican hats. Pkt $1.50

YELLOW PRAIRIE CONEFLOWER #WF112
(*Ratibida columnaris*) Hardy perennial. A lovely, perennial flower that is a common sight in the great prairies of the West. Lovely, yellow, daisy-like flowers have a tall seed cone; easy to grow. Pkt $1.50

CHINA ROSE (Edible)

ANGEL WINGS #FL127 *New!*
(*Rosa chinesis*) Perennial, often grown as an annual. Precious little true rose blooms the first season from seed! Foot-tall plants yield sweetly scented miniature roses in white, shell pink and deep rose-red. The blooms are mostly double or semi-double. Ever-blooming plants flower all season. Ideal for containers. Plants will overwinter outdoors in most of the country, eventually reaching a height of 2-3 feet. Plants flower more strongly each year. So lovely in cottage-gardens! Pkt (25 seeds) $2.50

'A good end cannot sanctify evil Means; nor must we ever do evil, that good may come of it."

-WILLIAM PENN

RUDBECKIA

GOLDILOCKS #WF131 *New!*
(also known as Gloriosa Daisy) Annual, biennial or short-lived perennial. Bright golden-orange, double daisies appear all season long! 'Goldilocks' is much more compact than wild Black-eyed Susans, and much freer flowering, too! Upright plants reach two feet in height, half that in width. Beloved by butterflies and bees as you would expect from this native flower. Makes a fine cut flower, too. Priceless! Pkt (100 seeds) $2.75

RUSTIC COLORS #WF143 *New!*
(also known as Gloriosa Daisy) Annual or short-lived perennial. Bright golden, orange, black, red and brown colored singled flowers are perfect for arranging. Plants reach two feet in height. Pkt (100 seeds) $2.25

BLACK-EYED SUSAN #WF101
(*Rudbeckia hirta*) Hardy annual. Often self-sows. A popular native variety from the Great Plains of North America. Large yellow daisies with dark brown centers. Good in heat and drought. Beautiful. Pkt (150 seeds) $1.50 *or 1 oz* $6.50

SALVIA - SAGE Annual. (150 seeds per Pkt)

BLUE MONDAY SAGE #FL700
(*Salvia horminum*) Wow, these produce long-lasting blue flower spikes over a long period! A lovely 2' plant that is becoming all the rage in cottage gardens. Pkt $2.00

PINK SUNDAY SAGE #FL701
(*Salvia horminum*) Lovely, romantic, bright-pink flower spikes that shine in any heritage garden! The 2' plants are covered in pink all summer and are very easy to grow. Pkt $2.00

BLUE BEDDER #FL253 *New!*
Perennial, usually grown as an annual. Slender, intensely colored violet blue spikes are produced non-stop, all summer long! Makes a colorful filler in arrangements, and an ideal dried flower. Attracts bees, butterflies and hummingbirds! Deer-resistant Texas native boasts well-branched plants that reach to 30 inches. Hardy to about 10 degrees F. Pkt $2.25

FARAO FORMULA MIX #FL254 *New!*
Perennial, usually grown as an annual. Intensely-colored spikes to about two feet in cream, apricot, salmon and dark rose. Mass plant for a serious jolt of color! Hardy to about 10 degrees F. Pkt $2.50

SCARLET SAGE #FL255 *New!*
(*Salvia coccinea*) Perennial, usually grown as an annual. Branched plant to 2 feet tall, making a lovely mound of gray-green foliage even before the blooming season. Flower spikes are insanely showy—each one four inches or so in length, covered with rich scarlet tubular flowers over a very long season. How's that for 'pop'? Pkt $2.00

ST. JOHN'S FIRE #FL702 *New!*
Tender perennial usually grown as an annual. Very early, very dwarf (to 12") plants cover themselves in the most incandescent flame red! Dazzling color is at its best in mass plantings, or when grown as a short "hedge" in the front of borders, blooming right up until frost. The bees, butterflies and hummingbirds love them too! Pkt $2.25

SCABIOSA OR PINCUSHION (Edible)

PAPER MOON #FL610
(Scabiosa stellata) Attractive pale blue flowers are followed by cool, everlasting seed heads that are perfect for dried arrangements. This pest-tolerant, annual plant is native to Southern Europe. Pkt (200 seeds) $2.00

TALL DOUBLE FLOWERED MIX #FL611
(Scabiosa atropurpurea) Annual. Also known as Sweet Scabious or Pincushion Flower. Free-flowering annual with large, intricate flowers on long branching stems to 30 inches. Sweetly fragrant blooms appear about midsummer, continuing until frost. Butterflies love the flowers at least as much as you will! Colors range from pure white through carnation pink, rose to a very rich maroon. Makes a superb cut flower. Liberty Hyde Bailey in 1917 wrote in The Standard Cyclopedia of Horticulture that Sweet Scabious "..are among the most popular of flower-garden annuals," and they should be much more widely grown today! Pkt (200 seeds) $2.00

OLYMPIA MIX #FL257 *New!*
Annual. Luscious mix of Pincushion Flower colors—purples, plums and blues and an occasional pink and white. With their long wiry stems and superb productivity, makes an excellent cut flowers. May persist as perennials where winters are fairly mild. Pkt (200 seeds) $2.50

SCHIZANTHUS

ANGEL WINGS MIXED #FL618 *New!*
(Schizanthus wisetonensis) Annual. Also known as Poor Man's Orchid, because the flowers do resemble orchids. Exuberant old-fashioned plant sports dozens of flowers in pink through red with yellow splotches at the center. Our mix includes pink, lavender, rose red and two-tone. Exotic-looking 10" plants are sublime in containers but equally at home in beds or borders. Favors cool summer conditions or light shade. Pkt $2.50

A lovely old packet of Schizanthus.

This packet dates to circa 1850s. Comstock, Ferre is one oldest seedhouse in New England and is now part of our company, providing us a base in the North.

Please visit our 200 year old seed store and gardens in Wethersfied, CT.
(263 Main St. Wethersfield, Connecticut)

SILENE

CATCHFLY #WF133 *New!*

Annual. Large clusters of pink-to-purple, 5-pointed stars bloom on 12-18-inch plants from midsummer on. This European native has been known, grown and loved in this country since at least 1804. Small insects frequently become stuck to the sticky leaves, hence the name, but not a truly carnivorous plant. Also called "Sweet William Catchfly" for its marked resemblance to its cousin, the true Sweet William. Super easy from seed sown in spring, summer or fall. Self-sows in favorable conditions; has naturalized east of the Mississippi.   Pkt (100 seeds) $2.25

SNAPDRAGON (Edible)

(Antirrhinum majus)

APPLE BLOSSOM #FL911

Lavish, full-sized old-fashioned snapdragons reaching 36 inches. Heavy trusses of large, velvety-textured blooms in true apple-blossom pink, contrasting with pale gold. Stunning massed at the back of the border or as an accent plant. Yields a commendable cut-flower as well. Snapdragons were cherished in the gardens of yesteryear! Pkt (600 seeds) $2.50

BLACK PRINCE #FL621

One of the best, this variety has beautiful dark leaves and stunning, very dark crimson flowers. This plant is so attractive when planted with light-colored plants. All parts of the plant are poisonous. So pretty! Pkt (600 seeds) $2.50

TALL DELUXE #FL620

Beautiful, 30"-36" flower spikes in a brilliant range of colors: pink, red, yellow, lavender, and rose shades. Native to southern Europe. Pkt (800 seeds) $1.75

"The regenerated do not go to war, nor engage in strife. They are children of peace who have beaten their swords into plowshares and their spears into pruning forks, and know no war." —MENNO SIMONS

SPIDER PLANT - CLEOME (Edible)

SPIDER PLANT MIX #FL237 *New!*

(Cleome hassleriana) Hardy annual to 4-6 feet tall. Also known as Rocky Mountain Bee Plant, Cleome was first described by the Lewis and Clark expedition. The shrub-like plants are topped by large open clusters of intriguing flowers, blooming late summer and into autumn. Color ranges from white, to pink to dark reddish purple. Thrives in heat, tolerates some drought, self-sows where conditions are favorable. Imposing at the back of the border, or when grown in large containers. And yes, the bees do love it!   Pkt (200 seeds) $2.25

SOAPWORT

ROCK SOAPWORT #WF123

(Saponaria ocymoides) Vigorous, low, trailing perennial plant--so beautiful used as a groundcover, in the rock garden or atop a stone wall. A carpet of deep pink, 5-petaled flowers is a bonus in late spring, nearly covering the plants. Fine for edging the border, and charming in containers as well. Evergreen plants are drought-tolerant once established. Another old-fashioned favorite. Pkt $2.00

STATICE   Annual. Occasionally self-sows.

BLUE SEAS #FL662

(L. perezii) This variety produces large clusters of deep blue flowers over a long season, perfect for using in both dried and fresh flower arrangements. Pkt (150 seeds) $1.75

APRICOT BEAUTY #FL663

(Limonium sinuatum) Annual. Classic statice long used in dried floral arrangements. Flowers in warm shades of apricot to salmon. Robust plants reach about 30" in height, yielding very large stems for drying. Very sophisticated employed in wreaths, centerpieces and more! Pkt (150 Seeds) $2.25

PASTEL MIX #FL665

(Limonium sinuatum) Annual. Charming pastel mix in cool shades of soft rose, pink and lavender. Pkt(150 seeds) $2.25

PACIFIC MIX #FL664

(Limonium sinuatum) Annual. This mix runs the widest possible range of rich jewel tones—purple, rose, and sunny lemon yellow. Plants reach about 30 inches, and do double duty in borders, being lovely when in bloom, before the flowers are cut for drying. An old fashioned favorite that is once again receiving the appreciation it deserves. Pkt (150 seeds) $2.00

STOCKS (Edible)
Hardy annual. Often self-sows.

STARLIGHT SCENTSATION #FL680

(Matthiola longipetala ssp. bicornis) Now you can grow this fragrant old-fashioned favorite in a whole mix of pastel colors. Lovely 18" plants are so beautiful when in bloom. Great for containers on the patio. Pkt (250 seeds)$2.00

DWARF TEN WEEKS MIXED #FL131 *New!*

(Matthiola incana) Annual. Spikes of richly fragrant flowers in jewel tones and pastels--cream, yellows, reds, pinks and purples, reach a foot tall or sometimes larger. The single to double blooms are densely arranged along the stems, and the petals are very deeply pleated and full. Makes a superb cut flower! This versatile, old-time cottage garden favorite is excellent for edging borders, bedding, and window boxes. Fast and easy from seed. Pkt (250 seeds)$2.00

STRAWFLOWER
Annual. Sow where plants are to grow.

TOM THUMB MIXED #FL190 *New!*

Annual. Dwarf Strawflowers in mixed colors. Scaled-down plants reach about 15" tall, thrive in hot and dry conditions. They would be worth growing even if they didn't make some of the loveliest dried flowers around but, fortunately, they do! A splendid mix of reds, yellows, pinks and whites add stunning diversity of color to your everlasting arrangements. Pkt (250 seeds) $2.50

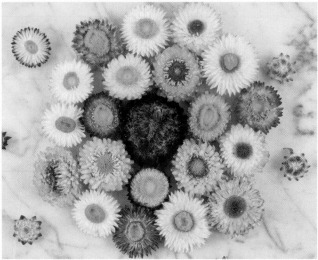

TALL DOUBLE MIX #FL640

(Helichrysum bracteatum) The popular everlasting flower that is easy and fun to grow. These come in red, pink, salmon, lemon, white, lilac, and more! Pkt (250 seeds) $2.50

SUNFLOWER (Edible)

(Helianthus annus except as noted) Annual. (35 seeds per pkt)

AUTUMN BEAUTY #FL720

A beautiful sunflower! Many 6" flowers in brilliant red, gold, yellow, rust, and burgundy. Blooms over a long period. Makes a wonderful display. Tall, 7' plants are a favorite. Pkt $2.00 *or 1 oz $6.00*

ARIKARA #FL736

This native variety produces 10-foot tall plants with many beautiful large, bright yellow flowers with black centers. The seeds are edible and were used by the Arikara nation in North Dakota. This heirloom produces flowers over a long period; it was a real winner in our garden! Pkt $3.00

DISTINTO MIXTURE #FL258 ↑ *New!*
Annual. Non-branching sunflower plants of very compact stature—maxing out at about 30". Single sunflowers in tones of red, yellow, and orange. Makes a very suitable choice for bedding, patio plantings or containers. Cheerful blooms feed the bees and butterflies, and mature seed heads for the birds, unless you beat them to the harvest! Pkt $2.50

EVENING SUN #FL733
This beautiful variety has medium-large blooms in shades of burgundy, rust, bronze, bright yellow, and crimson, with many being bi-colored. The 7' plants produce many flowers over a long season. This is one of my favorite varieties. Gorgeous! Pkt (35 seeds) $2.50

GIANT PRIMROSE #FL734
Tall plants grow 8' to 12' and produce multiple blooms that are a soft, creamy yellow in color with a chocolate center. A striking variety for the garden's edge. Pkt $2.25

HENRY WILDE #FL745
The classic-looking heirloom sunflower with pure yellow petals and dark centers is perfect for using as a cut flower and perfect for planting along a fence or barn. Pkt $2.00

HIDATSA #1 #FL822
Plants running about 8 feet tall produce a large central flower head and numerous smaller heads on side-shoots. Seeds are large enough to be processed for food, although smaller than the mammoth types favored today. Originally a staple crop of the Hidatsa people, who grew this variety in their floodplain gardens along the Missouri River. Pkt (15 seeds) $2.25

ITALIAN WHITE #FL723
This heirloom produces white and creamy-yellow, 4" flowers with dark chocolate-brown centers and many blooms. Tiny seed. Pkt $2.25

CRIMSON QUEEN #FL751

Velvety, deep burgundy flowers with dark centers. Multiflora type produces many small flowers, 3-5 inches across, on bushy, six-foot plants. Splendid at the back of the border; stunning in a mass planting! Pkt $2.50

LEMON QUEEN #FL722

Best seller! Beautiful, lemon-yellow blooms with chocolate centers. This one is very unique; tall plants produce many brilliant blooms that are a favorite of many bees. Pkt $2.50 *or 1 oz $6.00*

GIANT WHITE-SEEDED #FL744

This classic giant variety produces large, yellow heads and big, delicious white seeds perfect for roasting. It also grows very tall, 10'-12'! Fun to grow and eat. Pkt (20 seeds) $2.25

MAMMOTH GREY STRIPED #FL735

The standard giant variety that produces delicious seeds. The 10' plants produce heads that average 12" across. A stately garden plant. Pkt (25 seeds) $1.50

MEXICAN SUNFLOWER, GOLDFINGER #FL746 (*Tithonia rotundifolia*)

Lovely soft-orange-colored flowers on a more compact, yet profusely flowering plant makes this variety stand out in the crowd. Pkt $2.50

MEXICAN SUNFLOWER, RED TORCH #FL729

(*Tithonia rotundifolia*) (GOLDEN FLOWER OF THE AZTECS) Brilliant, red-orange, 2"- 3" flowers; an excellent butterfly plant. These bloom over a very long season, and the plants produce masses of blooms. The large 5' plants are very beautiful. I enjoyed these as I traveled along the roadsides in the high mountains in central Mexico. Pkt $2.25

MEXICAN SUNFLOWER, YELLOW TORCH #FL747 (*Tithonia rotundifolia*)

Here is a yellow version of this most popular plant with delightful apricot-yellow flowers that really cast a glow. This plant produces loads of flowers till frost. Superbly easy to grow. Pkt $2.50

RED SUN #FL912 *New!*

Stately branching plants reaching 5-6 feet tall are covered with dozens of ornamental blooms. Red to red-orange single flowers are highlighted with a hint of yellow around the centers. Blooms over a very long season, attracting bees and butterflies. Later, the tiny seeds attract birds. Pkt $2.50

SUN SPOT DWARF COLA #FL135 *New!*

Annual. Single, large flowers are very impressive for their size—10" flower heads on 2-3 foot plants. Color is a warm sunflower yellow with a dark center. Excellent container subject, placed where the geometry of the flowers' centers can be appreciated close up. Pkt $2.75

TAIYO #FL929

Annual to 6-7 feet—An old Japanese variety, non-branching and grown for cut-flower use. Equally attractive in arrangements or in mass plantings in the garden. The tall, non-branching plants produce a single large flower in tones of yellow-orange, chocolate and sable. Florists adore the 8- to 10-inch flowers! Pkt $2.75

TALL ORANGE SUN #FL825
Clear yellow-orange, six-inch, fully double flowers look for all the world like super-sized chrysanthemums, perched atop plants reaching 4-5 feet in height. Pkt $2.50

TARAHUMARA WHITE SEEDED #FL741
Grown by the Tarahumara tribe for their mostly white seeds, plants produce beautiful 8"-10" golden yellow flowers on tall plants. We are proud to offer this rare heirloom that may have originally been brought to Canada by Russian Mennonite farmers. Pkt $2.75

TEDDY BEAR #FL724
Beautiful 3"- 6" double, deep yellow blooms. Plants grow to only 18"- 24" tall, and the double blooms are very unique! This is a superb variety. Pkt $2.50 *or 1 oz $6.00*

TITAN #FL749
Massive, record-setting flower heads have reached a fantastic 24" across in some areas. One of the largest you can grow, it also produces lots of really big seeds. Fun for the kids and adults as well. Pkt (10 seeds) $2.50

TIGER EYE MIX #FL743
This mix is a stunning assortment of bronze, red, brown and yellow, and many are multicolored with an "eye" look. Mostly double blooms. Medium to large flowers. Many blooms per plant make these some of the showiest flowers in the garden. Pkt (15 seeds) $2.75

YELLOW PYGMY #FL137 *New!*
Dwarf, single-flowered variety in warm sunflower yellow. Plants reach 18 inches tall. Lovely in beds, or in the border where their formality can be employed to advantage. Pkt $2.50

SWEET SULTAN

IMPERIALIS MIX #WF125
Centaurea moschata Hardy annual. To 2 feet.Fragrant, thistle-like blooms look like large, silky powder puffs! The flowers run from deep, dusky rose purple through pink to white, and so fragrant! Makes a lovely addition to the border, and the 2-inch flowers are wonderful for cutting. Bees and butterflies adore them, as did the cottage gardeners of a bygone era. Often listed by seedsmen as Amberoa moschata. Pkt (300 seeds) $2.25

SWEET ALYSSUM

SWEET ALYSSUM TALL WHITE #FL108 *New!*
Annual. This cheery white denizen of cottage gardens since who-knows-when hardly needs an introduction! Tiny, snow-white flowers are produced by the hundreds on spikes reaching just a foot in height. The fragrance is just like honey! Tuck them at the edge of borders, or along walks. The small plants are also great in window boxes or in pots--anywhere their sweet scent may be savored! Pkt $2.00

SWEET PEAS

(Lathyrus odoratus) We offer a wonderful collection of old heirlooms and many are very fragrant. Plant in early spring, or whenever the weather is cool and moderate. Annual except as noted. Soak seeds 24 hours before planting. Sow in place in early spring into rich, moist soil. Plants thrive in the moderate conditions of spring, and tolerate some low temperatures. In most climates, hot summer weather will put a stop to the blooming season. (25 seeds per Pkt) (Warning: The seeds, pods and plants are poisonous!)

AZUREUS BLUE #SW160
(*L. sativus azureus*) Brilliant azure-blue flowers about 1 inch across, borne on semi-trailing or bush plants reaching about 2 feet in height. Really distinctive accent or container plant! This Chinese native tolerates heat much better than ordinary sweet peas. Pkt (10 seeds) $2.75

BEAUJOLAIS #SW134
Gorgeous, large, fragrant blossoms are a rich, burgundy wine color, truly stunning. Pkt $2.50

BLACK KNIGHT #SW103
Dark purplish-maroon blossoms are nearly black! Introduced in 1898 by Henry Eckford, a pioneering sweet pea breeder. Very fragrant. Pkt $2.50

BLANCHE FERRY #SW104
Beautiful rose-red blossoms are blushed with white. Very profuse bloomer, sweet fragrance. The oldest American introduction, from 1889, was by D.M. Ferry & Co. and named after his daughter. Pkt $2.50

BLUE REFLECTIONS MIX #SW147
Superb blend of fragrant Reflection sweet peas in all shades of blue and white. Truly a market winner. Bred by Keith Hammelt! Pkt $2.50

BUTTERFLY OLD SPICE #SW105
The Old Spice types carry intense fragrance, and Butterfly is no exception. White blooms are tinged with lavender toward the petals' edges. Introduced in 1878, by Suttons of England. Pkt $2.50

CHOCOLATE STREAMER #SW150
Gorgeous, chocolate-speckled blossoms are fragrant. Rare and unusual. These will steal the show in your home or market garden. Pkt $3.00

COUNTESS CADOGAN #SW169
Fragrant Old Spice selection in blues. Bluish-purple standard with clear blue wings. As the flowers open and mature, the color seems to change,

running through a lovely series of soft blues. Delicate and very pretty! Another Eckford introduction, dating to 1899. Pkt $2.50

CUPANI ORIGINAL #SW131
The original strain of sweet pea, sent to England in 1699 by Franciscus Cupani, a Sicilian monk. Colorful burgundy and purple bi-color blossoms with a very strong fragrance. Pkt $2.50

BELINENSIS RED YELLOW #SW171 *New!*
Annual. Strikingly different, recently discovered sweet pea species in a color previously unknown in sweet pea—bright buttercup yellow! The red-veined standard looks orange until viewed up close—then the curious intricacy of the red veins over paler background can be appreciated. Rather small, very fragrant flowers, but the scent is different from ordinary garden sweet peas—very distinctive! Delicate-looking vines appreciate some support; reach 3-4 feet. Also excellent in hanging baskets. Native to Turkey, and looked upon as a prospective resource for future breeding work. Pkt (10 seeds) $2.75

FLORA NORTON #SW111
Lovely clear-light-blue flowers, that have a powerful fragrance. Introduced by Morse-Vaughan in 1904. Delightful. Pkt $2.50

HENRY ECKFORD #SW158
Named after Mr. Eckford himself. The vines produce loads of spectacular bright orange flowers! One of the most beautiful we sell. Pkt $2.50

LATE SPENCER CHOICE MIX #SW133
The mix includes selections from the entire range of the Spencer types: pure white, dainty bicolor pinks and salmons, scarlet, burgundy and midnight purple. The Spencers were among the earliest large-flowered types; all are heavily ruffled; fine for cutting. . Pkt $2.50

MELODY MIX #SW154
A new series of sweet peas bred in Australia by Keith Hammelt. Gorgeous bi-colors that are perfect for your flower sales! Truly stunning. All seven stupendous bi-colors are in this mix, and these fragrant flowers are sure to please! Pkt $2.50

PAINTED LADY #SW135
One of the most fragrant sweet peas, the flowers are striking bi-colored deep pink and white. This variety is quite old, dating to the 1730's. It is becoming very popular with seed savers and is a very good producer of flowers with rich, old-time sweet scent. Pkt $2.50

OLD SPICE MIX #SW122 ↑
A gorgeous and fragrant mix of the finest sweet peas. Selected from varieties dating 1901-1907, has many brilliant shades of colors. Great heat resistance. Modern varieties are just not the same. Pkt $2.00

PERENNIAL SWEET PEA MIX #SW156
(*L. latifolius*) Hardy perennial. Sow in place fall or spring. Here is the wild sweet pea that comes in pink, red and white. Long blooming vines are very drought and winter hardy. Slow to germinate; soak 24 hours before planting in early spring. Beautiful clusters of blooms but are not fragrant like annual sweet peas. Pkt $2.50

PRINCE EDWARD OF YORK #SW168
Brilliant-hued Old Spice selection. The large, wondrously perfumed flowers are subtly two-toned, in cerise and a soft carmine, almost salmon. Very striking! Extremely fragrant, like all the Old Spice series. Bred by Henry Eckford in 1897. The flowers may not last well when cut, so enjoy this one in the garden. Robust plants climb up to 8 feet, are relatively tolerant of hot weather. Pkt $2.50

PRINCE OF ORANGE SPENCER #SW164
Late-flowering "multiflora" type, producing large, many-flowered trusses. This one is pure, clear orange, having flowers of excellent substance. Pkt $2.50

QUEEN ALEXANDRA #SW125
Startling, bold scarlet blossoms; this variety was bred by Eckford in 1906, and named after the Queen. One of the finest varieties Eckford ever developed, far excelling other scarlet varieties of his time. Fragrant. Pkt $2.50

ROSE PINK MAMMOTH #SW165
Very large, mildly fragrant blooms on long stems, but with a difference: these are shaded white towards the center of each precious, deeply ruffled bloom. Pkt $2.50

ROYAL FAMILY MIX #SW155
A standard old selection; needs to be grown in cool spring weather. The flowers are very large and solid colored. Sweet fragrance and very beautiful. Many stunning colors. Pkt $2.50

TASSEL FLOWER (Edible)

IRISH POET #FL790

(*Emilia javanica*) Beautiful bright orange variety for naturalistic gardens. This annual has long stems and small, bright orange flowers in clusters. These flowers were once described as the windswept hair of an Irish poet. Suitable as a specialty cut flower, it is a colorful filler for summer bouquets. Grow in full sun in a soil with good drainage. Tassel Flower was introduced to England from Asia in 1799 and was also known as "Flora's Paintbrush" in Victorian times. Pkt (150 seeds) $2.50

VINCA

ROSEA DWARF LITTLE MIXED #FL270 New!

Tender perennial usually grown as an annual. (also known as Madagascar Periwinkle) 5-pointed stars in a mix of snow white and cheery rosy-pink. Prefers full sun, yet looks so pretty peeping out from a shaded corner! Glossy leaves, always fresh-looking, are a bonus. Thrives in heat, not bothered by humidity or dryness. Height runs to about 10". Pkt Pkt (40 seeds) $2.50

WALLFLOWER

SIBERIAN WALLFLOWER #WF113

(*Cherianthus allionii*) Hardy perennial. Vibrant yellow-orange, phlox-like flower clusters are very fragrant and colorful. The 18" perennial plants bloom early in the season; adds a great splash of color to your meadow. Pkt $1.50

YARROW (Edible)

Hardy Perennial. Sow fall or spring.

PARKER'S VARIETY #FL795

(*Achillea filipendulina*) This hardy yarrow has beautiful, feathery gray-green foliage and lovely flower clusters with many tiny yellow flowers. Makes a beautiful and long-lasting cut flower. An easy perennial to grow almost anywhere! Pkt (900 seeds) $1.75

YARROW, COLORADO MIX #HB235 *New!* Perennial. Mix of blood red, cerise, cream, yellow and white. All the good traits of yarrow, but in an irresistible blend of colors. The large flower clusters are in reality made up of scores of tiny daisies, last a long time and bloom until very cold weather. Pkt $2.00

ZINNIAS (Edible)

(*Zinnia elegans*) Introduced from Mexico in 1800 and have been very popular ever since. They have huge flowers in many striking colors and are so easy to grow. Many of our zinnias are double, but many still produce fairly large amounts of single flowers.(100 seeds per pkt.)

BONBON MIX #FL827

Dahlia-flowered variety in a range of zinnia colors. The petals are exquisitely colored, often having two colors running the length of each petal. Height is about 30 inches. Great for cutting or for a veritable splash of color right in the garden. Pkt $2.50

BURPEE ROSE GIANT CACTUS #FL812

Lovely, big blooms in shades of rose to "bubble gum" pink; they have the unique pointed "cactus" type petals that make giant zinnias so unusual! Easy to grow and perfect for stunning bouquets. A hard to find variety that was introduced by Burpee's. Pkt $2.00

CANARY BIRD #FL805

Large dahlia-type blooms are a beautiful yellow, 4"-5" across. Great cut flowers for home or farm markets; an old favorite. Pkt $1.75 *or 1 oz $8.00*

CHERRY QUEEN #FL838 *New!*

Annual. Spectacular color in a zinnia--assorted shades of brilliant cherry red! Dahlia-flowered, fully double blooms are held atop 30-40" plants. A massed planting of these is sure to attract attention. Makes a sensational cut flower, or leave them in the garden where the bees and butterflies can enjoy them, too! Pkt $2.50 or 1 oz $8.00

CHIPPENDALE DAISY ZINNIA #FL913

Petite bedding zinnia, the same species and proportions as the well-known 'Persian Carpet.' However, Chippendale Daisy is much more sedate in color, the flowers being a fairly uniform deep burgundy with the outer tips of the petals picoteed in very intense golden yellow. Excels in more formal settings. Pkt $2.00

CUPCAKE MIX #FL273 *New!*

Annual. Jewel-toned blooms are so incredibly double that they resemble florist's mums! Blooms are on the small side (for zinnias), about 2" across, but so packed with petals that they describe almost complete spheres! Full-sized plants keep 'em coming all summer long! Pkt (25 seeds) $4.00

DREAM #FL814

Dreamy looking, lavender-rose blooms are good sized and add a wonderful effect to the garden. Provides great color all summer and into the fall. Pkt $1.50

ENVY #FL800

Exciting chartreuse-green blooms that are very unique. The beautiful flowers are 3" across. A wonderful variety that is a very popular color for marketing. These always are a favorite here! Pkt $2.50 *or 1 oz $8.00*

ILLUMINATION #FL808

A lovely Dahlia-type zinnia with large, double blooms that are a blushing, soft rose color. Great cut flowers. Pkt $1.75

GIANTS OF CALIFORNIA #FL801

Very large, 4"- 5" double flowers. This California heirloom dates back to 1919. The plants bloom all season and make superb cut flowers. This mix contains cherry, orange, pink, purple, scarlet, yellow, and white. Pkt $2.00

LAVENDER QUEEN #FL809

Very large blooms are a lovely lavender color. This is an attractive "California Giant" type; causes a sensation when planted in large groups. Pkt $2.00

LILAC EMPEROR #FL816

Cactus-flowered type to 36 inches boasts quilled petals of unusually heavy substance. Extra-large flowers are a lovely lilac-purple and make a bold statement in any garden. Pkt $2.50

LILLIPUT MIX #FL803

Cute 1½" beehive-shaped double flowers, in colors of white, yellow, pink, scarlet, purple, orange, and more. This mix is blended by formula. Plants grow 18" tall. Lovely! Pkt $1.75 *or 1 oz $8.00*

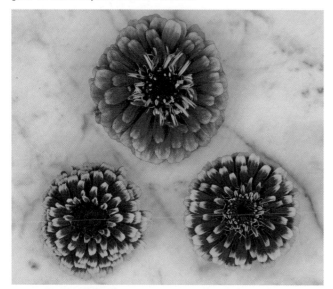

MACARENIA #FL861 *New!*

Annual. Ravishing flowers look like crimson velvet laced with gold! Large dahlia-flowered blooms are very double, two-toned in gold and red. The full-sized plants are just a bit compact, and the generous yield of blooms makes this an especially good variety for cut flowers. And if it's a trifle gaudy, well, that's just how we like our zinnias to be!   Pkt $3.00

"Ninety-nine percent of the failures come from people who have the habit of making excuses."

——GEORGE WASHINGTON CARVER

MAZURKIA #FL862 *New!*

Annual. Each scarlet petal is tipped in cream, and both are set off by the circular golden tracery at each flower's heart—sumptuous! Dahlia flowers, large bloom size, robust plants: what more could a zinnia connoisseur ask for? Pkt $3.00

METEOR #FL817

The big, bright red zinnia—truly majestic—grows up to 5" across, being double and rich red in color. This giant beauty is hard to beat and great as a cut flower. Pkt $2.00

MISS WILLMOTT #FL811

Huge, soft pink flowers can be as large as 6" across. An unusual but very attractive pastel shade, these have long stems and are perfect for bouquets. Pkt $2.50

ORANGE KING #FL818

Tall plants produce big, double, bright mandarin-orange flowers. A stunning color that really makes a bold statement. Pkt $2.00

QUEEN LIME #FL863 ↑ *New!*

Brilliant apple-green companion to 'Queen Lime Red' and stunning when paired with it, either in the bed or border, or in the vase! Dahlia blooms are incredibly double, tightly packed with brilliant green petals. Large plants are believed to be sturdier and more robust than 'Envy,' our previous old favorite for green-flowered zinnias. Pkt (25 seeds) $4.00

↑ QUEEN LIME RED #FL864 *New!*

Art shades in zinnias? The answer is yes! This large-flowered, dahlia type zinnia combines ruby tones with apple green, and the result is sophisticated ethereal loveliness! Flowers are very double, borne all season long on productive, full-sized zinnia plants, to about three feet tall. Intriguing! Pkt (25 seeds) $4.00

ORIOLE #FL819

Stunning, giant double flowers in shades of gold and orange, this beauty really gets attention. Lovely in the garden or the vase. Pkt $2.00

PEPPERMINT STICK #FL830

30 inches. Dahlia-flowered mix is splashed in crimson, similar to Candy Stripe except that the spangles are smaller, more uniform, and overall a bit more refined. A lovely variety. Pkt $2.25

PERSIAN CARPET #FL802

Stunning gold, red, chocolate, orange, and cream. Many of the 2" double flowers are bi-colored. This brilliant heirloom is still a favorite of many. Was a 1952 AAS winner. Plants produce loads of stunning flowers. Pkt $2.50 *or 1 oz $9.00*

PINK SENORITA #FL831 *-best seller!*

Enormous, mostly fully double cactus-type flowers are superb for cut flower use. Their color is confined to a sophisticated range of the best pinks the zinnia clan has to offer, coming as they do in near salmon through cerise. Pkt $2.50

POLAR BEAR #FL810
The white dahlia-type zinnia with very large blooms that are quite magnificent looking. Pkt $1.75

CUT AND COME AGAIN - PUMILA MIXED #FL866 *New!*
Annual. Smaller-flowered zinnia specially bred for maximum flower production. Rich colors run the full range that zinnias have to offer— amethyst, scarlet, rose, tangerine, orange, lemon yellow and snowy white! Plants are rather compact, seldom exceeding two feet. At 2.5- to 3 inches, the double blooms are small enough to be manageable in arrangements, but definitely large enough to provide the pop of color for which we adore zinnias. Drop-dead gorgeous! Pkt $2.00

REDMAN SUPER CACTUS #FL820 *New!*
A magnificent, huge red-flowered variety of the giant cactus family. These flowers are stately, being a deep red and having the pointed cactus-type petals. An old favorite that has now become rare. Pkt $2.50

PURPLE PRINCE #FL836 *New!*
Annual. Dahlia-flowered type is one of the tallest we've seen! The flowers are extra large and brilliant amethyst-purple, with pale green centers. Fine for cut flowers but the lavish display is best appreciated right in the garden, especially in mass plantings. Beloved in gardens since 1949. Fabulous! Pkt $2.25

ROYAL PURPLE #FL806
These lovely, large, light purple, dahlia-type flowers are perfect by themselves or in mixed bouquets. A real show stopper. Pkt $2.50

WILL ROGERS #FL821
This variety was named after the famous American, Will Rogers, and produces stunning, big, red flowers that really stand out. Pkt $1.50

DAHLIAS

The most popular flower at our farm each summer. Plant dahlias in full sun to partial shade with rich soil and even moisture. Plants grow about waist height and usually bear from June through October. Dahlias are perennial in frost- free areas, but anywhere with a killing frost you will have to dig up the bulbs and store them inside for the winter. You will know when to dig up your dahlias for the season, the plant will die back in the late fall, at that point just dig up the enlarged bulbs and save for next season.

Order these now and we will ship you good-sized tubers in March, April or May, depending on shipping conditions and your climate location.

MOM'S SPECIAL DAHLIAS #DA101 *New!*
These dinnerplate dahlias look good enough to eat! Lavender streaks the brilliant white petals of this massive edible beauty. Mom's Special makes a brilliant statement in a bouquet or atop a wedding cake. One of Jere's all-time favorite flowers! 1 tuber $7.00

KELVIN FLOODLIGHT DAHLIA #DA102
New! Dahlias are native to Mexico, Central America, and Columbia; you will find them eager to put out robust blooms late into the season. Kelvin Floodlight Dahlia's intense, pale-yellow blooms are an incredible 10-12 inches. These gorgeous dinner plate dahlias are easy to grow and are edible. Sasha's favorite flower! 1 tuber $7.00

THOMAS EDISON DAHLIA #DA103 *New!*
This is a velvety purple variety that dates back to the 1920s. It is a dinnerplate dahlia with a rich, deep purple color, Flowers are usually about 8 inches across for unbelievable flowers that are known to take home blue ribbons at the fair. 1 tuber $7.00

AVIGNON DAHLIA #DA104 *New!*
This Lovely dinnerplate dahlia is white with burgundy and purple streaks. Avignon has a very full flower head that reaches 8 to 10 inches across.. Beautiful petals can be to be sprinkled atop a salad or intricately arranged to design baked goods. 1 tuber $7.00

ISLANDER DAHLIA #DA105 *New!*
Pretty pink dinnerplate dahlia, with slightly wavy petals. Islanders grow best in full sun where they are known to grow up to 4 feet tall with 8-10 inch flower heads. 1 tuber $7.00

KOGANE FUBUKI DAHLIAS #DA106 *New!*
This lovely Japanese variety is likey the most beautiful Dahlia we grow! So unique looking in type, and the blooms have a soft yellow center that gives way to brilliant peach then pink on the tips. Dahlias are known in the gardening world as a very generous plant. This variety will produce heavily and each bloom will astound you. 1 tuber $7.00

Mom's Special

Kelvin Floodlight

Avignon

Thomas Edison

Islander

Kogane Fubuki

FALL BULBS

We adore fall planted bulbs because they are so easy, and they make the first flowers each spring! These tend to be hardy from zones 3 through 8. It is important to plant bulbs soon after you receive them; don't let them lay around outside! **Pre-order now and we will ship your bulbs in September, right before planting time!**

PARROT TULIP MIX #BL201 *New!*

The most flamboyant by products of tulipmania are the Parrot tulips. They arrive fashionably late, usually blooming mid to late spring just after the more traditional, early varieties of tulips. They finish off tulip season with a bang; colors are often bright flames of color with frilly, twisted or wavy petals. Parrot tulips are a favorite of macro photographers for their gracefully contorted flower forms and stark color contrasts. 25 bulbs for $22

HISTORIC DAFFODIL MIX (NARCISSUS) #BL202 *New!*

There is a spectacular range of daffodil varieties, they showcase beautifully beside one another in mass plantings. An entire bed of daffodils will range from large yellow trumpets to delicate white flowers with bright orange cup. Here you will find some of the varieties that were beloved by gardeners of the past as well as a few new varieties that are so special we just cannot help sharing with you. 25 bulbs for $22

HISTORIC CROCUS MIX #BL203 *New!*

This mix will liven up your bleak late winter landscape with the colors of the past and present. You can plant these sturdy little flowers in light shade under trees and even on your lawn! The flowers and foliage will be long gone before your first lawn mowing of the season. 50 bulbs for $22

HISTORIC HYACINTH #BL204 *New!*

The common garden Hyacinth originated in Turkey and has been cultivated commercially since the second half of the 16th century. Here are some old varieties that have withstood the test of time and remain in cultivation today. It isn't hard to understand how these fragrant old friends have secured their place in gardener's hearts; they are delightful! 10 bulbs for $22

SAFFRON CROCUS #BL205 *New!*

Talk about a cash crop, the dried stigmas and styles of Crocus sativus are known as one of the most expensive spices by weight; now you can grow your own saffron in your garden. Saffron is revered for its unique flavor that has been described as a slightly metallic honey with hay notes. Saffron has a remarkable history; it is said that Cleopatra liked her bath scented with saffron. 50 bulbs for $22

Parrot Tulip

Daffodil Mix

Crocus Mix

Hyacinth Mix

THE GENERAL STORE
BOOKS & GIFTS FOR HEIRLOOM GARDENERS

We sell only select books that we ourselves enjoy! Having the right info is so important. Learning how to grow and save seed and reading the history of heirlooms is really exciting.

NO EXTRA POSTAGE CHARGED FOR BOOKS SHIPPED WITHIN THE USA!

ALL NEW SQUARE FOOT GARDENING:
Grow More in Less Space #BK146
by Mel Bartholomew

This beautiful, full-color book offers instructions and plans for Mel's square foot gardening methods. Great tips and ideas throughout. It's definitely one of the best books we've seen on growing a lot in a small space. In this new version the author unveils 10 new improvements that save you time and money, all with a lot less work. Mel was a speaker at our 2007 Spring Planting Festival. 271 pages. $19.95

CARROTS LOVE TOMATOES: *Secrets of Companion Planting for Successful Gardening* #BK135
—*Customer Favorite!*
By Louise Riotte

This classic has now taught generations of gardeners how to use the natural benefits of plants to protect and support each other. Here is a reader's complete reference to which plants nourish the soil, which keep away bugs and pests, and which plants just don't get along. 224 pages. $14.95

GOOD BUG, BAD BUG #BK180
—*Customer Favorite!*
By Jessica Walliser

The best book we have ever seen about insects in the garden. Learn to recognize the good bugs from the bad ones, how to prevent attacks, what plants they damage, organic products that control each insect and more. Very

easy to use; spiral-bound and full color photos of each insect make this the funnest guide to garden insects ever! We found ourselves using this multiple times over the summer, as it is so easy to find what to use for each problem. 91 pages. $17.95

GOOD MUSHROOM, BAD MUSHROOM #BK234
By John Plischke III

A guide to some of the more common edible wild mushrooms and their poisonous look-alikes. A useful tool to use in identification, most of the photos in the book show different aspects of the mushroom: the cap and how

it is attached, interior of the mushroom, or its habitat. The book's spiral-bound small size makes it fun and easy to use. Semi-hardcover. 87 pages $17.95

GOOD WEED, BAD WEED #BK230
By Nancy Gift

A full-color weed identification guide that is designed to provide you with a quick and easy reference tool. The book's spiral-bound small size with its up-close photos makes it easy and fun to use. Categorized into Good Weeds, Bad Weeds, or Not-so-bad Weeds, each weed is described along with its benefits or drawbacks and the best methods of control. Full color. Semi-hardcover. 95 pages. $17.95

GREAT HERB MIXES YOU CAN MAKE #BK139
By Jim Long

With this book you can start your own herb business, make herb products to sell, or make lots of gifts for your friends. It includes over 100 herb seasonings, dream blends, bath herb mixes, allergy eye pillows, relaxing aromatherapy pillows, body care products, patterns, tips for selling and a very helpful resource list. 102 pages. $10.95

HONEY BEE HOBBYIST: *The Care & Keeping of Bees* #BK216
By Norman Gary, PhD

A practical, easy-to-use, fundamental guide to the hobby of honey bee keeping. Learn everything from how to start your own hive, how to have fun with bees, and how to harvest your honey. Its large size and colorful photographs will be a good addition to any bee hobbyist's library. Full color. Soft cover 176 pages. $14.95

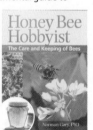

HOW TO STORE YOUR GARDEN PRODUCE:
The Key to Self-Sufficiency #BK182
By Piers Warren

This book has been completely revised and is the modern guide to storing and preserving your garden produce, enabling you to eat home-grown goodness all year round. The easy-to-use reference section provides applicable storage and preservation techniques for the majority of plant produce grown commonly in home gardens. A must for budding gardeners and homesteaders. 143 pages. $14.95

KEEPING CHICKENS: *All You Need to Know to Care for a Happy, Healthy Flock* #BK243
by Ashley English

A great source for the DIYer joining the movement to start and maintain a flock of chickens: everything

from choosing breeds suitable for various needs to how to feed, clean, house and care for chickens. The text portraits of chicken owners make the book a pleasurable, as well as a practical, guide. Also included are plans for making nesting boxes and a mobile chicken housing structure, followed by practical and delectable egg recipes. Hardcover. 136 pages. $19.95.

SEED TO SEED
(2nd Edition) #BK113
—*Customer Favorite!*
By Suzanne Ashworth

The expanded 2nd edition now includes seed starting info, too! Complete seed-saving guide for 160 vegetable crops, with detailed information on each vegetable: pollination methods, isolation distances, caging and hand-pollination techniques, proper methods for harvesting,

drying, cleaning and storing the seeds. This is the best book ever written on seed saving. Easy to read, it is a must for all seed savers & is our best seller! 228 large pages. $24.95

SEEDS OF DECEPTION #BK121
By Jeffrey M. Smith

Genetically Engineered Food Endangers Health; Political Corruption Exposed. An explosive exposé shows that the foods are, in fact, unsafe. The book, Seeds of Deception, presents overwhelming evidence documenting serious potential health risks. We love this book! 289 pages. $17.95

THE BEGINNER'S GUIDE TO GROWING HEIRLOOM VEGETABLES #BK269
By Marie Iannotti

Longtime Master Gardener and heirloom expert, the author gives more than just a list of the 100 easiest-to-grow, tastiest vegetables for your garden. The book is filled not only with

fascinating stories about the heirlooms but also tells which varieties to grow for the best flavor and how to cultivate each one successfully. Learn how to plant, grow, harvest, and save seeds. Paperback. 250 pages. $19.95

THE VEGETABLE GARDENER'S BIBLE #BK166
By Edward C. Smith
If you could only have one gardening book, this might be the one to pick. Well-written and nicely illustrated with lovely color photographs, this extremely comprehensive guide covers everything you want to know about sowing, harvesting, composting, soil testing, raised beds, no-till, vertical gardening, water, soil, mulch, fertilizer, cover crops, natural methods for disease and pests, AND includes an awesome 118-page A-Z Plant directory. 309 pages. $35.00

THE YEAR-ROUND VEGETABLE GARDENER #BK268
By Niki Jabbour
Proven techniques for year-round growing and harvesting. Read all the tips to get the timing right and grow the right crops. Learn Niki's intensive gardening methods and some affordable and easy-to-assemble protective structures that will help you to enjoy fresh and delicious produce throughout the entire year. Hard cover. 246 pages. $29.95

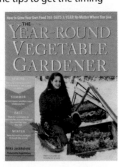

WEEK-BY-WEEK VEGETABLE GARDENER'S HANDBOOK #BK245
By R. Kujawski & J. Kujawski
The key to gardening success is having a plan. Beginning and experienced gardeners will benefit from this week-by-week plan for the growing season. Because the timing of gardening activities is largely determined by temperatures, this book bases the plan on the average date of last frost, which differs according to location. Intended to be used as a work book, it is spiral bound with pages for notes interspersed. 200 pages. $14.95

THE ORGANIC SEED GROWER
#BK537 *New! By Dr John Navazio*
A must-have, comprehensive manual on producing quality organic seed crops on the homestead or small commercial farm. Plant breeder and organic seed expert has filled the book with practical techniques and theory for home seed savers, commercial seed growers, and small scale farmers. 390 pages Hardcover $49.95

Our very own books...

THE BAKER CREEK VEGAN COOKBOOK:
Traditional Ways to Cook, Preserve, & Eat the Harvest **#BK267** *New!*
By Jere and Emilee Gettle
The cofounders of Baker Creek Heirloom Seed Company take you through more than 125 vegan recipes that are healthy and easy to make. They share tips and tricks on canning and preserving, as well provide a list of pantry staples to have on hand. Paperback, 194 pages. SALE, $9.95 (Half-price)

THE HEIRLOOM LIFE GARDENER: *The Baker Creek Way of Growing Your Own Food Easily & Naturally* #HG114
By Jere & Emilee Gettle, with Meghan Sutherland
A book for heirloom gardeners and want-to-be gardeners, a book that covers all the basics, from seed starting, growing, organic methods, harvest, storage, seed saving, as well as stories of our life in the soil, growing and eating from the land. Learn about our seed collecting trips and stories from our seed's history. We wrote this book as a colorful and simple guide book that will inspire you to garden the easy and heirloom way, the way our ancestors gardened! Full color, hardcover. 228 pages. **Customers in the U.S. who order** *The Heirloom Life Gardener* will also receive a one-year new or extended subscription to *Heirloom Gardener* magazine—all for only $29.95!

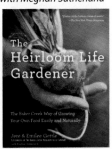

COPPER WATERING CAN #CWC101
This beautiful indoor watering can is a must-have for the serious indoor horticulturist. Made of beautiful polished copper, its functional design with its tall neck allows for precision watering of indoor plants without spillage from the tipped can. The removable watering rose lets you choose a fine spray or a steady stream of water. One liter capacity. Made in England by the Haws company. $112

Handy products for your garden

BOSMERE 5" WHITE PLANT LABELS.
#WPL101 Economical to use, the plastic plant labels come in a resealable plastic bag and can be reused in either the garden or containers. Package of 50. $6.00

NUTSCENE GARDEN TWINE #NGT101
All purpose garden twine is made of 3-ply all natural jute from sustainable sources. Soft, pliable, and strong. Made in Scotland since 1922. Approximately 26 meters total on 2 spools. $4.50

BOSMERE TWINE TIES #BTT101
All purpose garden ties made from soft foam with a galvanized steel wire core is ideal for tying and training most plants without damaging the stems. The 30-feet by 3/8-inch roll can be cut into any length required. $10.50

CLYDE'S GARDEN PLANNER #CGP101

This unique chart presents gardening events in a "time-phased" format so that it is possible to see at a glance the entire planting, growing and harvesting period. It shows proper indoor and outdoor planting times relative to spring and fall frost dates for 22 common garden vegetables. Since frost dates vary from region to region, the chart will slide, making it useful in most parts of the Northern Hemisphere where frost is a critical gardening factor. The front of the chart shows the spring season, and the flip side acts as a guide for fall gardeners. Frost dates are included in the directions. Developed by a friend and customer, this handy chart is a favorite of our staff and customers to our store. A must for new gardeners. Just $3.00!

OUR VERY OWN BOOKS...

THE BAKER CREEK VEGAN COOKBOOK:
Traditional Ways to Cook, Preserve, & Eat the Harvest **#BK267** *New!*
By Jere and Emilee Gettle
The cofounders of Baker Creek Heirloom Seed Company take you through more than 125 vegan recipes that are healthy and easy to make. They share tips and tricks on canning and preserving, as well provide a list of pantry staples to have on hand. Paperback, 194 pages.
SALE $9.95

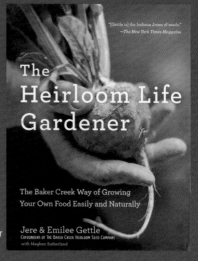

THE HEIRLOOM LIFE GARDENER: *The Baker Creek Way of Growing Your Own Food Easily & Naturally* **#HG114**
By Jere & Emilee Gettle, with Meghan Sutherland
A book for heirloom gardeners and want-to-be gardeners, a book that covers all the basics, from seed starting, growing, organic methods, harvest, storage, seed saving, as well as stories of our life in the soil, growing and eating from the land. Learn about our seed collecting trips and stories from our seed's history. We wrote this book as a colorful and simple guide book that will inspire you to garden the easy and heirloom way, the way our ancestors gardened! Full color, hardcover. 228 pages. Customers in the U.S. who order *The Heirloom Life Gardener* will also receive a one-year new or extended subscription to *Heirloom Gardener* magazine—all for only $29.95!

COBRAHEAD HAND HOE #CDT101

The CobraHead® precision weeder and cultivator is the closest thing to a universal garden hand tool. It weeds, cultivates, scalps,

edges, digs, furrows, plants, transplants, de-thatches, and harvests with ease. Jere's favorite tool ever! He uses this tool for nearly all his planting. The best tool we have seen; the shape of the head really makes this tool easy to use, fun and perfect for nearly every garden project. It can even dig 12" holes in even the hardest Ozark garden soil. A new favorite! Made in the USA. *Caution: these are sharp and must be kept out of reach of children.* $24.95

COPPER PLANT MARKERS #CPM101

Durable and attractive plant markers made of beautiful copper-plated metal. These permanent plant markers are rustproof, weatherproof, won't fade in direct sunlight, and can be used year after year to record plant name, date of planting and plant origin. These easy-to-use copper markers can be etched with a ball point pen or similar smooth pointed instrument. Face size is 3½ x 1⅛ inches. Sold in packages of 10 tags with stakes. $10.00

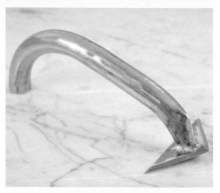

SERIOUS HAND WEEDER #SHW101

New! This wonderful weeding tool is designed and built by an engineer turned organic farmer who needed a hand weeding tool that could withstand the rigor of hand weeding over 4 acres of sweet potato. The ergonomic handle enables the serious weeder to both push and pull easily cutting weeds off just below the surface. This tool works especially well on tough hard clay soils that tend to bend or break many tools. We love it! Made in the USA. *Caution: these are sharp and must be kept out of reach of children.* $24.95

Looking for the perfect gift for the gardener in your life—or a special something for yourself? Here are a few of our favorite items, including Baker Creek exclusives.

SEED COLLECTIONS

We offer several packages containing some of our best seeds. This is the perfect way to save money and acquire a safe, secure food supply. Most of the seeds in these packages will store 4-10 years if kept cool and dry. What a great way to try many of our best varieties!

LARGE HEIRLOOM PACKAGE

Our Large Heirloom Package is a great package for a medium to large garden. It contains 50 full-sized packets of at least 30 varieties. Also included is Clyde's Garden Planner. It comes packaged in a metal container for long-lasting storage. This collection is packaged for either Southern or Northern climate.

#HPN101 Northern LARGE Package $99
#HPS102 Southern LARGE Package $99

JUMBO HEIRLOOM PACKAGE

A giant package great for large groups, schools and families; selected seeds for a sure supply of delicious home-grown produce. Contains 250 full-sized packets of more than 30 varieties of vegetables, specially chosen for either the Northern or Southern climate. Both *The Heirloom Life Gardener* and *The Baker Creek Vegan Cookbook* are included in this collection.

#JPN121 Northern JUMBO Package $395
#JPS122 Southern JUMBO Package $395

HOME GARDENER'S COLLECTION

This collection is perfect for the home gardener or container gardener. It contains 20 full-sized packets of seeds and *A Clyde's Garden Planner*—all packaged in an attractive burlap bag with a drawstring closure. Varieties in this package are chosen to be productive in both Northern and Southern climates. **#HGC Home Gardener's Collection $40.00**

ORGANIC BAKER CREEK T-SHIRTS
100% pre-shrunk organic cotton shirts with an original tomato print on the back by Ginger Irwin of Petaluma, CA. Sport our cool shirt in the garden, farmers' market or anywhere that persons of high class assemble. Available in:
Men's Sizes: Small, Med, Large, XL, XXL
Ladies Sizes: Small, Med, Large, XL
Your Choice, $16.95 each

BAKER CREEK GIFT CERTIFICATES
Available Online!

"A garden was one of the few things in prison that one could control. To plant a seed, watch it grow, to tend it and then harvest it, offered a simple but enduring satisfaction. The sense of being the custodian of this small patch of earth offered a taste of freedom.

-NELSON MANDELA

The Ozark Herbalist

By Kathy McFarland

Jim Long grew up with a love of gardening and developed a particular interest in herbs. As his love of herb gardening grew, he traveled the world to such places as the jungles of New Guinea and the markets of India and Thailand in search of rare and unusual culinary herbs.

Jim is fortunate to have turned his passion into a successful career. His gardens at Long Creek Herb Farm in the Ozarks Mountains of Missouri include not only several hundred varieties of culinary herbs, but also rare and unusual vegetables he's collected from his travels. There he photographs, writes about and develops recipes for the plants he grows.

Jim is also author of more than two dozen books on herbs, gardening and historical subjects. He writes for a variety of gardening and herb magazines, writes a syndicated newspaper column, has appeared on numerous television programs, and is a frequent speaker at conferences, garden shows and festivals. Visit www.longcreekherbs.com

Jim shares one of his favorite herb recipes:

Cold-Pressed Mint Tea

This herb recipe is so simple you may laugh, but once you've tried it you will see why it is one of my favorites. The flavor of the fresh herb is so much lighter and more refreshing than when made with dried herbs and hot water. While you can use almost any herb for this, I prefer using either mint or lemon balm for the herb ingredient. You'll need one big double-handful of fresh mint (or fresh lemon balm). Wad it up like a dishcloth and twist it slightly, to release the essential oils of the herb.

Put the herb into the bottom of a 2 quart pitcher. Fill the pitcher to the top; with ice, then add enough water to completely cover the ice, to the top. Set it aside for 10 minutes for the herbal essential oils to be extracted. Pour into glasses and serve with an herb sprig.

Add Jim's Great Books to Your Order!

Home Remedies That Work #BK447 Jim Long. A collection of folk remedies the author has collected over the years from various sources. Some are his own formulas he has used himself, while others were recommended by friends or reliable sources. $6.95 Paperback $6.95

Herbs Just for Fun: How to Grow and Use Herbs #BK154
by Jim Long. This book is a good introduction to growing herbs, whether you are on a shoestring budget or want to grow on a grand scale. It includes a list of common herbs and their uses. 20 pages. Paperback $4.95.

Easy Homemade Crackers Using Herbs   #BK446
by Jim Long. This is a collection of recipes for making both crackers using herbs as ingredients and crackers to be eaten with herbs. All are quick and simple to make using fresh or dried herbs. 36 pages. Paperback $6.95

Making Herb Vinegars #BK154
by Jim Long. Learn to make in your own kitchen the fabulous gourmet vinegars you buy at specialty stores. This book discusses the different types of vinegars, as well as recipes, for both culinary use and body care. 36 pages. Paperback $6.95

Make Your Own Hot Sauce #BK455
by Jim Long. A collection of basic recipes for making your own hot sauces, along with lots of tips and a few cautions. Learn the different methods for preserving your hot sauces made from a variety of peppers. 38 pages. Paperback $6.95

Sensational Salsas #BK137
by Jim Long. Dozens of great-tasting and high-nutrition salsa recipes made from a variety of ingredients from apples to zucchini. Many recipes include suggested accompaniments. 34 pages. Paperback $5.95.

HERBAL NAIL FUNGUS SOAK #NFS101
This amazing remedy for nail fungus and persistent athlete's foot fungus is nothing short of incredible. Developed by Long Creek Herbs, this remedy has become very popular with gardeners who report that it really works! Complete directions are included for mixing a packet of herbs with one quart of apple cider vinegar to make enough soak to cure the average case of nasty nail fungus. Was a top seller last season! (Net wt. 0.65 oz) $14.95

GMO Food Action

Genetically Modified Organisms, or GMOs, are unsafe. Yet GMOs appear in over 70 percent of all foods consumed in America, and the number of GMO crops increases each year, with GMO beets and GMO alfalfa, as well as GMO salmon, recently winning regulatory approval.

THE SAFE SEED PLEDGE

"Agriculture and seeds provide the basis upon which our lives depend. We must protect this foundation as a safe and genetically stable source for future generations. For the benefit of all farmers, gardeners and consumers who want an alternative, we pledge that we do not knowingly buy or sell genetically engineered seeds or plants. The mechanical transfer of genetic material outside of natural methods and between genera, families or kingdoms, poses great biological risks as well as economic, political, and cultural threats..."

This pledge was signed by us & other companies that are concerned about this issue. For more information on this project, contact:

THE SAFE SEED INITIATIVE
c/o Council for Responsible Genetics
5 Upland Road, Suite 3 • Cambridge, MA 02140
www.gene-watch.org

OUR COMPANY WORKS TO FIGHT GMO FRANKENFOOD!

SEND A LETTER to your US House Representative and Senator, asking what he or she is doing to support truth in labeling and a pure food supply. Also, please write:

SECRETARY OF AGRICULTURE, USDA
200-A Whitten Building
1400 Independence Ave. SW
Washington, DC 20250

BUY LOCAL FOODS & GROW YOUR OWN:

Buying local supports small farmers and organic production and keeps money in the local area, growing your local economy. Find farmers' markets & natural food stores. Find local producers at *www.localharvest.org.* Go to *www.greenpeace.org/usa* for a great list of brands that are GMO-free. Also, read the Non-GMO Report: *www.non-gmoreport.com.*

WE SUPPORT:

ORGANIC CONSUMERS ASSOCIATION
www.organicconsumers.org

INSTITUTE FOR RESPONSIBLE TECHNOLOGY
www.responsibletechnology.org

FOOD DEMOCRACY NOW
www.fooddemocracynow.org

"Back in Europe we have that choice. Our food is labeled and it hasn't increased any costs to the consumer or the farmer."
—SIR PAUL MCCARTNEY

Other Resources

Here are other great sources for information, plants, and seed. You may be able to find what you are looking for at the following sources:

SEED SAVERS EXCHANGE
www.seedsavers.org

SAND HILL PRESERVATION CENTER
SEEDS & POULTRY
www.sandhillpreservation.com

THE GREAT PUMPKIN PATCH
www.the200acres.com

SEEDS OF DIVERSITY CANADA
www.seeds.ca

ABUNDANT ACRES *Heirloom Plants*
www.abundantacres.net

MARIANNA'S SEEDS
www.mariseeds.com

RAINTREE NURSERY
www.raintreenursery.com

SLOWFOOD USA
www.slowfoodusa.org

SMALL FARM TODAY MAGAZINE
www.smallfarmtoday.com

MOTHER EARTH NEWS
www.motherearthnews.com

HOBBY FARMS MAGAZINE
www.hobbyfarms.com

IDIGMYGARDEN FORUMS
www.idigmygarden.com

RODALE INSTITUTE
www.rodaleinstitute.org

NATIVE SEEDS/SEARCH
www.nativeseeds.org

CAROLINA GOLD RICE FOUNDATION
www.carolinagoldricefoundation.org

INSTITUTE FOR RESPONSIBLE
TECHNOLOGY
www.responsibletechnology.org

NAVDANYA
www.navdanya.org

MODERN FARMER
www.modernfarmer.com

COMSTOCK, FERRE and COMPANY
www.comstockferre.com

SOUTHERN EXPOSURE SEED EXCHANGE
www.southernexposure.com

ORGANIC GARDENING
www.organicgardening.com

Please support these 'Pure Food' advocates!

America's Only Magazine Devoted to the

heirloom
GARDENER

We have expanded our quarterly publication to 84 pages! Each issue is filled with mouth-watering, lavish photos and articles tailored to the heirloom food enthusiast. Home gardeners, market growers, chefs, and homesteaders have been subscribing to our publication since 2003. Each issue is filled with interesting articles surrounding heirloom gardening, GMOs, vegetarian cooking, homesteading, and more. Learn how to grow organically, eat locally, save your own seed, preserve the harvest, homestead, and live self-sufficiently!

Subscribe Today!

ONLY $15/YEAR (4 ISSUES)

REQUEST A SAMPLE: $4.95

Write item #HG112 on your order form to subscribe.

www.rareseeds.com

ORDERING INFO

Send orders to:
BAKER CREEK HEIRLOOM SEEDS
2278 BAKER CREEK ROAD
MANSFIELD, MO 65704

Online orders: *(The quickest way!)*
WWW.RARESEEDS.COM
FAX ORDERS TO: 417-924-8887

TELEPHONE : *We have limited phone lines and are no longer taking orders by phone,* **417-924-8917.** Please mail, fax or place your order online. You're welcome to call if you have questions or need help.

We accept checks, money orders, cash and all major credit cards! (If paying by credit card, please write number, expiration date and CVV on order form.)

PLEASE INCLUDE ITEM NUMBERS ON SEED ORDERS! They are listed right after the variety name (e.g. *ROMA #TM110).* This will help us get your order to you quickly.

YOU MAY USE OUR ENCLOSED ORDER FORM, OR JUST WRITE CLEARLY ON A SHEET OF PAPER. Remember to include your name, address and phone number!

POSTAGE & HANDLING: (USA, CANADA AND

MEXICO) Just $3.50 per order! *(INTERNATIONAL POSTAGE & HANDLING: (All other countries) 20% of the total of your order, Min. $5.00)*

SALES TAX:
California customers, please add 8% for all products except vegetable and herb seeds, which are non-taxable.

Connecticut customers, please add 6% for all products except vegetable and herb seeds, which are non-taxable.

Missouri customers, please add 5.225% on all products, except for vegetable and herb seeds; for these add 2.225%.

Other areas are not subject to sales tax.

TERMS AND CONDITIONS:
All orders are shipped by the U.S. Postal Service or FedEx. Estimated time until fulfillment is usually 3 to 5 business days. It is our goal to ship all orders in 48 hours.

Seeds are guaranteed to germinate at reasonable rates for one year from the date of purchase. Seeds are also guaranteed to grow true to type. Seed packets may be returned for only these reasons, and are only eligible for an exchange or refund up to the purchase price of the item. We are not responsible for return shipping costs. We are in no way responsible for crop failures, insects, disease, floods, drought, terrorism and acts of God.

Merchandise is guaranteed to be free of defects. Any faulty or broken merchandise may be returned for a full refund or exchange up to 10 days from time of arrival. We are not responsible for return shipping costs. We will never sell or give away your information. However, we may contact you at any time in the future.

All live plants are guaranteed true-to-type and to live for 30 days.

ORDER FORM

Phone #_____Date_____

Name_____

Address_____

City_____State_____Zip Code_____

Email_____

# of Items	Order #	Name of Item	Price $
1	FR000	FREE GIFT PACKET - A gift with all orders! (Our choice)	$0.00

Order Form Side 2

Do you have a comment or suggestion? We would love to hear from you!

# of Items	Order #	Name of Item	Price $

Cut on line

Request a catalog for a friend!

Friend's Name

Address

City   State   Zip

Send orders to:
Baker Creek Heirloom Seeds
2278 Baker Creek Road
Mansfield MO 65704 USA

Or place online for quicker
prosessing! Rareseeds.com

USA, CAN. MEX.
SHIPPING $3.50

CA, CT & MO Customers:
Add Sales Tax!(See Order Info)

TOTAL
$

Did you subscribe to The Heirloom Gardener
Magazine? If not, just add $15.00 for a year!

THANKS FOR YOUR ORDER! IT WILL HELP US PRESERVE MORE RARE SEEDS.

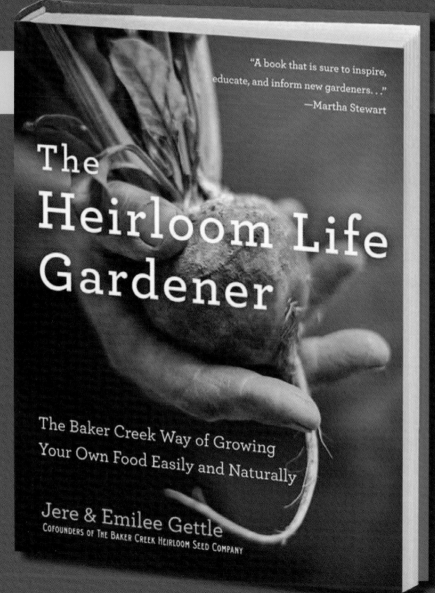

BAKERSVILLE
HERITAGE DAY FESTIVALS
MANSFIELD, MISSOURI

FIRST SUNDAY MONTHLY MARCH-OCTOBER

← Our Restaurant!

HERITAGE DAY FESTIVALS

Round up your family and come to our exciting, fun-filled festivals that celebrate the growing season with produce, music, crafts and garden speakers!

Spring brings a plant lover's paradise to our festival. Guests will be tempted by hundreds to thousands of rare and heirloom plant varieties. In May, our largest festival of the year, you can hear top of the line garden speakers that truly are America's cream of the crop!

Then, celebrate summer and fall by savoring the fruits of our labor as we display our garden's bounty. Vendors sell many varieties of fruit and produce as well as handmade crafts. Start the day off right by picking up a cinnamon roll fresh from our bakery, then rock the day away on the front porch listening to one of our many fine bands.

COME ON OUT TO THE FARM...

These events are held at our village and farm. In 2007 we saw the beginning of our historic town. Besides the Baker Creek Seed Store, located on our historic property are a speaker barn, restaurant, an old-time mercantile, herbal apothecary, a natural bakery, garden museum and blacksmith shop, two music barns, a Western jail, a native rock oven, a windmill and many breeds of historic poultry and livestock.

We offer free tent and RV camping; no need to register. There are also hotels in the local area. Some food is available at the festivals. All pets over 20 lbs must be pre-approved. No weapons.

Vendors are welcome! Bring your crafts, garden produce, plants, garlic, seeds, natural products, garden tools, and more. Space is free to non-profits & those providing historic demonstrations. For more information or to register, call 417-924-8917 or visit www.rareseeds.com.

We are 10 minutes from the home of the Laura Ingalls Wilder Museum and only 90 minutes from Branson. Come to Mansfield, MO and follow signs. We are open 6 days a week, Sunday-Friday.

THE RESTAURANT

Enjoy a hearty meal in our Asian-themed vegan restaurant during our festivals. Our meals are always made from scratch with as many local ingredients as we can procure. Many of our meals are represented with recipes in our Baker Creek Vegan Cookbook. Our restaurant is run by donations only, so all our guests can dine. While we are generally open for lunch Monday through Friday, winter hours may vary according to weather and other concerns. Travelers planning to visit October through March should call ahead to check availability.

JOIN THE FUN AT BAKER CREEK SEEDS AND BAKERSVILLE!
FIRST SUNDAY OF EACH MONTH, MARCH-OCTOBER.

Seeds For Peace
Our Seed Donation Program

Our donation program here at Baker Creek has grown tremendously over the years. Each year we donate hundreds of thousands of seed packets. The renewed and increasing interest in gardening around the country has provided an inspiration for us to help many people obtain seeds they would not normally have access to.

We love helping classroom garden projects, as well as other educational garden projects. We are always delighted to send seeds to food-aid projects in developing countries to help the people improve their food supply. In the past we have sent large amounts of seed to Haiti, Honduras, South Africa, Congo, Zambia, Ecuador, and many other countries.

The urban garden movement is well underway across the globe, and we are helping it to grow when we send seeds to inner-city agencies and volunteers trying to grow healthy food in plots intermingled with apartment buildings and businesses. All kinds of charity groups around the world seek donations from us so they can help to spread the knowledge of good food and how to grow it.

Seed donation requests, along with your 501-c non-profit organization number, should be mailed or faxed to Baker Creek Heirloom Seeds. We will also need your physical shipping address rather than just a P.O. box number.

When submitting donation requests, please keep in mind that it can take up to a month or more for us to process your request, depending on the season and how busy we are. It is also good to remember that you should request only types of seeds rather than specific varieties (i.e. "carrots" rather than "Atomic Red Carrot"). All donations are filled on a first-come, first-served basis, and as available. We reserve the right to limit or cancel any request, for any reason.

We appreciate the photographs of beautiful gardens that our donation recipients send to us. Please take time to share photos with us after your garden comes to fruition. For more information about our donation program, please call 417-924-8917, email seeds@rareseeds.com, or fax 417-924-8887.

Our goal is to educate everyone about a better, safer food supply and fight gene-altered Frankenfood and the companies that support it.

BAKER CREEK HEIRLOOM SEED CO
2278 Baker Creek Road
Mansfield, MO 65704
417-924-8917
www.rareseeds.com

BAKER CREEK HEIRLOOM SEED COMPANY

*T*hroughout the ever-changing seasons we are constantly busy. From picking your seed orders when the winter winds blow, to tending our spring gardens and harvesting the produce, saving the seed and sending you this catalog. It's a yearly cycle we never tire of. Join us at our farm during our Planting Festival and Heritage Days for *a small taste of what life on our farm is really like!*

WWW.RARESEEDS.COM

HEIRLOOMS OF THE FUTURE!

Brad Gates--Owner of Wild Boar Farms in St. Helena California. Named after his favorite animal, his farm includes a wholesale tomato business that supplies Bay Area restaurants and businesses with outstanding organic tomatoes, as well as marketing plant starts in the spring, and seeds to seedsmen throughout the country. And he doesn't just market seeds—he breeds the varieties he sells as well!

Gates started saving his own seeds and crossbreeding many years ago. Wild Boar Farms varieties often have some whimsical reference to pigs in their names. But the whimsy extends to the tomatoes themselves. All colors of the tomato rainbow are represented, and often several of them on a single fruit: bicolored striped fruits abound, with not a few possessing three colors! Wild Boar Farms has been at the forefront of "blue" tomato breeding as well, with the "Indigo" series already approaching near-legendary status. Gates' varieties come in all sizes, ranging from currants, like Indigo "Gold Berries," to enormous slicers like "Large Barred Boar", "Pineapple Pig" and "Pink Berkeley Tie Dye", which may be his most beloved release.

Gates' offerings have heirloom ancestors in their background. He selects from crosses and mutations; many of his varieties have been chance discoveries rather than deliberate breeding. It helps that he has so many tomato plants to work with: he grew over 14,000 of them in 2013! "A lot of them have been lucky finds which I attribute to growing tens of thousands of plants and actually being the one going up and down the rows... to notice them... With a lot of plants to choose from you can get some pretty bizarre looking tomatoes; the key is selecting for flavor to go along with that unique look." he said. Only a very few of his test tomatoes are selected for planting the following year. "I like to grow about a hundred plants or more, then I'll select seeds from just a couple each season." "It's like a...Christmas present that takes a year to open," he adds, referring to the colors, shapes and flavors.

Life and Death in the Cart

There is one business in every town in America that makes me incredibly sad. It doesn't matter if I am in a town with a population of one million or one hundred, it is there...

BY: EMILEE GETTLE

The doors open and people flood in from miles around. Visiting this place is a life necessity now for most people. You probably visit at least once a week yourself. I would call it your local supermarket, but the word "local", generally speaking, can't be used for it anymore.

I've got a confession to make. I rarely shop in a grocery store. I mean, it is really, really rare. It isn't a weekly event for me any-more. I'm literally disgusted by the food that lines the shelves. Come on people, let's be real. It can't even be called food any-more! If I have to don a lab coat to whip up a recipe based on the ingredients list, I have decided it isn't going on my table, let alone in my cart. So, on those rare occasions when I stumble into a grocery store, I shop the perimeter. Why? Because that is where the least processed foods are. The further you venture from the perimeter of the store, the further from the farm you food comes from. Even then, I narrow my purchases even further to being sure that I'm buying as much organic food as possible. I would rather dish out a little more cash on my food than on my doctor bills down the road.

Ok, here it comes--another con-fession... I am a people watcher too. Growing up I was shy, like hide-behind-momma's-apron-strings shy. So, that's when I developed my ability to observe the public. Anyway, when I roll up with my oh-so-small cart load of what might resemble REAL food at our grocery store, my jaw drops when I see what rolls up around me. There she is, the mom who wants to give her kids the best birthday. So, what food does she have? The chemi-cally processed cupcakes topped with icing. Now, we are not talking about your grandmother's buttercream anymore. It is vibrantly colored with, as the Center for Science in the Public Interest so adequately names it, the "rainbow of risk". And then there is that case of soda cans, each can containing ten teaspoons of sugar. Can't forget the sports drinks for dad and why not throw in some fried food for a quick super. Vegetables, fruit? I'm not seeing it. When I checkout, the clerk doesn't even know what to ring up my produce as, because she hasn't even seen asparagus before, let alone ate it. Don't get me wrong, I'm not trying to be a pharisee here. I know that most moms genuinely don't know about food additives, preservatives, and colorings and what they are doing to their health. THAT, my friends is what infuriates me. The public is inundated every day with a barrage of food advertisements pushing us to buy unhealthy food. Even though it might be labeled "natural," it can be far from it--think pesticides. Personally, I feel that grocery shopping shouldn't be like navigating a deadly mine field. It's a fact, we need to learn how to shop again and what to eat.

As a child visiting the grocery store, it was a social outing. We lived in a small farming community, but we'd often find our cousins, friends and neighbors at the store on a weekend evening. There we'd be propped up against the end cap hashing out the latest news. Shopping for food has historically been a social event and equally a way to support your local community. In our rush-rush busy lives we now roll up to the big box store, dash in and fight through the aisle with mega carts. The goal: getting through the store without breaking the bank, satisfying a few cravings and managing to keep the kids from adding too much while backs were turned. There is something seriously wrong with this picture and I think it is high time we change it.

I have a passion for helping people learn how to find healthy food in our chemically-immersed society. I want Moms to have the tools necessary to be able to feed their kids right and teach their children how to shop too. I find that we have been robbed and royally sold a bill of goods over the last several decades. No one wants to be a guinea pig. Yet, we, as a nation, have unknowingly filled checkout lines and laid down our hard earned cash to purchase boxes of gmo-laden cereals, preservative laced fast food and antibiotic pumped proteins for our family. It's time we take a stand for those we love and turn the tide. Are you with me?

So, first things first, we need to get back to the ground floor. Literally, we need to get our hands in the dirt and learn how to grown our own food again. The markets of days gone by were originally meant to supplement what you were already producing on the farm. I don't care if all you have is a fire escape, plant something edible. Reconnect with the soil and your food.

Next, skip the big box store for one week. Sounds scarey, huh? Just b.r.e.a.t.h.e! Try a REAL local market that sells local produce and supports your local farmer, or go to a farmer's market. See if you can create your weekly menu from the organic ingredients you purchase there, and don't be afraid to swap out a few ingredients for something fun and new.

Whatever food we don't produce on our farm, I buy through a food co-op. I have been doing this for over 10 years! You can start your own buying club and have all the organic grains and ingredients, along with your favorite health foods delivered by the case to a local drop off. In the winter, I supplement our orders with organic produce, too. This is how I avoid stepping foot in the grocery store.

While on a recent family vacation we enjoyed stopping at some of our favorite old-fashion grocery stores. The wood floors creak with age and the buildings have such a nostagic atmosphere. These spontaneous stops brought back some wonderful childhood memories!

I am so surprised how many people don't cook anymore. There is something seriously wrong if we can't find enough time to cook a few meals a week at home. Don't feel embarrassed if you don't know how, either! Have a cook-along with a friend, find a simple recipe online or watch Youtube videos and start small. While we're on the topic, don't forget to sit down together as a family when you eat, too. Studies prove that having a sit down meal with our kids at least three times a week lessens their likelihood for behavioral problems and eating disorders down the road, not to mention the awesome memories you will cherish. Imagine how special it is when that meal includes food from your own garden (or fire escape), that you've cooked together as a family!

Two more words of wisdom, educate yourself. Learn how to eat wisely and add more fruits and vegetables to your diet. It will literally help you live longer! Plus, make the nutrition label your friend and don't buy anything until you've read it. Make it a point to know what is in any processed food you are purchasing. A good rule of thumb is, if you can't pronounce it, your body probably wasn't built to process it.

Need more help? Feel free to email me! You can visit my website at www.heirloomgirl.com. Together we can make a difference in the health of our loved ones; it just requires not being afraid to take a stand and tie on an apron.

Emilee Gettle is a Certified Health Coach and editor of Heirloom Gardener magazine. She is the wife of Jere and mother to Sasha and Malia. She lives a full life of gardening, homeschooling and crafting She also has the distinct pleasure of associating with some of America's most interesting people--heirloom farmers. Read her blog at: www.heirloomgirl.com

Ethnobotanical wonderland:
PERU

By Joseph Simcox

As the great agronomist Nikolai Vavilov designated "hotspots" for the origin of domesticated crops, Peru was definitely one of them. When Patrick and Joseph Simcox visited Peru in late summer 2014, their goal was not too much different from Nikolai's so long ago: to record and document food plant diversity. The Peruvian Andes are home to corn, beans, mashua, oca, ullucus, yacon, lima beans, potatoes, peppers, papayas and many others. The great US agronomist Jack Harlan once wrote: "Crops are artifacts made and molded by man as much as a flint arrowhead, a stone ax-head, or a clay pot." Indeed, when my brother Patty and I made our way through the high mountain villages and markets, we were reminded that the natural wonders we were witnessing were indeed artifacts that were in ways lovingly maintained by man, through the rituals of planting and harvest.

I may like to intellectualize too much, but I often ask the question if the people growing this stuff really love it or if they are just doing it because they have no better choices. Why do I ask this? Because in our own world of modern day America, most people, the overwhelming majority, seem very content to not be bound to the toil of the soil. Are the colorful folk in Peru just as susceptible to losing their agricultural traditions as we did?

In the USA, only 50 years ago people were growing far more of their own food; men and women gathered the harvest and prepared it for some type of storage. Most of that home processing is now gone. In a recent survey, 40% of teenagers could not properly identify milk as coming from an animal—the cow! It sounds absurd, but when you think about the aisles of the grocery store (where most kids are exposed to food), there are no cows there. Now, the dairy section presents diverse "milks": soy, almond, coconut, flax etc. Where is the cow in those? Processed foods make the acquisition of food seem painless, and I fear that those in Peru, who are my examples today, are as easily vulnerable as our populace was when conveniences in the food trade were being rolled off the production line. What then, if any, does love have to do with it? My brother and I hope that there is something deeper to the human psyche, some figment that is not vulnerable to easy seduction, something that conveys a supra-natural significance.

My brother and I believe that there is that spirit of tradition in Peru. In 2013, Peru denounced all GMO crops by banning their cultivation within its borders. Peru had also been "victim" to the bio-piracy efforts of large corporations. A notable case involves a foreign company's "patenting" of Maca (Lepidium meyenii). The absurdity of the patent only requires knowing that the people of the high Andes have raised Maca for centuries, and, that it was not a modern nutraceutical firm that discovered it. Those international intrusions have galvanized a sentiment against large corporate domination and have enabled the precious country folk to realize their riches.

Patrick Simcox enjoys finding rare seeds in the high mountains of Peru